Imperial Caesar

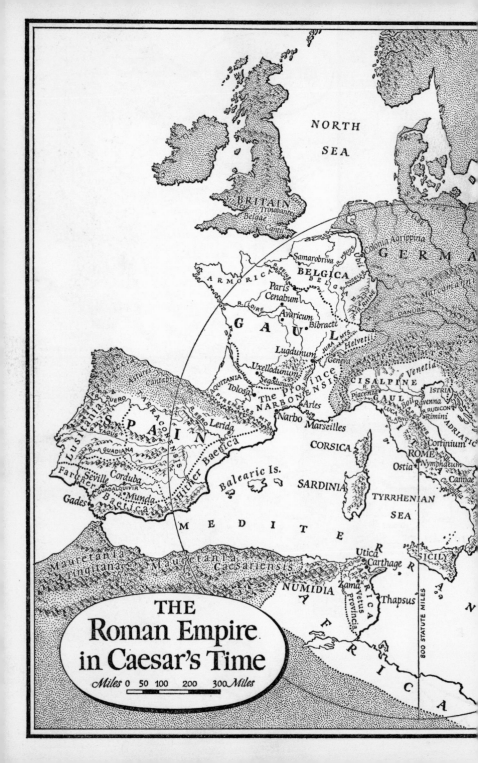

NORTH SEA

BRITAIN
Trinobantes
Belgae
Cantii

GERMA

ARMORICA

BELGICA
Samarobriva
Colonia Agrippina
Ubii
R. MEUSE
R. RHINE
R. MOSELLE

GAUL
Paris
Cenabum
Avaricum
Bibracte
R. LOIRE
Marcomanni
R. RHINE

Lugdunum
JURA MTS.
Helvetii
Uxellodunum
Segodunum
Geneva
AQUITANIA
Tolosa
The Province
NARBONENSIS
PYRENEES MTS.
Arles
Narbo
Marseilles

CISALPINE
GAUL
Venetia
R. PO
Piacenza
ISTRIA
Ravenna
Rimini
Boii
LUCA
R. ARNO
ADRIATIC

R. DANUBE
ALPS MTS.
APENNINE MTS.

SPAIN
Gallaecia
Astures
Cantabri
R. DUERO
TARRACONENSIS
R. EBRO
Lerida
R. TAGUS
Hither
Baetica
R. GUADIANA
Farther Baetica
Corduba
Seville
R. GUADALQUIVIR
Munda
Gades

Balearic Is.

CORSICA

SARDINIA

ROME
Ostia
Nymphaeum
Cannae
Corfinium
VIA APPIA
VIA LATINA

TYRRHENIAN SEA

M E D I T E R R A N E A N

Mauretania
Tingitana
Mauretania Caesariensis

NUMIDIA

Utica
Carthage
Zama
AFRICA vetus
Africa provincia
Thapsus

SICILY

AFRICA

800 STATUTE MILES

THE
Roman Empire
in Caesar's Time

Miles 0 50 100 200 300 *Miles*

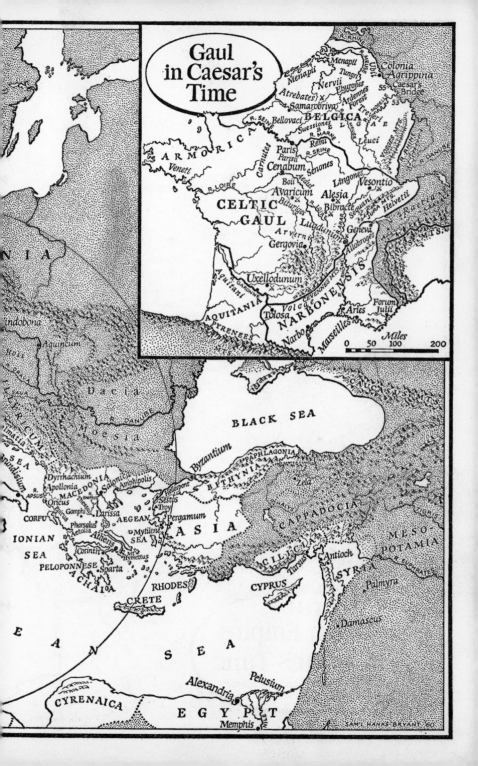

Books by Rex Warner

Novels

THE WILD GOOSE CHASE

THE PROFESSOR

WHY WAS I KILLED?

THE AERODROME

MEN OF STONES

THE YOUNG CAESAR

IMPERIAL CAESAR

POEMS AND CONTRADICTIONS

THE CULT OF POWER (*essays*)

VIEWS OF ATTICA (*travel*)

Imperial
Caesar

By REX WARNER

An Atlantic Monthly Press Book

Little, Brown and Company
Boston · Toronto

FIRST EDITION

ATLANTIC—LITTLE, BROWN BOOKS
ARE PUBLISHED BY
LITTLE, BROWN AND COMPANY
IN ASSOCIATION WITH
THE ATLANTIC MONTHLY PRESS

PRINTED IN THE UNITED STATES OF AMERICA

Contents

BOOK TWO

Imperial Caesar

Prologue

Cicero has made a number of rather good jokes about my supposed divinity. I must get him to repeat them (he will be vain enough to tell them to Balbus or Matius, if he is afraid to tell them to me) so that I can include some, at least, of them in the next edition of my little book of "Witty Sayings." No doubt he would have something to say now either witty or solemn, and certainly well expressed, if he could see how for some hours I have been attempting in vain to go to sleep. Though here he might not be funny after all. He is apt to be malicious and, in an ineffectual way, envious; these defects of character often blunt both his judgment and his wit; they even interfere sometimes with the precision and elaboration of his style.

So, from malice, he might regard my sleeplessness as being the result of indigestion, which is, obviously, not an ailment from which a god should suffer. Or, from envy (since for so long people have ceased talking about his consulship), he might suggest that I, as a tyrant or at least as one who has considerably modified the Constitution, must be the victim of alarming nightmares, as my Uncle Marius was in his old age — the effects of a guilty conscience. But in both suppositions he would be wrong. I can eat, without any ill effects, food which a good centurion would hesitate to issue to his men; and I can also enjoy a lavish enter-

tainment such as the one which was in fact offered me tonight by
Lepidus. Nor do I suffer from nightmares. I have never betrayed a
friend and never acted savagely towards a Roman enemy.

If one may be said to deserve anything, I deserve sleep more
than the gods deserve it. I have done more for men than they
have. There is certainly a sense in which the notion of my divinity
is far from fanciful.

Again those lights in the sky. It cannot be torchlight. This is
the silent hour, the only silent hour in Rome. Even Antony
must be asleep. Why cannot Caesar sleep? Calpurnia too tosses
from side to side. Her forehead is all wet with sweat. Her lips are
moving. Twice already she has called out my name. She is frightened evidently, and that is unlike her. Why indeed should she
be alarmed by terrors in the night or by any dreadful anticipa-
tion? She is fond of me but she will not mind it when I leave her.
She is used to that. Never since the time I married her, in my
first consulship, nearly fifteen years ago, have I lived with her
for more than a week or two at a time. Yet she is satisfied with
her position and she enjoys her loyalty. I, on my side, though I
seem scarcely to have seen her, have been careful to respect her
and am, in one way, deeply fond of her. If only she had been
able to give me a child — a son — I should have loved her as I
loved Cornelia whom I married in my early youth and who gave
me the only child that I can confidently declare to have been mine.
Cornelia is dead and so is Julia. As it is I have given the Queen
of Egypt permission to call her child Caesarion; but naturally I
shall watch the boy's development before I reach any definite
conclusion. Cleopatra will always believe what she wishes to believe. I have not ruled out the possibility of marrying Cleopatra,
though, if I were to do such a thing, I am aware that public
opinion in Italy would be shocked. The conquest of Parthia must
come first and with that, perhaps, a new conception of kinghood
or of divinity.

Again Calpurnia cries out in her sleep. She would be sorry if
anything were to happen to me. And at some time or other, god

or no god, I shall die. But it is not likely that I shall die in Parthia. I shall not make the mistakes which Crassus made. And, surrounded by my own soldiers, I feel safe from the danger of assassination. That is a danger which, though I take no precautions against it, is something, I suppose, to be reckoned with in Rome. But I only have one more day in Rome.

I shall be glad once again to leave this city from which for so many years I have been absent and yet which has somehow determined my life since the time when, as a young child, I would listen enthralled to stories of the exploits of my Uncle Marius. The old man was savage, cruel, politically inept and utterly uncultured. Yet he was real. (Was he also a god?) His vanity was not a disease, as it was with Pompey. His savagery was not an intellectual vice, as it was with Sulla. He saw, dimly and in his own egotistical way, a different and a truer Rome. He saw the soldiers and the provinces and he saw how both were being betrayed by the blind self-interest, the narrow judgment, the antiquated pomposity, the inefficiency of a few whom he would describe with contempt as "aristocrats." Since he had married into our family he should, in decency, have avoided the use of this particular word and my Aunt Julia would often tell him so. But he was not interested in verbal accuracy. Like the ordinary workingman or legionary, whom he so much resembled (though I should prefer to say that they, in a Platonic sense, partook of his nature, rather than that he resembled them) he had to have a convenient label for his ideas. It was necessary for him to simplify. On the one hand he saw, and drew his strength from, the people, the army, Italy, the provinces; and on the other side he fancied a narrow, inefficient and cowardly clique of the nobility. He neglected some obvious facts. In our times, for example, the leaders of the people have invariably come from the nobility and indeed have usually belonged, as in the case of Catiline, Clodius and myself, to the most ancient families of all. Also, though he saw better than anyone that the fighting quality of an army depends, first and foremost, on the discipline and devotion of the centurions, he seems to have been unaware that in politics also and in administration we need experts and that these are still to be found mostly among members of the senate.

Yet, confused or childishly oversimplified as the ideas (if they deserve such a name) of Marius may seem to be, what is important is that they do, however surprisingly, correspond with the realities of our times. Was it accident, a childish loyalty or the beginnings of percipience which made me, so young, defy what looked to be the permanent establishment of Sulla? Then I could have followed in the paths of Pompey or of Crassus; yet instead I risked my life and sacrificed, to all appearance, every hope of distinction whether in politics or war. Much too slowly for my ambition events began to turn my way and gradually I became able myself to influence events. In the future I shall be regarded, rightly, as an important general and administrator — as have been so many others of my class. But I had little or no military experience until I was past the age of forty, and I should not have survived to reach that age if I had not shown a rather exceptional grasp of politics both in their widest and in their meanest and most squalid sense. I owed my success in politics and indeed my survival to various qualities of my own — fearlessness, extravagance, loyalty to my friends, a love of display; yet Clodius and Catiline possessed these qualities too and achieved very little with them.

I think that what a historian of the future may admire in me, and will be surprised to find, is my consistency. I am surprised myself sometimes when I reflect on the fact that, in spite of some hesitations, of many improvisations, of accidents and of adventures into the unknown, my life seems to have proceeded as it were in a straight line towards a certain aim. The aim may be, I suppose, described as "order," though my enemies would be more likely to describe it either as "tyranny" or as "revolution." They will never realize that I did all I could to avoid the necessity of taking power so obviously into my own hands and they fail to notice that I have a great and increasing reverence for antiquity. I even think of restoring the monarchy. Their own "order" stands self-condemned. It was the order of Sulla, which was a mere bloody repression; or the order of Cicero, which was based on nothing more durable than a temporary panic of the moneyed classes; or the order of Cato, which was a hypocritical display of harmful or unnecessary rectitude, taking no account whatever of the conditions in which men live. Instead of the violence, inefficiency and restriction of these "orders," I have consistently worked for a wider and in some ways a more complex world in which others apart from myself may be able to achieve greatness and to display initiative. I have seen the Roman people as my uncle Marius used to see them. I have seen them as individuals with every kind of fault and weakness, yet capable of immense endurance and the most unlikely heroism. I can see them also in a somewhat abstract way — a mass of related lives, instincts, needs, affections and antipathies — and I know that, although in many directions I am able, because of my peculiar training and endowments, to see more clearly than can any member or any section of this mass, it is the mass itself from which I draw my strength and which, in the last resort, determines my plans and my ambitions.

In my youth I thought only of this Roman people and, of course, of my own position among them. By various tricks and by much sincerity I won their affection and, with their help, was able both to preserve my own life and to win back for them all the liberties which Sulla had taken from them. It was for their glory as well as for my own that I subdued Gaul and carried the standards of the legions into remote Britain. And when, tomorrow or the day after, I set out for Parthia and the East, I shall still be thinking of this people, of this complex and concentration of fact and tradition, of this Rome from which I sprang. Both my flatterers and my well-wishers say that I am on my way to India in order to equal or surpass the achievements of Alexander the Great. Naturally this is an idea which has occurred to me also. I was, indeed, rather pleased with the design of the new equestrian statue of me in the Forum Iulium. It is not unlike the Alexander of Lysippus and has a certain distinction of its own. But I know how misleading these comparisons are. There was a time when everyone used to refer to Pompey as "Alexander," and that was simply because he was lucky, good-looking and a competent commander in his early youth. In my case, if indeed there is any resemblance to be found between me and the great Alexander, that resemblance is, I think, rather spiritual than physical, rather political than military. Alexander began life as a Greek and ended by bringing Greece into the furthest corners of the world. In the process he became something more than a Greek — indeed one may almost say something more than a man. In the same way, perhaps, I, the child of a Roman patrician family, a leader of the Roman people, a general known to his men both as comrade and commander, can perceive an extension of Rome and an extension also of my own personality. The mere extension of Roman citizenship is an old idea and, like every good idea in our times, has been bitterly opposed. When I first campaigned for it and when, very late in the day, I was able to confer citizenship on the whole of Northern Italy, I used to think in terms of the recruiting of armies and the use of voters at elections. Now I am inclined to think much further ahead and almost in a different way. I see Rome not in this old-fashioned city (which, nevertheless, I shall continue to adorn with buildings) but at the ends of the world. One must never plan too far ahead, but still I can imagine, supposing that my campaigns in Parthia and India turn out in a certain way, that it might be desirable to shift the capital of our empire — to Byzantium, to Troy, to Alexandria, to Antioch. This would be a question of efficiency. And so, it may be, Alexander thought of Greece. He respected his native Macedonia, he revered Athens and knew her history. But, with Bactria and Sogdiana and India confronting him, how could he consider, except in a literary and philosophic way, the local loyalties of a remote peninsula? His mission was to bring Athens to the world, not to bring the whole world into the restricted area between Hymettus and the sea.

So now I begin to think of Rome, and no one yet — not even Balbus — quite comprehends me. If I were to remain in Rome and still pursue these views, I should become increasingly hated even by those members of the aristocracy whom I regard as my friends. In fact I am assisting, with some authority and some skill, at the birth of a new era; yet my midwifely, or medical, task is sure to be denounced as tyranny, impiety or interference by all those who cannot see that a birth is imminent or who wish, by all means possible, to prevent it. There is now no armed force in the world which I need fear; but I ought, I suppose, to have taken some precautions against the honest distaste which I inspire among a few doctrinaires. The other day someone told me that Antony was plotting to murder me. That, of course, is ridiculous. But of some others I am not so sure. My very existence conflicts, I know, with the theories of Marcus Brutus; but he is honorable as well as able. He will be able to see further if he lives longer. At the moment, though I believe him to be fond of me and though I have often talked with him and with his mother about my aims, he is probably unable to see that if, by some chance, I were struck down either today or tomorrow and if after that he and his friends were to attempt what they would no doubt describe as "the restoration of liberty," the result would be absolutely disastrous. Our world, the Italian world of the future, would be plunged once more into a state of war; the opportunity would have been lost, perhaps forever.

How angrily the wind blows tonight! There are still those lights in the sky and now I hear a sudden crash in the courtyard, as though some ornament had fallen from the roof. Calpurnia is sitting up in the bed, her eyes wide open, though she is asleep. Now she falls back again, still restless and disturbed. Probably in the morning, when I inspect the sacrifices, she will try to find some pretext for persuading me to stay at home. For something in her sleep has certainly alarmed her and she is not as a rule superstitious. She fears for me, and perhaps it is right to fear for the gods. In particular it is proper to consider the safety of such gods as I am, since we do, unlike the gods of the poets, intervene in human affairs.

It seems that with regard to gods as with regard to so much else we must learn to change our ideas. Men need gods, though, as is admirably pointed out by Lucretius in his poem, they are injured and weakened by superstitious fears. In one sense Epicurus did a great service to men when he proved scientifically that the gods of the mythographers, though there is some reason for supposing them to exist, cannot conceivably play any part in the process of our lives and consequently cannot be objects of fear. He might, I think, have gone further still and said that they could not be objects of admiration either; for we cannot admire anything that is wholly ineffectual. Yet it is a fact of nature that most men desire to look up to something more powerful than themselves, something capable of affording protection, of rewarding good actions and of punishing or preventing what is wrong. In childhood many people find such beings in the persons of their parents and, when they grow up, can impose themselves in the same way upon their own children. But few men ever fully grow up. From youth to old age they will always demand an assurance that cannot be found in their own natures. And this demand for assurance will, of course, become particularly urgent during periods of history when a society is obviously not living in accordance with its own pretensions. It is at these times that some people will talk particularly loudly about "liberty"; but what really disturbs them is the collapse of authority, with the inevitable sequence of violent untrue assertion or else impotent well-meaning doubt.

Liberty can only exist within a framework of convention, and a particular framework, once shattered, can never be replaced. It will require luck and genius to discover or create another framework in which it will be possible once again for men to live in reasonable activity and ease. The lucky discoverers, the creative geniuses are, for their times and, in a sense, for all time, gods, although the atomic structure of their bodies and minds are mortal and lack that smoothness which Epicurus attributes to those impractical divinities who live in the spaces between the worlds. The idea is not absurd. Men will find no divinities outside themselves, and they will be comforted in acknowledging in a fellow human being something which is too great for them to comprehend. Yet men retain a sense of humor. Everyone knows, for example, that I can be killed. They are often happier if their god can also be a king and if the king, as in the very ancient ceremonials of our remote ancestors, can be encouraged or expected to die for his people. Though I am intensely interested in antiquities, I do not propose voluntarily to make a sacrifice of myself. This is because I have too much to do.

Still the wind blows; still there are some hours before dawn. It is the Ides of March. Not long ago a soothsayer told me to beware of this day. As it happens it is a time of year that has nearly always been most propitious for me. It is the opening of the campaigning season — though often enough I have had to move into action in the dead of winter. But this is the best time. One can travel faster. I did eighty-five miles a day when I left Rome, nearly fifteen years ago now, and went north to take over the Tenth Legion from Titus Labienus at Geneva. I can see the men now and can still remember the precise situation with which I had to deal. It was not a difficult one, but at that moment of my life it seemed immensely important. And in a way it was. What dreams I had! And how closely have I followed these dreams, recognizing and respecting their reality, forcing sometimes upon them a reality of my own. Now, waiting for the dawn, I see and feel those cold dawns in Gaul. I see the face of every centurion and of half the soldiers of the Tenth Legion as I saw them when, after my consulship, I arrived to take command.

Book One

Chapter 1

Arrival in Gaul

I HAD WISHED TO BE IN MY PROVINCE MUCH EARLIER IN THE YEAR, but had been detained near Rome for two and a half months after laying down my consulship on the first of January. Once I reached my province I could not legally leave it again for five years (in fact it was to be ten years before I left Gaul and then I left it, strictly speaking, illegally). Meanwhile, before I went north, it was essential to safeguard the arrangements which I had made during this first consulship of mine. In this period I had been forced by my enemies to act in a somewhat highhanded manner. Most of the legislation had come not from the senate (though I did my best to make the senate see sense) but from the people's assembly, and nearly all of it had been carried out entirely under my own auspices. My colleague Bibulus, after some unsuccessful attempts at opposition, had retired to his own house and had issued from there various edicts declaring that everything I did was illegal. It was for this reason that instead of calling this year "the consulship of Caesar and Bibulus" people used to refer to it as "the consulship of Julius and Caesar."

I had been able to overcome the opposition of my enemies partly because of my own popularity with all classes and partly because I had, to the surprise of everyone, secured for myself the support of the two most powerful figures in Rome — Pompey and

Crassus — each of whom had grievances against what had been the dominant party in the senate. These two had long been enemies, but I was able to convince them that they would have much to gain from becoming friends and from supporting me. I had often in the past been associated politically with Crassus and found him easy to deal with. Pompey was another matter. He was, with all his excellent qualities, extraordinarily vain and very suspicious of all merit other than his own. But he was capable of seeing reason. On the whole I got on well with him and he became more closely bound to me still when he married my only daughter, Julia, who loved him with the same passion and devotion as her mother Cornelia had loved me.

Pompey's prestige (backed, as it was, by his veterans), Crassus's wealth and my popularity formed a combination of forces that, for a year at least, was absolutely irresistible. I still find it agreeable to reflect that my opponents never even imagined the possibility of such a combination being brought about until they were confronted helplessly with the fact. It remained true, however, that the combination was uneasy and precarious. During the year of my consulship all our aims had been secured. Pompey was now able to satisfy the demands of his veterans for land; Crassus had gained still more power and influence in both political and financial circles; I had not only received the governorship of Cisalpine Gaul for the exceptionally long period of five years, but, owing to the fortunate accident of the death of Clodia's husband, Metellus Celer, had also acquired the province of Gaul across the Alps — a small enough area in those days. We had also succeeded in promoting the election to office for the following year of candidates who could be relied upon to support us. One of the consuls was Gabinius, an old partisan of Pompey and a friend of my own; the other was my father-in-law, Piso. I had only just married Calpurnia then.

Nevertheless even before the end of my consulship it had become apparent that trouble was to be expected in the future. Some of the difficulties were personal. For example it seemed that not even the clearest recognition of self-interest could permanently reconcile the old antipathies and jealousies of Pompey and Crassus. Then there was the party of Bibulus and his friends who, however discredited for the moment, were at least armed with something in the nature of a legal argument. If, by any shift in the political balance, they could get the rest of the senate behind them, they might even find it possible to pass a decree declaring that all the acts of my consulship were null and void. One of the means we adopted for meeting this danger was to support Clodius as tribune. This was a plan of my own, and though Crassus, who was used to working through disreputable agents, was in favor of it, Pompey was at first reluctant to be associated with a character who, to his mind, was so utterly irresponsible and whose moral reputation stood so low. He even remarked that he was surprised that I myself would tolerate Clodius, who had been the lover of my previous wife and had involved me in some rather disagreeable scandal. As I had been the lover of Pompey's wife, Mucia, before he divorced her to marry my daughter, I considered this remark of his curiously tactless. In fact Clodius did do some harm to Pompey's dignity (and Pompey used to cherish his dignity above everything); but he also kept the Roman people in a mood of independence, hostile to the extremists in the senate and therefore, in spite of some appearances, friendly and cooperative to those policies which I had designed for the benefit of both Pompey and myself.

I knew that it was impossible entirely to control Clodius, but I fancied that he could be guided. He did, in fact, exactly what I wished him to do in the important period which immediately followed the end of my consulship. He entirely disarmed, for the time being, what might have been a dangerous opposition. Owing to him we got rid both of Cato and of Cicero. Cato, by a vote of the people, was sent on an official mission to Cyprus. Cicero was exiled. I had wished, certainly, that matters could have been arranged differently. As for Cato, he was, I knew, an irreconcilable enemy and I should have liked to see him removed forever to some corner of the earth where he might be comparatively harmless. But for Cicero I have always felt the greatest respect. He is the best prose stylist in our language, a brilliant lawyer and an agreeable conversationalist. I wished very much to have him on my side. However he would neither throw in his weight with us (I entreated him to do so) nor keep quiet nor, when the danger from his enemy Clodius became really threatening, accept my offer of an honorable and lucrative appointment with me in Gaul. It was therefore necessary for me to abandon him. When I left Rome I knew that in a week or two he would be forced into exile. With him and Cato out of the way, it seemed that, for a year or two at least, no serious opposition could be organized against the legislation that had been carried out in my consulship. Indeed, if only I could have been sure that Pompey and Crassus would, during my absence, work together, I should have regarded the position of all three of us as perfectly secure. But I could not count on this. Moreover I knew that my own future would depend not only on the intricate workings of Roman politics but on my success in my new command in Gaul. No one, up to this time, had ever known what precisely to expect of me; but everyone expected something unusual. I could afford neither to fail nor to be forgotten.

From the very first I had to make quick decisions, some of which were mistaken. It took time to acquire anything like an accurate knowledge of the country and the people and the constantly changing rivalries and friendships between the tribes. The Gauls, even more than most people, are prone to believe what they want to believe; moreover they change their opinions with the most extraordinary ease and rapidity. The result is that hardly a single Gaul who is actively engaged in tribal politics will, however well-intentioned he may be, find it possible to give one accurate information. Further difficulties proceeded from the fact that, until my time, Rome had never followed a consistent policy with regard to Gaul. Most governors had been content to safeguard the narrow limits of our existing Province and in order to increase security had entered into treaties both with Gallic tribes and with Germans. Both Gauls and Germans had sent deputations to our senate in Rome and these deputations had had their requests granted or refused by people who lacked the necessary knowledge for coming to a correct decision. I myself, for example, during my consulship agreed to the recognition of the German king, Ariovistus. That was before I knew that I was to receive the governorship of the Transalpine Province and when I was entirely unaware of the great ambitions which Ariovistus entertained. Certainly I never had at any time a mandate from the senate and Roman people to complete the conquest of the whole of Gaul or to invade Britain or to cross the Rhine. These exploits were unexpected by public opinion and, if ever anything went wrong with us, my enemies in Rome were quick to attack me for waging unnecessary and expensive wars of aggression. It was therefore necessary for me to move carefully, though, in the nature of things, it was impossible for me to move slowly. I had, of course, resolved to make use of my army, but up to the time when I actually arrived in Gaul I had made no definite plans of precisely how it was to be used. Not till the end of the first year's two campaigns did it suddenly dawn upon me that I possessed an opportunity of achieving conquests as important, as durable and as glorious as anything that had been done in the East by Lucullus or by Pompey.

Strictly speaking, I had only two legal pretexts for intervening in the affairs of Gaul. It was my duty, of course, to protect both northern Italy and the small Roman Province across the Alps from any threat of invasion. And there was also a rather loosely worded decree of the senate which instructed the Roman governor of the Province to do what he could to look after the interests of the large Gallic tribe of the Aedui, with whom we had for some time been in friendly relations. I found both these pretexts useful in the course of my first campaign.

This campaign, against the Helvetii, was not one which I had expected to have to fight. Two years previously there had certainly been some alarm at Rome when it was reported that this large and formidable tribe was planning to turn westward in the direction of our Province. It was even feared that they might invade Italy and two competent commanders had been sent north — Metellus Celer to the Transalpine Province and Afranius,

Pompey's friend, to Cisalpine Gaul. But the threat had, to all appearance, disappeared — much to the annoyance of Metellus who, before he died, wrote to his friends complaining that he had been deprived of the opportunity of showing the world that he was a better general than Pompey. (This, at the time, was everyone's ambition). I myself had, by the end of the year of my consulship, received no information to suggest that any serious danger could be expected from the Helvetii. If I had expected danger or if, as some of my enemies have made out, I had planned from the start to wage aggressive warfare in Gaul, I should, at the beginning of my governorship, have disposed the legions differently. As it was I had four legions under my command. Only one of these, the Tenth, was beyond the Alps. So, when I heard from Labienus that the Helvetii were already beginning to muster in large numbers on the Rhone opposite Geneva, I was aware at once that we had at the moment neither enough troops on the spot nor sufficiently strong fortifications to stop them.

On reaching Geneva I discussed the situation with Labienus and other officers. It became clear that the Helvetii had planned a mass migration of the whole tribe — men, women and children. Estimates of their numbers varied, but all our informants were agreed that we had a large horde to deal with and that the fighting men among them were troops of high quality. Later we discovered their exact numbers. There were three hundred and sixty-eight thousand of them, one quarter of whom were men capable of bearing arms. Their leaders had, it appeared, decided to abandon entirely the somewhat barren and mountainous territory in which they had always lived and to move westwards into Gaul where, somewhere or other, they would find land for themselves by conquering and dispossessing the present owners. They had already burned their towns and villages, so that there should be nothing to tempt them to return, and they had equipped themselves with adequate supplies for a long march. There were only two possible routes leading westward from their country. One was an extremely narrow track between the Rhone and the Jura mountains. It went through the country of the Sequani and was quite impassable without the co-operation and permission of this tribe. The other route, running in a southwesterly direction, was a very much easier one. It led across the Rhone and then into the northern part of our Province.

Within a few days of my arrival at Geneva I was visited by a deputation of Helvetian notables. They were tall impressive men and had a natural dignity which prevented them from being made to look ridiculous by their barbaric headdresses and the ornaments which they wore. They spoke respectfully, but not humbly, clearly regarding themselves as a power to be treated by me on a basis of equality. They pointed out to me the difficulties of the northern route out of their country and asked my permission to march for a few days through the Roman Province, promising that they would do no harm to the inhabitants or to their property.

It is, I think, quite possible that they sincerely intended to keep this promise and it could not have occurred to them that, once they had marched out of our Province, I or any other Roman could be justified in controlling their future actions. But I had several reasons for thinking that I ought not to accede to their request. There was the obvious risk that so great a horde would not be sufficiently disciplined on the march and would be tempted into acts of excess by the riches and superior civilization of our Province. And also it seemed to me that, from the Roman point of view, the Helvetii had been fulfilling a very useful function in their own country, where for many years they had acted as a barrier against the Germans to the north and east of them. These Germans would now be likely to occupy the land left empty in Helvetia and would thus become neighbors, and dangerous neighbors, of our own. I realized, however, that not even the senate in Rome, let alone the Helvetii themselves, would admit that I had any right to dictate to any Gallic tribe outside the frontiers of our Province. It would therefore be necessary to move carefully — although, so far as public opinion in Rome was concerned, I was aware that I could win great distinction by any successful action I might take against this particular tribe. For in the last generation the Helvetii had utterly defeated one of our armies and had inflicted on it the humiliation of sending it under the yoke. My wife Calpurnia's great-grandfather had been killed in this battle.

I determined, therefore, to resist the Helvetii, although I knew that I was not, at the moment, strong enough to do so effectively. I informed their deputation that I could not at once give a definite answer to their request to be allowed to go through our Province and I asked them to return in about three weeks' time, when I would tell them what I had decided. I could see that my attitude surprised them and this was an anxious moment for me. With one legion and no fortifications I could not possibly have prevented them from crossing the Rhone, had they determined then to force their way over. But they evidently had no wish to engage in hostilities with us, at least at this early stage of their migration. They went away and gave me time not only to raise more troops from the Province but also to construct eighteen miles of fortifications to guard the crossings of the Rhone. When the Helvetian representatives returned I informed them that it was our settled policy to allow no one at all to march through our Province and that, if they attempted to do so, I should meet force with force.

The Helvetii were offended by my answer, but avoided the use of any threatening language. Some few of them afterwards did attempt to break through our lines; but there was nothing in the nature of a concerted action and I much doubt whether those attacks which were made, and were easily repulsed by us, had been authorized by the Helvetian leaders. These leaders had observed the preparations which I was making to defend the line of the Rhone and, evidently not wanting to become involved in war with us, had been exploring the possibility of taking the other, difficult, route through the country of the Sequani to the north. I must own that I was taken entirely by surprise when I was informed that the Sequani had given permission to this huge invading army to march through their territory by a road which could quite easily have been defended even by a small number of troops; and I was still more surprised to find that it was through the good offices of a nobleman among the Aedui, Dumnorix by name, that the Helvetii had secured this concession from the Sequani. I was surprised because the likelihood was that, after crossing the country of the Sequani, the Helvetii would turn westward into the territory of the Aedui themselves; and I was also disconcerted, since, unless I were to receive an appeal for help from the Aedui, it would not be easy for me to find a pretext for interfering with the great Helvetian migration. Frankly I was puzzled. I had not yet discovered that among the Aedui, as among most Gallic states, there existed a permanent condition of civil war. Sometimes I found this condition helpful. I soon discovered on this occasion, for instance, that, in spite of the fact that Dumnorix, a leading Aeduan, was evidently acting in collaboration with the Helvetii, there was a large, indeed a predominant, party in the state which, for one reason or another, was anxious that both Dumnorix and the Helvetii should be checked. This party was, greatly to my relief, prepared to ask me to intervene in accordance with the existing treaty of friendship between the Aedui and Rome.

Neither the pro-Roman party among the Aedui nor I myself had at the time any idea of how important would be the effects of this request of theirs for our help. Without it I should have found it, both for political and for military reasons, very difficult to march with a considerable army into the heart of Gaul. I might indeed have been diverted from Gaul altogether and have undertaken instead campaigns in Germany which, because of the geography and the low standard of civilization of that country, could not have led to important results. As it was I was offered by a small party in one state, and almost by accident, an opportunity to appear in the role of a protector of Gaul from foreign invasion.

I took the opportunity without delay. Leaving Labienus in charge of the fortifications at Geneva, I crossed the Alps into Northern Italy, joined the three legions which were stationed there, quickly enrolled two more legions, and with this force marched back across the Alps by the shortest route into Gaul. We marched fast and, in these early days, there were some complaints from the soldiers, who were unused to the kind of exer-

tions which I demanded of them. After a little time these troops of
mine would be prepared to follow me anywhere and to put up
with every kind of hardship; but at this stage they watched me
closely, and with some suspicion. I was known to them as a politician, not as a general. It was necessary for me to gain their confidence which, finally, could only be gained by leading them to
victory. And in this first campaign we were outnumbered by
at least three to one — not serious odds in some conditions, but
in this case serious enough, since the Helvetii were good soldiers
and full of confidence, while I was not yet sure of the morale of
my own army.

By the time we had marched out of the Province into Gaul the
Helvetii had already entered the country of the Aedui who now
sent me the expected appeal for help. I summoned a number of
Aeduan leaders, including Dumnorix, to my camp, gave them
detailed instructions as to the supplies I required from them and
also asked them for a force of cavalry.

The huge slowly moving host of the Helvetii had now reached
the river Arar. They took nearly three weeks to cross this river
and their extreme slowness over the operation enabled me to win
my first victory in Gaul. When my patrols informed me that
three quarters of the Helvetii had crossed I led out three legions by
night, reached the river just before dawn and attacked the division
of the enemy that was still waiting to make the crossing. They
were taken completely by surprise and were nearly all killed or
captured. This particular division of the Helvetii constituted one
of the four clans into which the whole nation is divided, and it so
happened that it was this same clan which had in the previous
generation killed a Roman consul and sent his army under the
yoke. I was careful to have this fact reported in Rome where I
knew that my enemies would already be accusing me of fighting an
unprovoked and unnecessary campaign. Whether the campaign
was necessary or not, it could now be claimed that at any rate
I had avenged a disgraceful military defeat of ours.

This first victory was, of course, very far from being decisive.
I followed it up immediately and on the next day threw a bridge

over the Arar and led the whole army across. The Helvetii were evidently impressed by the fact that we had accomplished in one day a task over which they had spent three weeks and now made what appeared to be a reasonable offer of peace. I was visited by their old chief Divico, a man who, fifty years previously, had been their leader in the battle in which they had defeated us and killed our consul. Even in his old age this Divico was strong and erect. I was impressed both by his wisdom and his resolution; and his words put me into a somewhat awkward position, for, while showing no fear of us, he made it clear that he did not wish to fight if fighting could be avoided. The Helvetii, he said, were willing to settle in any part of Gaul I liked to choose for them. If, however, I continued to make war on them, they would defend themselves. They had defeated Romans before and could do so again. As for my recent victory, that had been the result of a surprise attack and could not be used as evidence to suggest that I could expect any such success in a pitched battle. It was for me, Divico concluded, to choose between peace and war. He and his tribe preferred peace but were not afraid of the alternative.

It was a good speech, made with much dignity. Many of my officers were impressed by it and I myself was aware that, with an untried army, I was taking a risk in confronting so powerful and resolute a tribe. I should have preferred to gain further experience and further knowledge of my men before hazarding everything on the result of one battle. But I did not want to lose the opportunity I had of intervening in the affairs of Gaul outside the Province; and I was also aware that, if I were to show the slightest hesitation on this occasion, the army might be less willing to follow me unquestioningly on other, and possibly more dangerous, ventures. I replied to Divico in a way that was calculated to offend his dignity. I told him that the previous victory won by his tribe against us had been due to treachery rather than to any soldierly qualities that the Helvetii had displayed. I accused him of bad faith in attempting to break through my lines on the Rhone and in plundering the land of tribes who were allies of ours. If he wanted peace, I concluded, he must pay compensation for the damage that his tribesmen had done and also give me hostages as guarantees that he would in fact march wherever I directed him to go.

As I had anticipated, Divico found my proposals unacceptable and my manner intolerable. He merely remarked that the Helvetii were in the habit of taking hostages, not giving them; this, he pointed out, was something which we Romans ought to know from experience. He then left me and next day the Helvetii resumed their march. It was now evident that nothing further could be achieved without hard fighting. The Helvetii were prepared to meet us in battle and for me, in this new command, it was absolutely essential that the battle, when it came, should result in a Roman victory.

Chapter 2

The First Battle

I SUPPOSE THAT AT THIS PERIOD OF MY MILITARY CAREER I WAS still much under the influence of textbooks on strategy and tactics. Also, of course, I bore in mind constantly the battles of the past and the commanders whom I had studied and admired: Alexander, Eumenes, Hannibal, Scipio, my uncle Marius and that master of stratagem and brilliant improviser, Quintus Sertorius. And in the most practical affairs I have always tried to contribute something theoretical or artistic. I would wish a victory in war or a success in politics to be something inevitable, complete and perfect, like a fine piece of painting or a lyric poem. By this time I know well enough that in warfare these set pieces are rare indeed. The enemy is very seldom obliging enough to act exactly as one would wish and most victories are won not by some careful stroke of genius on the part of the commander, but simply by the superior quality of the soldiers under his command. Nevertheless it does sometimes happen that, owing to the folly or carelessness of the enemy, an opportunity presents itself for winning what may be described as a perfect victory. I was particularly anxious to find such an opportunity in this first campaign of mine in Gaul. This was partly because I was not yet sure of my army and I wished, by leading them to a total and inexpensive success, to give them the confidence in my command which they did not, at this stage, have; and partly, no doubt, I was thinking, as I often do, theoretically and artistically. There is something aesthetically satisfactory in attaining one's aims with no waste and with complete certainty.

So, after the departure of Divico, I took no immediate steps to bring the Helvetii to battle. I was waiting for the chance to inflict a crushing blow on them, and I was daily becoming better acquainted with my own troops and officers. For a whole fortnight we followed in the track of the long straggling column, cutting off any of them who strayed aside to plunder, but making no attempt to fight a general engagement. All this time we were seldom more than five or six miles away from them.

It was during this time that I became aware that the political situation in Gaul was very far from being as simple as I had imagined. I had a number of the leading men of the Aedui with me and I often conversed with them by means of interpreters. So long as one can rely on one's interpreters, this is a good method of dealing with foreigners. It is possible to watch them closely when their attention is occupied with the interpreter and, if one has even a little knowledge of their language oneself, it is usually easy to see whether they are speaking sincerely or not. I soon noticed with regard to the Aedui that while some of them — the old chief Diviciacus, for instance — were genuinely trying to be helpful, many were, for some reason or other, ill at ease and perplexed. I thought at first that this attitude might be the result of fear. It was possible that they considered our army no match for the Helvetii, and certainly their own cavalry — a force in which most Gallic states take a particular pride — had proved singularly disappointing in action. Soon after my interview with Divico I had sent out all the cavalry I had — most of which was Aeduan — in pursuit of the Helvetian column with orders to slow down its march and do all the damage possible. The Helvetii only had about five hundred horsemen of their own but had nevertheless succeeded in beating off and inflicting quite severe casualties on my cavalry who numbered four thousand.

It had never occurred to me that this cavalry defeat of ours

could have been the result of treachery; but that was because I
had not yet learned how intricate and how quickly changing are
all the moods and policies of the Gauls. What finally opened my
eyes was my discovery that not even half of the supplies originally
promised by the Aedui had in fact appeared. The excuses made
by the Aeduan nobles in my camp seemed to me entirely uncon-
vincing. Up to this time I had treated them with the greatest
courtesy, but I now spoke to them with some severity. I told
them that, as a result of their failure to keep their promises, I
would be unable to issue full rations to the troops when these became due and I accused them of first asking me to help them and
then betraying me. My words were effective, so that I was able in
the end to discover from two or three of the Aeduan chiefs the
surprising truth that about half of their number secretly hoped
that our army and I myself would be wiped out by the Helvetii.

There were, as usual in Gaul, several reasons for this split in
the tribal council. There was some genuine anti-Roman feeling,
based on the supposition that we intended to deprive the Gauls of
their liberties and gradually bring them all into subjection. Incidentally I had not yet even conceived of such a plan, so I was
interested to hear of this view. It was, it appeared, a view held
particularly firmly by the rich and popular Aeduan chief Dumnorix; but, according to the others, Dumnorix was exploiting what
may be called the patriotism of his tribe for his own ends. He
was married to a Helvetian woman and he had hopes of getting
Helvetian help in making himself king over the Aedui. It was because of these hopes that he had used his influence with the
Sequani to obtain permission for the Helvetii to go through the
mountains unmolested; and since then he had given our enemies
further proofs of his devotion to them. He had kept them constantly informed of our movements; he, with the Aeduan cavalry
which he commanded, had been the first to turn tail in the recent
engagement; and it was because of his influence among the officials
of the tribe that the promised grain had not been collected and sent
to us. There was, certainly, among the Aedui a strong party opposed to the ambitions of Dumnorix and perfectly willing to co-

operate with us. This party could see that there were very solid advantages to be gained from accepting Roman support. One of its leaders was the Druid Diviciacus, a brother of Dumnorix, and a most farsighted man who was one of the very few Gauls to have grasped the fact that the chief threat to his country as a whole and to each Gallic tribe was from the east, from Germany. Diviciacus imagined that his own tribe, if backed by Rome, might succeed in uniting Gaul and making the whole country into a powerful and prosperous nation. For some time I shared his views and only gradually became aware that Gaul could only be united and pacified by being incorporated with our empire. At this stage of operations I had scarcely begun to think in terms of Gaul as a whole. I saw only that I was in a singularly dangerous position. What particularly impressed me was the fact that even my well-wishers such as Diviciacus had not, up to this moment, dared to inform me of what the true situation was.

I had to decide rapidly between conciliation and punishment. My tendency has always been to mercy, when mercy can be exercised safely. This is partly because I dislike cruelty — having seen too much of it in my boyhood — and partly because I know that in the end, however much violence one may have to employ to gain power, one can only retain it by winning the good will of those who are, in fact, in subjection. Certainly with regard to the Aedui it was most important, both with a view to my future operations in Gaul and with a view to opinion in Rome, that I should appear as a friend and ally rather than as a governor or dictator. I would have been justified in making an example of Dumnorix, since he had betrayed me in battle; and I could have used my authority to have him condemned by his own people, since he had certainly disobeyed the instructions of his government. But I saw that any such action, taken so early against so popular a figure, might result in widening the already existing division among the Aedui. It might also discredit Diviciacus, who was one of the few on whom I could rely. I was therefore content with reprimanding Dumnorix severely and informing him that he owed his life to his brother's intervention on his behalf. Dumnorix pretended to be grateful and promised loyalty for the future. But I had him watched continually. He realized this and did, in fact, behave correctly for some time.

I now saw more clearly than ever that what I needed in order to impress both my own army and the one Gallic tribe which was, at any rate officially, friendly to me was a victory. The day after I had dealt with Dumnorix a perfect opportunity presented itself. The Helvetii had perhaps come to the conclusion that we were not formidable. Certainly they had, for once, encamped in a very badly chosen position. Behind them a hill sloped gently down to their great host with its countless wagons and fires. My patrols informed me that this hill could be easily climbed from the further side and I at once saw what could be done. I discussed the plan with Labienus, who was as enthusiastic about it as I was. He set out with two legions about midnight with orders to occupy the summit of the hill behind the Helvetii. I, with the rest of the army, was to attack them in front soon after dawn and, when Labienus heard the sound of fighting, he was to move down the hill and take the enemy in the rear. Nothing could have been simpler or more effective. It would have been, had it happened, a textbook victory. Unfortunately my advanced patrols were commanded by a man who considered himself a military expert. He was called, I think, Considius, and he used both to interest and to amuse us by recounting stories of the campaigns in which he had served with Sulla and with Crassus. If one were to have believed him one would have thought that neither Sulla nor Crassus (who, incidentally, was, in spite of his final disaster, an excellent general) would ever have won a battle without the aid of Considius, who, I remember, was particularly emphatic about the importance of carrying out all reconnaissance work with the utmost speed and care. It was Considius who now deprived me of this certain victory. We had moved up into position to attack and, as we discovered later from prisoners, the Helvetii had no notion of our intentions. Within half an hour I should have given the signal for action, when suddenly Considius appeared, breathless and excited with his own importance. The ridge behind the

Helvetian camp, he informed me, was strongly held by the Helvetii themselves. He had seen them with his own eyes and taken particular note of the barbaric crests on their helmets. What had happened to Labienus and his two legions he did not know.

This was to me, at this time, a most disturbing report. Could it be, I wondered, that the Helvetii had been thinking along the same lines as I had been thinking and had outwitted us? Had Labienus and his force fallen into an ambush and been annihilated? There was nothing to do but wait and to send out other patrols along the route which Labienus had taken and in the direction of the main Helvetian encampment. Most of the day had been wasted before my patrols returned with the news that the Helvetii were once again on the march and that the summit of the hill was and had been since dawn occupied by Labienus. What Considius had imagined to be barbaric crests had been either tree trunks or else the standards of our own legions. Labienus, naturally enough, had been amazed by my inaction; but he was too good a soldier not to obey his instructions precisely and so, after watching the Helvetii moving quietly out of danger, he had led his men back again and was on the way to rejoin me. At the time I was furious with Considius; but his inefficiency did teach me a useful lesson — to mistrust all "old soldiers" above the rank of centurion.

The effect of our failure to make use of this opportunity was serious. We were now within a day's march of the important Aeduan town of Bibracte and I decided to go there, partly in order to make certain of my supplies, partly in order to impress the Aeduan people with the sight of six Roman legions which, I should suggest, had answered their call for aid. I proposed to leave the Helvetii alone for a day or two and then, when I had settled matters to my satisfaction among the Aedui, to go after them again. They moved so slowly that it would be easy to overtake them. But as soon as we turned in the direction of Bibracte the Helvetii were informed of what we were doing. This did not surprise me. I was uncomfortably aware that many of our Gallic cavalry were still unreliable and still in contact with the enemy. I was surprised however to find that the Helvetii, as a result of this information, had evidently decided that we were frightened of them and had determined to engage us in battle. They also had changed the direction of their line of march and were now pursuing us as we had been pursuing them. Advanced elements of their column were soon in action against our rear guard.

I saw that I was now compelled, whether I liked it or not, to fight a battle that might be decisive for my whole future. I should have to fight on ground that was not of my own choosing against a tough and experienced enemy who was greatly superior to me in numbers. Even if I had been able to think out some brilliant or bewildering tactical plan, there would have been no time to put such a plan into operation. I should have to fight this battle in a perfectly conventional way and rely for victory simply on the discipline, training and courage of my troops.

First I sent out the cavalry to drive back the small numbers of Helvetii harassing our rear guard. It would not have surprised me altogether if the cavalry had deserted; but in fact they did as they were required to do. Probably they were waiting to see how the battle would go. While the cavalry were in action I proceeded to form up my army exactly in accordance with the prescriptions of military textbooks (which, in fact, are full of useful advice). I had four veteran legions. These were drawn up on rising ground in three lines. Behind these, on the summit of the hill, I placed the two legions which I had recently raised in Italy. I set the veterans in the third line to work immediately on entrenchments which were to protect the baggage and which could be manned by the two legions of recruits. On this occasion I made the somewhat histrionic gesture of having my own horse and then the horses of all the officers sent to the rear. I wished to show the men that we were all in this action together and that, if our lives were to be preserved, they could only be preserved by victory. Such gestures as this became, of course, quite unnecessary later. After the campaigns of this first year in Gaul, no soldier of mine, I think, would ever imagine that he could be deserted by his commander in chief. As it was, after having my horse sent away, I put on the scarlet cloak that I always wore in action and, before battle began, went along the lines on foot, speaking by name to the centurions in whom I trusted most and stopping from time to time to say a few words of encouragement to the men. I said the usual things (these too can be found in textbooks); but in saying them I was able, I think, to communicate some of my own enthusiasm for battle and determination to win. At these moments I feel exalted. And it would be not quite accurate to describe this exaltation as a form of egoism. In a sense it may be true to say that I see the long line of the legions as an extension of my own personality. They occupy more space than I can and they represent more physical power than can be concentrated in my body. Their activity, and even some of their thoughts and aspirations, are functions of my will, my ambition, my careful loving training and my determination of aim. In such a sense I may feel an army to be an instrument in my hand. But at these moments when battle is about to be joined, I feel much more than that. I feel the friend and comrade of every soldier who is about to face death or wounds and I am convinced that it is in my power to impart to each of them some of my own vehemence and assurance. At such times the soldiers too will speak to me easily, knowing that our language is the same.

All these sensations I knew well enough already, though I had only once previously commanded a considerable army, and that was against the comparatively disorganized opposition of Spanish tribes. Here in Gaul I had a much larger force to handle; I was confronted by a disciplined and powerful enemy who had already defeated armies of ours in the past; and my whole future hung upon the issue. This is therefore a battle which I often recall to mind.

While the legions had been forming line of battle and beginning to entrench a position on top of the hill, the Helvetii had been arranging their wagons in a great circle, also as a defensive position. Their main army had rapidly formed up into a dense phalanx, with the men standing shoulder to shoulder, their great shields overlapping. It was now possible to see in reality those

barbaric crests and helmets which Considius had imagined. They
seemed to add stature to the men who were big enough already
and who, as I had frequently been told by my Gallic interpreters,
despised us Romans for our puny and insignificant physique.
Looking down from the hill, I could see how utterly ineffective our
cavalry were proving against this mass of men. This was as I had
expected. There would be no further use for cavalry in the
battle except in the event of a general pursuit.

After brushing aside our cavalry the Helvetian phalanx began
to move steadily up to our front line. I was glad to see that they
were confident enough to advance uphill, since this was bound
to put them at a disadvantage. A volley of javelins coming even
slightly from above is twice as effective as when discharged on
the level. I knew that my veteran troops were fully aware of this
and would do their duty. They behaved indeed with exemplary
steadiness. They waited until the last moment before hurling their
spears and the weight of their first volley had the effect of dis-
rupting the whole Helvetian line. Indeed the Helvetians had
made a serious mistake by attacking in such close order. Often
two or more of their interlocked shields were pierced by one and
the same javelin, so that the holders of the shields found all their
movements impeded and could not even use their right arms effectively. Our men by now had drawn their swords and were going in to close quarters, yelling and shouting, cursing, grunting,
even laughing (since men at the moment of action will express
themselves in many different ways). We appeared, by contrast
with the dense mass of the enemy, to be a ridiculously thin line; yet
if one looked more closely one would see that our looser order enabled each one of our men to strike two blows where the enemy
struck one. Nevertheless, in spite of the initial shock caused by
our volley of javelins, the enemy, their front ranks still pressed
forward from behind, stood firm or swayed indeterminately, now
in one way now in another. It seemed as though our thin line was
hacking at some almost impenetrable forest. I was beside myself
with the suspense and longed to hurry forward and show myself fighting in the front line. But I knew that this was not the mo-

ment for such a display. Our men were doing well; it remained only
to be seen whether it would prove to be well enough.

Then I began to see deepening depressions in the Helvetian
line. They were falling back, first very slowly and then faster,
though not a single one of them turned to run away. By now our
second and third lines were in action and the Helvetii, under increasing pressure, fell back to the level ground at the foot of
the hill. We pushed them across a stretch of plain and began to
drive them up another hill at the further side. They were now
moving more quickly. The ground was covered with dead and
wounded. Our men were cheering each other on, in the belief
that at any moment all serious fighting would be over and the
retreat turned into a rout.

At this moment I saw fresh troops away on our right and realized instantaneously that in this my first battle in Gaul I had
been entirely outmaneuvered by old Divico or whoever was acting as the enemy commander in chief. I had fallen into precisely
the same trap (except that it was only half closed) as that in
which Hannibal had destroyed the Roman army at Cannae. My
main force had been drawn too far forward so that it was now
exposed to a crushing blow on its exposed flank. Had I had reserves on which I could rely, I might have used them; but I
hesitated to expose the two legions of recruits at this critical moment. If they were to panic, the situation would become hopeless.
I therefore sent orders to the third line of veterans which was now
joining in the pursuit of the main Helvetian force. My instructions
were that they were to turn about and engage the new army
which was bearing down on our right flank and which had somehow succeeded up to now in concealing itself among the Helvetian
wagons. It was, as we discovered later, a force composed of two
tribes, the Boii and Tulingi, who were allied to the Helvetians and
numbered about fifteen thousand fighting men.

On their appearance the Helvetii who had been retreating up
the hill first stood firm and then began to push our men back to
the level ground. These were agonizing moments. If our line
had cracked, the whole army would have been annihilated. But

our men, once they were on level ground, re-formed and fought back. Behind them and to their right they could hear the shock of another battle, as our third line engaged the Boii and the Tulingi. Here too a local defeat for us would have meant complete disaster, and here too, for the critical first moments of the attack, our men stood firm and fought back magnificently. After a few minutes I could see that the danger of total defeat was past. It was now a soldiers' battle and the better soldiers would win gradually and not necessarily decisively. So it happened. After nearly three hours' fighting the main body of the Helvetians, who had suffered very great losses, again retired up the hill; and at the same time the Boii and Tulingi fell back towards their wagons. There was nothing that could be called a flight, and our first two lines, who had suffered many casualties themselves, allowed the enemy to disengage. They were certainly in no condition to attempt a pursuit.

It was now late afternoon and I called upon the troops for a final effort before darkness. With the whole of our third line and additional cohorts which I had summoned from the other two lines an attack was launched on the circle of enemy wagons which contained much of their property and many of their women and children. Here the fighting was fierce and the din indescribable. Our men were now almost maddened by the blood they had shed already; the screams of the Helvetian women, who stood on the wagons, their breasts exposed and their hands stretched out, or else who joined in the fighting with the men, acted on us as though it were a battle cry of our own. When finally we broke through we took very few prisoners.

It was indeed a victory and I was soon receiving the congratulations of members of my staff. But I myself was fully aware that this victory had been won, not by any skill or prescience of my own, but entirely by the discipline and fighting qualities of the troops. If it had been merely a matter of generalship, I deserved to be defeated. Moreover, though we had inflicted enormous casualties on the enemy, we had suffered badly ourselves. About a hundred and thirty thousand of the Helvetii were still left. They marched off during the night and I would have liked to be able to pursue them. As it was, we had to spend three days on the battle-field, burying our dead and attending to our wounded. I spent much time during these days in seeing to it that every soldier and centurion who had distinguished himself in the fighting was prop-erly rewarded.

It was a victory. Of that there can be no doubt. And the results which immediately followed were of the greatest importance. But I could not afford many more victories of this sort.

Chapter 3

Protector of the Gauls

THE HELVETII HAD LOST MOST OF THEIR SUPPLIES. THEY CONtinued to march westward, but had, I knew, no chance of survival unless they could gain the alliance and support of some tribe or other on their way. I had already learned enough about Gallic politics to know that this was a possibility to be reckoned with and so I sent messengers to all the tribal councils along the Helvetian route to make it clear that I would treat as enemies all who gave the defeated army any provisions or any help at all. Fortunately my orders were obeyed and the Helvetii were left with no other course than to surrender.

I gave them very generous terms. Most of them were directed to return to their own country and rebuild the towns and villages which they had destroyed. I made arrangements for having them supplied with grain until they could support themselves once more. The survivors of the Boii, who had special relations of friendship with the Aedui, were settled in Aeduan territory. However I wished to be certain that my instructions were carried out and, since I knew that the Helvetii still constituted a formidable fighting force, I demanded the surrender of their arms for the time being. Later I wanted them to use these arms of theirs to defend their country against the Germans and indeed I was already apprehensive about the danger of German hordes occupy-

ing their old lands. Perhaps my order for the surrender of arms
was misinterpreted by some of the tribesmen who may have
thought that I intended either to massacre or to sell my prisoners
as slaves. Certainly six thousand of them did attempt, after
agreement had been reached between their leaders and myself, to
escape in the direction of the Rhine. I at once sent instructions to
the tribes through which they had to pass and these instructions
were obeyed. The escaped prisoners were rounded up almost to
a man. They had put themselves outside all rules of war and I had
the whole number sold as slaves.

I was still in the neighborhood of Bibracte and here I was visited by chieftains from all over Gaul, who came ostensibly to offer me their congratulations, but really out of curiosity or to find
out how the presence of a Roman army could be used to further
their particular interests. During these days I greatly increased
my knowledge of the country. I was well served by my interpreters, who were mostly Gauls from the Province or from Northern Italy, and who had been chosen not only for their knowledge of the language but for their general intelligence, charm,
good looks and devotion to me. Many of them are still dear
friends of mine and all of them have become immensely rich.
With their aid and the aid of various Italian merchants and
Gallic chiefs, I began to form for myself a more or less accurate
picture of Gaul as a whole, and at the same time I quite suddenly
conceived the idea that it might be possible to force or induce
the whole country, from the Atlantic to the Pyrenees, to accept
the supremacy and, in the end, the customs and civilization of
Rome. When first this idea occurred to me, I experienced that
agreeable thrilling of the nerves which must be felt often, I
think, by great poets and can be felt sometimes even by those
who, like myself, have some pretensions to style in prose. It is a
thrill which seems to accompany the contemplation of something
created, or of some transformation of nature, of existing material,
into a new thing. The idea must be audacious and also strictly
practicable. So, in a moment and before the long hours of con-

sideration and the long years of struggle, I saw the conquest of Gaul.

I think I may say that the idea was peculiarly my own. When I began to explain it to Labienus, he was enthusiastic in his support. He saw before him a long career of victory and honor and wealth — and at the time when he deserted me he had achieved all of these. I, of course, also felt the pull of such attractions. In particular I longed for a military reputation that might be comparable with that of Pompey; and I also looked forward to a time unlike any that I had known, when I would be able to lend rather than be forced to borrow money. But it was something more than the prospect of honor or wealth which thrilled my nerves. I saw order being born out of disorder, something certain in the place of vagueness, vacillation and the aimlessness of personal ambitions. It was only gradually that I saw my way, and I am still, in some directions, groping for it.

So far as Gaul is concerned, one of those who, in these early days, gave me particular help was the Druid Diviciacus, the Aeduan whose popular brother, Dumnorix, was still, I suspected, an enemy both to me and to Rome. I learnt from Diviciacus much about Gaul, including some simple geographical facts which I should have known already. But in those days people in Rome were almost wholly ignorant of Gaul beyond the Alps. Even senators and ex-governors knew little more than the names of a few tribes beyond the Cevennes or the Jura. Our merchants were better informed than our administrators or military commanders; but our merchants had never penetrated as far as the Belgic tribes to the north or the Armoricans in the west. We tended to think of all Transalpine Gauls as Celts; but I learned from Diviciacus that the Celts only constituted about a third of the whole country. South and east of them were the Aquitanians; north of them were the Belgae, reputed to be the best warriors in Gaul. There were differences in language, customs and laws among these three areas; indeed, as I listened to Diviciacus, I could see that there were differences everywhere. In Gaul each state was as likely as not to be at war with its neighbors and within each state there were certain to be at least two parties struggling for power. I saw to it that memoranda were prepared for me by members of my staff to cover the whole country and even began at this stage to collect information about the island of Britain. But I realized that for the next year or so my activities would necessarily be confined to Celtic Gaul and so I took particular care to become as well informed as possible about the problems and possibilities of this area.

Diviciacus told me that in his boyhood there had been in the whole of this part of Gaul two predominant tribes — his own tribe of the Aedui and another tribe, the Arverni, who lived in the mountainous country north of the Cevennes. About ten years ago the Arverni, as part of their policy against the Aedui, had allied themselves with the Sequani, who had a frontier on the Rhine. The Sequani had called in the help of German mercenaries who had come in larger numbers every year until by now a great horde of these savages, under their king Ariovistus, had become established on the Gallic side of the Rhine. These Germans had defeated the Aedui and other Gallic tribes in battle, had taken the children of their leading men as hostages and compelled them to give hostages also to the Sequani. However the Sequani themselves had been the next to suffer. Ariovistus had first annexed a third of their territory as a reward for his intervention and recently, since he was constantly being joined by fresh bands of German warriors, he had demanded that they should evacuate another third. In all his dealings with the Gauls, Ariovistus had behaved like a cruel, arrogant and capricious tyrant. The Aedui and all other tribes in the west of Gaul were convinced that his final aim was the conquest of the whole country and, since Germany appeared to have unlimited reserves of manpower, he was quite capable, unless checked at once, of achieving his aim. Diviciacus suggested that I should win the gratitude not only of the Aedui but of the whole of Gaul if I were to use the prestige of my recent victory and, if necessary, my army to make Ariovistus realize that Rome was prepared to defend her allies.

I knew already, of course, something about Ariovistus and the German menace, though I had not met Diviciacus at the time, some years previously, when he had come to Rome in person in order to try to persuade our senate to see the danger that could be involved in a German invasion of Gaul. This mission of Diviciacus had taken place two years before my consulship, when I was governor in Spain. It had not been very successful, though the senate had indeed passed the vague decree, of which I was to make full use, empowering the Roman governor of the Province to defend the Aedui, if he could do so without risk. Our policy, if it could be called a policy, was to remain on friendly terms with all powerful tribes, whether Gallic or German, beyond the Alps in the hope that no tribe would become so powerful as to threaten our own interests. Neither I nor anyone else had taken the threat from Germany very seriously. Indeed it was during my consulship that the senate had bestowed on Ariovistus the title, which he certainly did not deserve, of "Friend of the Roman People."

At that time I did not know that I should be in a position to intervene myself in western and central Gaul. Now, having seen with my own eyes the mass migration of the Helvetii, I knew how formidable these movements of tribes could be; and I saw too that Diviciacus was offering me an opportunity which, if I took it, might have the most far-reaching consequences. He was inviting me to represent myself as the protector, first of the Aedui and then of the whole of Gaul. And from "protector" to "governor" is a small step. Naturally I was impelled to accept the invitation, although I realized that in doing so I should be running an enormous risk. Success would give me just that position which might make possible in the end the fulfillment of my wider aims; but failure would almost certainly mean the annihilation of my army and myself. And, though Ariovistus could not be described as an unknown quantity, many factors in the situation were obscure. Without having an exact knowledge of the size of his army, I knew that it greatly outnumbered my own and that it was continually being reinforced from across the Rhine. His troops had constantly defeated the best soldiers in Gaul and I knew that the

Gauls themselves were no mean antagonists. To make contact with him I should have to advance into a part of the country which was practically unexplored, leaving my communications to be guarded by Gauls on whose loyalty I could not depend. Finally, and most important, I was not yet quite sure of the morale of my own army. They had won a victory, but they knew quite well what it had cost them.

I determined that I must risk everything and made the necessary preparations. First, largely because of the influence and initiative of Diviciacus, I was invited to preside over what was called, somewhat euphemistically, the council of the whole of Gaul. In fact the Gauls are very rarely capable of co-operation or of taking counsel together, though for a short time, in later years, Vercingetorix did succeed in uniting nearly the whole country against me. I have hardly ever known a council of Gaul to which all tribes sent representatives. On this occasion however the leading men of quite a number of tribes did put in an appearance. The main business had, of course, been arranged beforehand and Diviciacus had undertaken to develop the theme. He made an admirable speech, describing accurately enough, though in a most emotional way, what Gaul had to fear from Ariovistus and appealing to me, as the ally of the Aedui and the friend of Gaul, to take a stand against this savage king who was depriving them all of land and of liberty. The speech was warmly applauded by all except the representatives of the Sequani, who sat with bowed heads in silence and would make no response to my requests of them to explain their views. Diviciacus intervened and stated that the Sequani, even in the privacy of this council, were so frightened of Ariovistus that they did not dare to open their mouths. He may have been right. More probably, though, the Sequani merely recognized the fact that, whatever happened, they would be the losers. They would either be incorporated in the empire of Ariovistus or else made by me once more dependents of the Aedui. They had, indeed, every reason to look dejected.

Among the other delegates, however, I noticed a keen excitement (the Gauls are excited by everything new) and also some evidence of genuine resolution. They had indeed suffered from Ariovistus and, as a nation of warriors, they had been particularly humiliated by their military defeats. They wanted security and they wanted revenge. It had not, I think, occurred to many of them to consider which was preferable — a Roman or a German domination. They still believed — like the ordinary politicians in Rome — in a kind of ineffectual license which they described as liberty. Though here my friend Diviciacus was an exception. He realized that his country could never be effectively united except under some dominant power and he saw that the choice to be made was between us and the Germans. He himself preferred civilization, though even he can scarcely be credited with the ability to have seen the possibility of a general and equal civilization in which the remotest areas of Gaul would share. He still thought chiefly of the greatness of his own tribe and he rightly believed that, if the Aedui loyally supported me, I should see to it that they received special privileges. And indeed I did treat the Aedui with the most particular consideration. It was they who gave me the opportunity for developing and following my idea. At this first council of Gaul over which I presided, I made a reassuring reply to the speech of Diviciacus and the appeals of the rest. I promised to defend Gaul against foreign invasion, but I was careful not to say anything which, if reported to Ariovistus, could be taken by him as a declaration of war. He was, after all, officially the "Friend of the Roman People," and I knew very well that, unless I acted correctly, my enemies in Rome would accuse me of waging an aggressive war in order to enrich myself or to gain further prestige. In fact these were secondary considerations. So I informed the Gauls that I felt sure that Ariovistus, as a faithful ally of Rome, would be prepared to listen to reason and would accept my demand that he should keep his hands off others who were also our allies. Both I and my audience knew that Ariovistus would do nothing of the kind.

My next step was to send a messenger to the German king, asking him to meet me at some point halfway between our present positions, as I had various matters to discuss with him.

Ariovistus insolently replied that, if I had anything to say to him,
I could come and visit him; he himself had nothing to say to me
and was not going to take the trouble and undergo the expense of
marching into my part of Gaul. My next message to him was
an ultimatum. I demanded an undertaking that he would not
bring any more Germans across the Rhine, that he would
restore to the Aedui all hostages of theirs whom he held, that he
would compel the Sequani to do the same thing, and that he would
guarantee in future to respect the rights both of the Aedui and
their allies. As I had expected, this message evoked a blustering
and bellicose reply. Ariovistus refused to admit that I had any
right whatever to intervene in Gaul. What he occupied, he
claimed, was his by right of conquest, just as the Province was
ours. If being a "Friend of the Roman People" meant giving up
what he had won in battle, he would prefer to be known as an
enemy. He concluded by pointing out that his army had never
been defeated and boasted of the fact that they had now lived in
the open for fourteen years on end; he claimed to command
troops who were physically fitter and better trained than any
in the world.

Emergence of an Army

AT ABOUT THE TIME WHEN I RECEIVED THIS MESSAGE FROM ARIO-
vistus more reports came in of the movements of German tribes.
A very large force had assembled on the farther bank of the
Rhine, evidently with the intention of crossing in order to reinforce Ariovistus's army of veterans. Soon afterwards I was informed that Ariovistus himself was moving westward in the direction of Vesontio, an important town of the Sequani, which was
full of military supplies. I realized that I should have to act
quickly and proceeded to do so. When I look back I am inclined
to think that this was the most hazardous of all my campaigns. I
have taken risks before and since; but on other occasions I have
had a clearer idea of what precisely were the risks involved. On
this occasion I had little knowledge either of the country or of
the enemy and I was not entirely able to depend on my own
troops, who had not yet acquired the habit of victory.

They were unused too to the kind of exertions which I would
require of them and which, later, they were invariably so willing
to undertake. Now, for example, it was necessary, in order to be
sure of reaching Vesontio before Ariovistus, to march in each
twenty-four hours at least four times the distance we had been
used to while following the Helvetian column. I was informed
that there were some complaints from the soldiers about these

forced marches and I had no doubt that there were some "military experts" with us (Considius, of course, among them) who were saying that I was impairing the efficiency of my army by demanding too much of them before a battle. Soon every soldier under my command would know as well as I did myself that speed before a battle is almost as important as the courage one displays in the battle itself. It became a matter of pride with us always to appear when we were least expected. So, on this occasion, we reached and occupied Vesontio long before Ariovistus was near the place. Thus we had time to make satisfactory arrangements for our supplies and to discover something about the routes which lay ahead of us in the direction of the Rhine.

Everything, in fact, had gone as well as I could have hoped, when I was suddenly confronted with a situation which I had never expected at all and which, I hope, I shall never be confronted with again. I was able to deal with this situation partly, I think, because of my long experience of politics which had taught me how people in a crowd are, quite often, entirely beyond the reach of reason. An unconfirmed rumor, a false insinuation, a promise that can never be redeemed may, by exciting a particular type of easily communicable emotion, deprive even intelligent people of the ability to consider some case or proposal on its merits. It is not reason that can bring them to their senses again but only some show of reason which in fact is directed not at logical conviction but at substituting one emotion for another. As a rule the framework and discipline of an army are fairly effective barriers to these outbursts of irresponsible feeling which are so common whenever civilians are gathered together in any numbers. But when, for whatever cause, an army does lose its inner cohesion, when the soldier begins to think as though he were a civilian, then the situation can become much worse than anything one is likely to find in the Forum.

At this time in Gaul I remembered well what Clodius had told me about the army of his brother-in-law Lucullus, in the disintegration of which, incidentally, he had himself played a large and discreditable part. Lucullus was one of the best generals we have had. In my youth I always attacked him, because he had been a friend of Sulla and might be an enemy of mine. But even then I could recognize his military genius. He conquered the East more quickly and with fewer troops than Pompey was to use later. And at a moment which should have been the culmination of his victorious progress, his own soldiers had mutinied. I like to think that my own agitation against Lucullus in Rome, carried out purely for political reasons, had no effect on this disgraceful desertion of a great general by his troops. Yet it must be owned that Lucullus, for all his very great ability, did not deserve devotion. There was no bond between him and his men. He was, as Marius would have said, an aristocrat; he was not, in my sense of the word, a god.

Now, on the borders of the Rhineland, with this incalculably important campaign in front of us, I suddenly became aware that all was not well with my own army. I had spent much of the time on the march with the Tenth Legion and had found the centurions, officers and men remarkably cheerful, keen and efficient. I had assumed that much the same spirit existed throughout the army and in fact I believe it did until we reached Vesontio. Here the troops got into conversation with local Gauls and with a few Italian merchants who were doing good business with the Gauls and hoped to be able to make profit out of Ariovistus too. The Gauls are particularly fond both of giving and receiving information and find it quite impossible not to exaggerate everything which they say or hear. They are also very prone to self-justification. These particular Gauls and others from the neighboring tribes had frequently been defeated by Ariovistus in battle; it was therefore natural that they should claim that Ariovistus was invincible. They began to spread the most alarming stories and, as no one in our army had had any direct experience of German warriors, there was no one to contradict these stories. Few people seemed capable even of thinking rationally; and indeed I have often noticed that in states of general emotional disturbance people prefer the miraculous to the intelligible. According to the Gauls of Vesontio these Germans whom we were about to meet were all of gigantic stature and of almost incredible courage. They had been trained in arms since boyhood and they had never in history been defeated. It was even said that they had somehow developed a certain look in the eye, or expression of savagery, which was enough in itself to rout armies, so that even seasoned troops had often turned and run before a single blow had been struck.

It is still difficult for me to understand how it happened that these absurd stories came to be widely believed. No doubt people are apprehensive before the unknown or the partly known; and we were now approaching an area of dense forest with, beyond it, what was still the almost fabulous river Rhine. We had only Aeduan guides to rely upon and we were entirely dependent on the Aedui and a few other tribes for our supplies. There was certainly plenty for me, as commander in chief, to worry about; but I was not unduly worried. I knew that I could trust Diviciacus; I had thought that I could trust my army. I was infuriated to find that, as it appeared, my army would not trust me.

The rot started (as no doubt Marius would have expected) among certain well-born officers who had had little military experience and had come out from Rome with the aim rather of making their fortunes than of engaging the enemy. There were quite a number who, at the beginning of my career in Gaul, used to ask me for commissions in the belief that I would give them comfortable and lucrative careers. Their mistake was understandable. They realized that I, having been since my early youth always very heavily in debt, needed to restore my own fortunes; and, since I have a certain reputation for generosity, they were sure that I would share my gains with others. They did not immediately grasp the fact that I have never been, as Crassus was, greatly concerned with money, though I have always wanted, for political or other reasons, the use of a great deal of it. In Gaul I myself, my officers, my centurions and my soldiers would, in fact, all become rich; but we would enrich ourselves, as it were, incidentally. And those who were not prepared to fight and march and dig and stay awake would not enrich themselves at all. At

this time some of those who had only known me as a politician
or man of fashion in Rome were still ignorant of what I expected
of them while on military service. After a day or two in Vesontio
I found that I was receiving a number of requests for leave. Some
of the reasons given were good and some bad, but all these requests came from that particular set of noble, though impover-
ished, young men who, as I knew, were under the impression that
they could get money without winning battles. I was glad to let
them go; but I probably showed by my manner what I thought
of them. The result was that some others of the same sort became
frightened of being considered cowards and determined to stay
on. Unfortunately, however, they remained, in spite of this resolution, just as frightened of the Germans as before. They kept on
making their wills and I was constantly being asked to witness
these documents. Some of them would hold farewell drinking parties in their tents, as though they were sure they only had a few
more days to live. In my presence they would often look at me
with a rather ridiculously affected devotion and would sometimes
burst into tears.

Such conduct, though disgraceful, would have been amusing if
it had not influenced others. Quite suddenly a state was reached
in which the whole army was rapidly losing its efficiency as a
fighting force. This state of affairs was a kind of infection. One
may say that it was caused by fear of the enemy or by a general
lack of confidence in my ability as a commander. Yet it is not
usual for a trained legionary to be afraid and there was no evidence to suggest that I was less efficient than most generals. And,
as events were to show, there was no good reason either for
fear or for lack of faith. But I was certainly aware that, as a result
of what might be called a kind of mental disease, we were in extreme danger. If Ariovistus had attacked, we should have been
defeated and my personal career would have been over. I discovered that even some centurions were affected by this pervasive failure of nerve. Naturally they would not admit that they
were frightened; in fact they would express the greatest contempt
for the enemy; but at the same time they would show them-

selves anxious to get as far away from him as possible. Difficulties of supply or the impossibility of properly exploring the route through the forests were the reasons they put forward for their anxiety, and, since no doubt they wished to disguise their cowardice even from themselves, they certainly believed in what they were saying. It was also convenient for them to exaggerate the cowardice of the rest. Some, for example, came to me and said that, while they themselves would follow me anywhere, they much feared that the others would refuse to march when I gave the signal.

I sometimes think that this was the most dangerous situation with which I have ever had to deal. My feeling of rage was intense, as also was that feeling of exaltation which I always experience at critical and compulsive moments. Labienus was as angry as I was. He wanted to parade the army and have every tenth man executed as a lesson to the rest. It was an old-fashioned disciplinary method which Crassus had found effective when his troops had disobeyed him during the war with Spartacus. But it was an unsuitable expedient for me at that time. Too many in the army were affected by the disease and the enemy was too close to us. As the disease appeared to me to be of an hysterical or, one might say, political nature, I determined to deal with it by the political means of oratory. But I was aware that this was something more important than a political speech — that upon my oratory depended our lives and my honor.

I summoned a meeting of all centurions in the army, of every grade, and began by abusing them in the most violent terms for their ignorant and undisciplined presumption. I asked them what business it was of theirs to inquire where I was leading them or why. Since when, I demanded, had it been the province of centurions and soldiers to organize supplies or to decide upon the direction of march? They were, after these preliminary remarks, startled by my manner and I could see that their minds were alert for what I would say next. I introduced the question of the Germans in a somewhat incidental way, as though it were not a matter of great importance. Ariovistus, I told them, was under great obligations both to Rome and to me personally. Once he saw that he was faced by a resolute army he would in all probability do as I had asked him to do, that is to say restore the Aeduan hostages and retire behind the Rhine.

Those words of mine had the effect which I had desired. My audience became much calmer and began to look as though they were as resolute as I had stated them to be. I immediately confronted them with the other alternative. Ariovistus, I said, might be mad enough to prefer war to peace. If he did, so much the worse for him. I reminded them of how my Uncle Marius and his army had annihilated the great invading hordes of Germans some forty years before. And I pointed out that the victories of Ariovistus over the Gauls were no evidence of any exceptional fighting abilities of the Germans. The Gauls had never put a united army into the field and, since they fought only in local detachments, every advantage had been on the side of Ariovistus.

I then referred briefly to the question of supplies, informing my audience that this was my business rather than theirs and that I had in fact dealt with it so thoroughly that there was not the slightest danger of any shortage. As for the route, they would soon have an opportunity of judging that for themselves. I closed on a personal note. I could not endure, I said, the idea of leading an army which had no confidence in me as a commander. I should therefore strike camp earlier than I had intended. We should begin our advance against the enemy before dawn. This would give me an opportunity of seeing how many men in the army retained their courage and a sense of honor and how many were miserable cowards. If no one else would follow me, I should go forward alone, with only the Tenth Legion. I had no doubt whatever about the loyalty of the centurions and men in that legion, whatever I might think about the rest.

This speech had the effect which I had desired. Now the whole army wanted to fight at the earliest possible moment. The men of the Tenth were delighted with the confidence I had shown in them. The men of the other legions spent much of the rest of the

day in sending deputations to me in order to explain that they
had never been reluctant to follow me and to assure me that they
were as brave as or braver than their fellow soldiers in the Tenth.

We marched at the hour which I had mentioned. As I had expected, Ariovistus refused my terms. I forced him to fight before
he was quite ready to do so. His army was annihilated. We killed
more than eighty thousand Germans, including two wives and
one daughter of Ariovistus. To my great delight we recovered
safe and sound my young friend Procillus, who had fallen into German hands. Ariovistus himself escaped across the Rhine. He
died soon afterwards. But more than this great victory, which
was won by ordinary skill, Roman discipline and by the fact that
each man fought like a tiger, I remember the anxious moments
which preceded it. This was the only occasion when troops of
mine have ever in the face of the enemy shown any reluctance to
meet danger or difficulty. It was an occasion which ended very
happily. From this time we trusted each other and felt ourselves
to be what we gradually became, invincible.

Chapter 5

War with the Belgae

THAT FIRST YEAR IN GAUL GAVE ME THE OPPORTUNITY OF EVEN-
tually conquering the whole country. My enemies in Rome could
not reasonably maintain that I had fought the campaigns against
the Helvetii and Ariovistus wantonly and for my own interest. In
both cases my help had been demanded by the legally constituted
government of the Aedui, who were friends and allies of the Roman people. And as for the Gauls themselves, those tribes, including the Aedui, who had suffered from German invasion were, at
least for the time being, genuinely grateful to me. It was therefore
possible to go further, and the first step which I took was to quarter the legions for the winter in the country of the Sequani, far
outside the Province, to which they had expected to return.
They were there, I gave out, to defend Rome's allies, and in a
sense this was true; but they were there to stay.

I spent the winter, as I intended to do every year, in my other
province on the Italian side of the Alps. There was much administrative work to be done there and it was also easier, from
that distance, to keep in touch with what was going on in Rome.
As always when I was away I left Labienus in command of the
legions. I had complete confidence in him and my confidence, up
to the very end of the Gallic wars, was fully justified. He was an
admirable general, being particularly expert in the use of cavalry.

He was thoroughly reliable in a conventional way, and was also able to confuse the enemy by rapid changes of plan or unexpected expedients. He inspired fear rather than devotion, but his men trusted his leadership and indeed, except when he was fighting against me, he never fought in a losing battle. His intelligence work too was remarkably efficient. During the winters his spies were operating all over Gaul and the dispatches which he sent to me, giving his own assessment of a situation which was always complex, were invaluable to me.

I had known Labienus from the days when he and I, as very young men, had, shortly after the abdication of Sulla, served together on the staff of Isauricus in Cilicia. Fifteen years later, when Labienus held the office of tribune, he and I worked closely together in politics. At that stage of my career the most brilliant success I could have imagined possible was to become Chief Pontiff. I secured this position as a result of a bill passed by Labienus which re-established the ancient right of the people, whose favorite I was, to be the electors. It was not till after my consulship that I was able to reward him for what he had done for me. I knew that he wanted a military command, though I could scarcely imagine how excellent a commander he would prove to be. He had the same love of distinction as I have and, whenever possible, I used to allow him to carry out operations independently of me. And he, on his side, would behave with the most scrupulous loyalty. He knew that his soldiers were my soldiers and when, in my absence, he led them into battle, he would ask them to behave as though I were watching them and as though I, not he, were their commander in the field. I sometimes wonder whether this great loyalty and these acts of magnanimity which I so much admired were, in fact, a violation of his true nature. Did this faithful and generous service rankle in his heart instead of liberating and invigorating his spirit? Was he always secretly jealous of me and did this jealousy become the stronger and more bitter through being repressed? Certainly in the end he hated me with a more than political bitterness.

He is the only officer of mine who has ever betrayed me. Up

to now, then, I have been luckier than that great commander Sertorius, who was assassinated by his own officers and those who were supposed to be his friends. In this case too, I suppose, the motive was jealousy. There was also the fact that Perperna and the other Romans who murdered Sertorius resented the fact that he was of comparatively humble birth and yet so infinitely superior to them, the nobility, as a general and as a man. No one in Rome can very well look down on me socially; but there are plenty who are jealous and some who, from a doctrinaire point of view, genuinely believe that I am infringing what they call their liberty. I have seen this "liberty" of theirs in action. It has resulted in the death or exile of every reformer I have known since my child-hood, in maladminstration abroad, oppression and inefficiency at home. I too should have been eliminated by the legal operations of their "liberty" if the officers and men of the Gallic legions had not been prepared to fight for my honor and my life.

How well I was served by my officers from the very beginning! Apart from Labienus there was young Publius Crassus, the son of the financier, who had that beautiful and intelligent wife whom Pompey married later. It was young Crassus who gave the decisive order in the battle with Ariovistus. Next year, with one legion, he pacified all the tribes along the Atlantic coast and in the year after he received the submission of Aquitania. I wish I had never given him leave to accompany his father to Parthia. He died gallantly there, and I shall think of him as well as of the lost legions when I take the field, in the eastern war which I have planned. They were all good, those officers of the army of Gaul. Some were brilliant like Decimus Brutus and Trebonius and, above all, Antony, though he was not there at the beginning. Then there were the perfectly sound, skillful and reliable commanders like Caninius, Fabius and so many more. Even Sabinus was good, till he made that fatal mistake. And Quintus Cicero, who is so lacking in his brother's eloquence and who used to spend his leisure hours in writing plays — I have known him hold onto an almost untenable position with a courage and resolution that are quite beyond praise. But his plays were really unreadable.

They were a varied and colorful lot, the officers and men of
that Gallic army, and they used to excite a good deal of unfavorable comment in Rome. At the beginning I had my friend
Balbus as prefect of engineers and he did this work, as he has
done all other work for me, brilliantly. Soon, however, it seemed
better for Balbus to remain in Rome. I trusted him entirely; he
was a friend of Pompey as well as a friend of mine; and he was an
expert diplomatist. In Gaul, Mamurra took on his job and the
sudden riches which Mamurra began to acquire offended everyone. Catullus used to write witty and obscene lampoons about
him and about me. I was distressed by these lampoons, partly because they were effective and partly because I much admire
Catullus as a poet. I am glad that I made friends with him before
he died. He was a clever and affectionate young man, but he
could not see human beings very clearly. Otherwise he would have
realized that neither Mamurra nor I are monsters; and he would
not have fallen so pathetically in love with Clodia. In literature
it may be that a kind of blindness is sometimes an advantage.
Catullus, for instance, may well be remembered as one of the
great love poets of the world. The object of his passion was a
grasping woman whom everyone in Rome has been to bed with.
He believed her to be first a goddess, then a fiend. She deserved
neither his love nor his hatred; yet both love and hatred were
genuine, however misdirected. Had Catullus been a better judge
of character, he would have felt neither of these emotions for
Clodia, and our literature would have been the poorer. Nevertheless there is a sense in which it is true to say that nature will
not tolerate falsehood or misdirection. It was probably Clodia
who killed Catullus in the end, though she certainly cannot be
blamed for it. He committed too much of himself to something
which did not exist.

One cannot afford such mistakes either in warfare or in private
life. And if, by any chance, I, like Sertorius, should ever be attacked or even assassinated by men whom I have trusted or forgiven, perhaps I should be accused of having made the same mis-

take as Catullus — of having failed to observe that where one trusts most one can be most deeply injured. Such an accusation would not be true. I understand ambition, prejudice, and envy. I can even understand the cold self-righteousness that Cato had and with which, I am afraid, he has imbued Marcus Brutus, who is otherwise so promising and admirable a character. No, I should not be surprised by any obliquity in human character. I have a fairly correct idea of how far any particular individual can be trusted. It is simply that I prefer to trust and to forgive. Let others be themselves, if they must: I will be myself. And I am lucky indeed to have many friends who can be trusted absolutely. Not only Balbus, Oppius, Matius and that intimate circle who have followed and aided my plans from the beginning; but hundreds of others, of all classes and all races. And the centurions too. I am bound to them rather more strongly and reliably than ever Catullus was to Clodia. I can still see, for example, as clearly as I did at the time the face of Gaius Crastinus of the Tenth as he listened to my words at Vesontio before we fought on the Rhine. He was a young man then and his eyes blazed with delight when I showed my utter confidence in his legion. He died like a hero, sure of victory, at Pharsalus. If, in the future, anyone reads my books, his name will be remembered with mine.

No wonder that with such officers and men I conquered Gaul. Yet, as I look back on those campaigns, I can see more clearly than I did at the time that every year, almost, we might have been destroyed. I was invariably, as it were, slightly in advance of my fortune. I was always compelled by events whether in Gaul or Rome to take risks. Something new was always happening and I had to move faster and faster in order to keep ahead of danger and to impose my own selection of alternatives upon necessity. Was I pursued or pursuing? Was I shaping or being shaped by events? To these questions there is no perfectly satisfactory answer, yet any answer that is given should, to be accurate, emphasize what is active in me rather than what is passive. I cannot refuse an opportunity.

All through that first winter and early spring when I was on the Italian side of the Alps, I kept receiving dispatches from Labienus which made it clear that in the campaigning season we should have to fight hard in order to maintain and extend our influence. My action in quartering Roman troops in the middle of Gaul had produced an immediate effect. Though in the neighborhood of our winter quarters things were quiet and though the pro-Roman party among the Aedui seemed to be firmly in control of that state, there was no doubt that many of the Celtic tribes were bitterly opposed to our presence among them. Some of these tribes had got into touch with the very formidable nations of the Belgae in the north and, so Labienus informed me, a great Belgic coalition had been formed with the object of destroying our legions or driving them back across the Alps. According to Labienus's information the Belgae were capable of putting into the field an army of nearly three hundred thousand men, some of whom were considered to be the best troops in Gaul. I thought this figure exaggerated, though in fact it was not greatly so. Nevertheless I raised two more legions in Northern Italy and sent them to join Labienus. I put my young nephew, Quintus Pedius, the son of my elder sister, in command of these legions and was glad to notice that he carried out his duties efficiently. I have always wanted to find someone in my own family to be, as it were, the inheritor not only of my money, but of my ambition and my abilities. For some time I had hopes of Pedius and I have indeed provided for him in my will. He is loyal and reasonably competent, but not, I am afraid, exceptional in any way. I now have much more confidence in a younger man, my great-nephew Octavius, whom I have made my first heir. His health is weak (as mine was at his age) and he is somewhat lacking in charm; but of his ambition, tenacity and intelligence there can be no doubt. At this time Octavius was a small boy. Pedius was handsome and was devoted to me. It gave me much pleasure to find that he had conducted himself well in the organization of the newly conscripted troops.

I myself arrived at our headquarters in Gaul soon after he did.

We took the offensive at once and I found that the Belgic confeder-
acy had indeed got together an enormous force. But it was badly
led and inefficiently supplied. I had arranged for Diviciacus and
his Aedui to threaten a diversionary attack on the territory be-
longing to the Bellovaci, who were supplying the largest contingents to the Belgic army. News of this move encouraged the
Belgae to attack us on ground most unfavorable to them, and
after the failure of this attack they began a general withdrawal,
but were too numerous and too badly disciplined to be able to
carry out this operation successfully. Our cavalry, followed by
the legions, spent a whole day in killing them. After this, tribe
after tribe submitted without a blow.

Among the Belgic tribes nearest to Celtic Gaul I had found one,
the Remi, which, having observed how I was treating the Aedui,
became genuinely pro-Roman and remained so. Both the chieftains of the Remi and old Diviciacus were extremely helpful to
me on this campaign. Disunited as Gaul was, there was still a
number of ties, whether of religion or family relationship, which
connected together individuals from all over the country. It was
therefore always easy to find someone influential who could represent me in negotiations even with the most remote tribes. I was
very careful to see that, once a tribe had made its submission,
it was treated as well as circumstances permitted. None of its
people were enslaved; no looting was tolerated. In most cases I
supported whatever government I found in power, though, as time
went by and I noticed more and more instances of inefficiency, I
began to insist that candidates whom I favored myself should be
elected to the chief magistracies, and in some cases I arranged
that particularly talented Gauls in whom I had confidence should
be made kings of their tribes. This was no very great innovation.
Kings had been common in Gaul until very recently. By reviving
the institution I hoped to show that I was not attempting any
fundamental disruption of Gallic custom. At the same time it is,
of course, much easier to deal with one man than with a set of
magistrates who, because of all kinds of personal rivalries, are
quite incapable of pursuing a consistent policy.

I was aware, of course, that some scope must be allowed for
that passion for distinction which is one of the strongest of human
feelings. So from the beginning I found posts for ambitious young
Gauls both in our cavalry and in our secret service. Later I enrolled a whole Gallic legion, the Larks, from non-citizens in the
Province. They have recently received the franchise and have
richly deserved it. But in these early days I had not begun to imagine a system of government for the whole country. I was living
and making decisions from day to day and I made some mistakes.
Labienus and others would have preferred a more openly acquisi-
tive policy and would suggest that my aims of conciliation were
doomed to failure. They were wrong; for, though it is perfectly
true that in the end the Gauls turned almost unanimously against
us, it is also true that, after their final defeat, they have become
reconciled to their lot. Had they not had before them old examples
of my clemency and practical demonstrations that obedience
would be rewarded, they, in their patriotic fervor, would have
fought to the last man and we, who in any case were so nearly
destroyed, might have been destroyed entirely.

I believe therefore that the policy which I initiated in these
first years was the correct one, though I was overoptimistic with
regard to its quick and certain success. Inevitably, of course, the
Gauls had some reason for resentment. To supply our large
armies, especially during the winter, was a considerable undertaking. Our men, too, naturally needed women from time to time.
There was not much rape, except when towns were taken by
storm; indeed a victorious army with money to spend can never
be short of women unless it is operating in a desert. But it is of
course certain that the local male population will harbor ill-
feeling. Undoubtedly, however, what created most ill-feeling was
the idea of subjugation. The Gauls are a proud race and are
particularly proud of their record in war. Man for man they are
physically stronger than we are, though they usually lacked the
resolution that comes from training and discipline. But they
showed no lack of individual courage. They are extremely quick
at learning new techniques. In a few years, for instance, they

were building siege towers and even entrenching camps on the Roman system. Their cavalry was good. Fortunately for us their leading men and best warriors regarded it as beneath them to serve as infantrymen. Consequently their infantry (with some exceptions) was a disorganized horde. Had they succeeded in developing this arm, they would have been insuperable. But, of course, to have developed their infantry, to have co-ordinated their command, to have remedied all those obvious defects of organization, they would have had to have been a different people with a different social system.

Once and once only did we come up against Gallic infantry of really first-rate quality, and here what caused us trouble was not so much the training or skill of the enemy as their outstanding courage and their great speed in action. The Nervii had the reputation of being the bravest of all the Belgae and they thoroughly deserved this reputation. Our engagement with them took place soon after we had disrupted the main Belgic coalition and received the submission of most of the tribes. We were in a confident mood as we marched northwards into Nervian country, though there was nothing slack or disorganized about our advance. From what I had heard, I imagined that we should have some hard fighting. I could not have imagined how hard it would be.

For some days the main Nervian army had retired before us, keeping itself hidden in the woods. This tribe is unique in having hardly any cavalry; the few horsemen of theirs whom we saw were engaged on reconnaissance and always avoided battle with our own cavalry or light troops. Much of the country presented a most peculiar appearance, being covered by lines of artificial hedges, some of which were quite high and all of which were nearly impenetrable. These hedges, I discovered, were used by the Nervii as we might use ditches or entrenchments — as defenses against hostile cavalry and as screens for their own infantry. In some areas this close and complicated system of vegetable fortification greatly delayed our advance. It interrupted visibility and I was, of course, always on the lookout for an ambush and was careful to choose sites for our camps which could not be easily attacked while our men were at work on the entrenchments.

We were marching with six legions, all ready for battle, at the head of the column. Behind them came the heavy equipment of the whole army and behind this followed the two legions who had been recently recruited. Late one afternoon I chose what seemed to me a particularly good position for a camp. It was on a hill which sloped down to a river about three feet deep. Beyond the river was a stretch of open ground suitable for the operations of cavalry and sloping gently upwards towards some thick woods. Enemy forces might well be hidden in these woods, but to reach us they would have to come out into full view of our cavalry, cross a stream and then ascend a fairly steep hill. I made the mistake of thinking that it was impossible that any commander would ask his men to undertake such a hazardous operation. After sending some squadrons of cavalry down into the plain, where enemy pickets were visible, I ordered the six leading legions to begin the work of measuring out the ground for our camp. It was a calm summer evening. Neither I nor anyone else in our army anticipated any disturbance.

I happened to be looking across the stream and up the further hill when the first of the Nervian infantry began to emerge from the cover of the woods. I saw at once that they were in battle order and were moving very rapidly. They brushed our cavalry aside as though it were nonexistent, swarmed across the stream and, without slackening pace, began to ascend the hill. What was happening was what I had imagined to be impossible. I realized the danger of our position without having the time to do anything immediately about it. Before any of the appropriate orders could be given, the enemy were upon us. The soldiers had no time even to take the covers off their shields. There was no possibility of detaching troops to act as reserves, nor, in any case, would I have known where such reserves could have been stationed. I could neither give the signal for battle nor put on the scarlet cloak which I always wore in action. In this emergency the soldiers behaved admirably. Each man, as he left his work, formed up under the nearest standard, so as not to waste time in trying to find his own unit. Among the six legions who bore the brunt of this battle, there was no panic or anything approaching disorder, though there were moments when the situation seemed desperate.

The Ninth and Tenth Legions were on our left, the Eleventh and Eighth in the center, and the Twelfth and Seventh on the right; but we had nothing which could be called a continuous line. Different legions were facing in different ways, and some battle groups were separated from others by the thick hedges which had been planted near the top of the hill.

When the Nervian attack began I was myself on the left. I just had time to say a few words to the men of the Tenth. I then went along the line towards the right, but found that everywhere our men were already in action. By the time that I reached the Twelfth and Seventh Legions on our right I began to have some idea of how the battle was going and could see that our position was critical. The Ninth and Tenth Legions, led by Labienus, had easily overcome a comparatively weak opposition. They had driven the enemy down the hill, killed great numbers of them in the stream and had continued the pursuit up the slopes beyond. No doubt they were under the impression that we were winning the battle. Next to them the Eleventh and Eighth Legion, engaged with a Belgic tribe allied with the Nervii, had had a harder struggle, but had forced the enemy downhill and were fighting on the banks of the river. But meanwhile the main Nervian army was engaged with our Twelfth and Seventh Legions who were now isolated on the top of the hill. Our men were heavily outnumbered so that the Nervii were able to envelop them on their exposed right flank and were also able to send other detachments against our undefended camp and the baggage train. Here there was a scene of indescribable confusion. The men in charge of the baggage, the light armed troops and our already defeated cavalry were rushing about in every direction that led away from the enemy. It was at this point of the battle that a contingent of our Gallic cavalry which had come from the Treveri — a tribe which particularly prided itself upon its courage — rode off home with the news that our camp had been captured and our army annihilated.

The two legions in this sector were still fighting, but the fighting was telling on them. The Twelfth Legion in particular was under tremendous pressure. Its Fourth Cohort had lost every single centurion. The men, as is natural in such conditions, were huddling together. Of course the closer they got to each other, the less able they were to fight efficiently. Most of them were standing their ground, but I noticed a few who were not seriously wounded preparing to give up the fight and I could sense a growing feeling of despair. These men must have felt that they had been abandoned by their comrades and left unaided to face the whole weight of the enemy attack. They had even lost contact with the Seventh Legion, which was quite close to them and also subjected to very heavy pressure. The situation was dangerous.

I snatched a shield from someone in the rear rank and pushed forward to the front, shouting at the top of my voice and making myself as conspicuous as possible. I called out to each of the centurions by name and gave words of encouragement to every soldier whom I saw to be exerting himself with courage and resolution. It was at this point, I told them, that the battle would be won and I ordered them to open out their ranks so that they could use their swords properly and to begin to push the enemy downhill. My intervention was effective. Everyone wanted to do his best while I was looking on and sharing in the fighting. There was a slight slackening in the enemy attack and I was able to send messengers to the Seventh Legion with orders that it should gradually join up with the Twelfth and that the two legions together should form a square. This maneuver was carried out. There was now no danger of being attacked from behind. The troops stood up well to the pressure which remained as heavy as before, since the Nervii realized just as well as I did that in the end we should be reinforced.

And so it happened. Labienus had halted his advance on the hill opposite. Looking back he could see the chaos in our camp, the disordered baggage train, and the dense enemy masses surround-

ing the two legions. Assuming correctly that I was myself fighting in
this sector he immediately sent back the Tenth Legion, instructing
them to win fresh glory for themselves by rescuing their commander in chief. The men of the Tenth hurried back across the
stream and up the hill to attack the Nervii in the rear; and at the
same moment the two legions of recruits under my nephew Pedius,
who had been marching behind the baggage train, came into sight in
the distance. In an instant the situation was transformed. The crowd
of camp servants who a moment before had been panic-stricken now
actually began to fight. The cavalry, or those of them who had not
run too far already, began to scour over the battlefield, cutting off
and destroying small detachments of the enemy, now showing a
courage which had been entirely absent in the early stages of the
battle. And in the legions, men who had been put out of action by
their wounds now began to struggle to their feet and, whether on
one knee or supported by their shields, renewed the fight. Still, in
their hopeless position, the Nervii fought on until in the end the
few survivors were standing on a mound made of the corpses of
their own men. From this ghastly eminence they still hurled down
their javelins at us. Not one man was seen to run away and the
slaughter continued until night.

Next day what was left of the tribe surrendered. I was told that,
out of their governing body of six hundred, only three men remained alive and that out of an army of sixty thousand scarcely
five hundred were left. I took care to see that the remnants of this
gallant tribe, the old men, the women and the children on whom
its future depended were preserved from hostile action by their
neighbors. I hoped that my generosity would be appreciated and
that the crushing nature of our victory would have the effect of
making other tribes prefer our friendship to our enmity.

In acting with such moderation I offended some members of my
staff and disappointed the men who, reasonably enough, expected
some profit from the campaign. But before the end of the season I
was able to satisfy all demands. A tribe allied with the Nervii, the
Aduatuci, after first submitting, subsequently made a treacherous

attack on us. I had no reason here to show mercy. The whole population were sold as slaves. I was told that the number was fifty-three thousand.

Towards the end of the season I received the news that young Publius Crassus had received the submission of the tribes on the western Atlantic coast. I also received envoys from the Germans across the Rhine. It almost seemed that in two years we had accomplished the tremendous task of subduing all Gaul and my mind was already turning towards Britain. When my dispatches were delivered to the senate in Rome, a public thanksgiving service was decreed. This service was to last for fifteen days on end. No one before in our history had received such an honor.

Chapter 6

Difficulties in Rome

MARCUS CICERO HAD SPOKEN IN FAVOR OF THE HONOR DECREED TO me by the senate. He had returned to Rome from his short period of exile at about the time when I was engaged in completing the subjugation of the Belgae, and the question of his recall had been the chief issue in politics for the whole of this year. I myself was visited in Gaul by Sestius, who was acting both for Cicero and for Pompey, and who came to me to secure my approval for measures by which the original sentence of exile, passed by Clodius, could be annulled. In consulting me on this subject Pompey acted most honorably. By this time he hated and feared Clodius much more than he had ever loved or respected Cicero; and there were plenty of people who were ready to try to convince him that Clodius was an agent of mine and of Crassus, selected by us simply to weaken Pompey's own prestige. This was not true, though neither Crassus nor I were unaware of the likelihood that Clodius would in fact turn against Pompey. I had hoped that, in my absence, Crassus would be able to some extent to control him, but I had not given sufficient weight to the fact that, however often some kind of friendship was patched up between Pompey and Crassus, and however obvious it might be that this friendship was in the interests of them both, nothing could alter the antipathy between the two. Pompey, on the strength of his military reputation, remained ostentatiously superior; Crassus, in spite of his enormous wealth and great, if tortuous, political influence, still kept from his early years an abiding jealousy of Pompey. He still remembered how, when the two of them were young men, it was he, Crassus, who at the battle of the Colline Gate had won the decisive victory for Sulla, whereas from that moment onwards it was Pompey who had received every important command and had won more distinction in war than any Roman before him. Crassus consequently was not displeased when Clodius, after having done as we wished by getting rid of Cicero and of Cato for the time being, turned next against Pompey.

I can see that, in adopting this attitude, Crassus was not actuated entirely by personal jealousy. He was aiming also, in his own overelaborate way, at preserving what seemed to him a proper balance. For at the time of my first consulship, when the alliance between Pompey, Crassus and myself had been formed, there was a kind of equality in the contributions which each of us had to offer. I had the prestige of my office, Crassus could bring us the support of the entire business community, and Pompey had his veterans. Indeed it was their presence and the threat that they might be used which had impressed public opinion more than anything else and which, in the last resort, had enabled me to carry through, against the opposition of my colleague, the legislation of my consulship. Those who most resented the events of that year would blame Pompey as much as me for them. They would even, in a rather foolish way, describe Pompey as "king" and me as "queen."

Crassus meanwhile occupied a position as it were behind the scene. This was as a rule in politics the position of his choice. Both his strength and his weakness proceeded from the fact that he would never show himself in the open and he was delighted with his own skill in keeping most people guessing as to what his real intentions were. But there was always a curious contradiction in his character. At the same time as he prided himself upon his apparent obscurity, he longed for just that prominence which, consciously, he rejected; and he very much disliked the sight of others, uncontrolled by him, standing full in the public eye. Oddly enough he was never jealous of me, although by this time I had already acquired a certain reputation as a general and had long been following in politics a line of my own. Probably the chief reason why I never aroused his animosity was that I had owed him money from the very beginning of my career. Over and over again he had saved me from my creditors and he knew that I was grateful to him. I showed my gratitude in many ways apart from the obvious one of repaying him his money. He was particularly pleased by the confidence which I had in his son Publius to whom I gave just that sort of responsibility which his father, at that age, had longed to be given.

It may indeed have been partly because of a mistaken notion of loyalty to me that Crassus encouraged Clodius in his attacks on Pompey. His aim, certainly, was to strengthen me as well as himself by undermining what seemed to him the too dominant position of our partner. But, as was very often the case with Crassus, he was taking an alarmist and overelaborate view of things. What he feared was that Pompey would become acknowledged as the leading member of our triumvirate and might then, by flattery or other means, be detached from us and used against us by that small but energetic section of the senate which had always regarded both Crassus and me as revolutionaries. This indeed was, as I had long known, a real danger. Pompey was always very ill at ease in the role of a reforming or "popular" statesman; he would have much preferred to be what he became in the end under the most tragic circumstances — the acknowledged leader of an apparently respectable reaction. But what Crassus failed to see was that Pompey was much more likely to join our enemies through weakness than through strength. And before I had been two years in Gaul there appeared to be a definite possibility that this might happen.

Pompey was peculiarly unfortunate as a civilian. He was not only a good general, but a fine, if shortsighted, administrator. He could turn his hand to any practical problem, however complicated, and deal with it successfully. But to use his great gifts it was necessary for him to be able to give orders and to know that they would be obeyed. He was not capable of forcing his will upon others except within the conventions that govern the relations between a general and his subordinates. In the senate he was never perfectly at his ease. He regarded himself, not without some reason, as the greatest man in the world; but when he spoke, he spoke either obscurely or pompously; and often, when it was particularly necessary for him to declare his opinion, he would not speak at all; he would sit still, staring with what appeared to be satisfaction at that purple toga of an Imperator which he had the right to wear on all occasions; his expression, at such times, may have been intended to be majestic, but in fact was either sulky or confused. And he was still less sure of himself at any assembly of the people. In his early youth, when he had been the hero of almost everyone in Rome — admired for his beauty, his courage and for the fact that he was the youngest imperator in our history — wherever he went he was greeted by throngs of supporters. His extraordinary political inconsistency was rewarded by the affections of all parties. He made his name as the youngest and most brilliant of Sulla's officers and went on to acquire the reputation of a friend of the people by restoring to the people's tribunes the rights of which Sulla had deprived them. He had, of course, no notion of politics at all and was uniquely interested in his own reputation. He would never have been guilty of the slightest innovation, indeed he would have supported the reactionary Constitution of Sulla to the end, if only the members of his own class had not been persistently jealous of him. Some of them honestly believed that he aimed at setting himself up as a supreme ruler, as Sulla had done. Even an intelligent man like Crassus sometimes held this view.

In fact, as I realized from the beginning, Pompey had neither the wish nor the ability to hold more than a limited amount of power. The wide powers which he did receive were always limited to some sort of military objective and these powers were admirably exercised by him. He usually obtained them against the will of the majority of the senate and as a result of a direct appeal to the people's assembly — just as I had obtained my five-year command in Gaul. And when he returned victorious from a campaign the senate had, as a rule, combined to obstruct him, to argue about his settlement of conquered areas and to make difficulties about allotting land to his veterans. Confronted by this sort of hostility, Pompey was simply bewildered, since he had no idea of how to deal with it. He might indeed have justified the suspicions of Cato and others by calling in the help of his legions, as Sulla had done; certainly there were times when he had the control of an irresistible amount of physical force. But he was by nature a constitutionalist — so long as the Constitution could be modified so as to give him exceptional commands and distinction; and, if he had grasped power, he would not have known how to use it. Thus, in periods of peace, he was amazed and indignant to find himself, in spite of his enormous reputation, frustrated and even controlled by lesser men. It was because of this frustration rather than because of any similarity in political outlook that he had thrown in his weight with me at the time of my first consulship. I on my side had given him everything that I had promised — land for his veterans and a ratification of his settlement of the East. And we had become even more closely united by the fact that he married and deeply loved my only daughter, Julia. Before I left Rome I had become genuinely fond of him. In ordinary private relationships he conducted himself with grace and charm, and I was delighted to see how particularly charming he was to my daughter and how she repaid his devotion with a devotion of her own.

I had, therefore, personal as well as political reasons for feeling distressed when I found that, two years after I had left Rome, there was a real danger that the alliance between Pompey, Crassus and myself might be on the point of breaking up. For this state of affairs Crassus was much to blame, since he could, if he had wished, have exercised some kind of control over Clodius. As it was, Clodius, who was remarkable for his ingenuity, had been doing everything he possibly could to humiliate Pompey and to render him powerless. There was always a certain irresponsibility about Clodius. To this day I am not certain why he hated Pompey with such a peculiar intensity. He was apt, certainly, to attack all military commanders and his successful agitation against his brother-in-law Lucullus had served to discredit one of the greatest generals we have had. Also, being genuinely a leader of the poorer classes (as I had been in my time), he was perhaps outraged to find Pompey, who was by nature a conservative, claiming to be the protector and benefactor of the people. I myself, at about the time of Catiline's conspiracy, used to feel annoyed with Cicero when he attempted to fit himself into a similar role. But it is perhaps not very profitable to attempt to find a coherent or sensible motive for the doings or feelings of Clodius. With great courage, beauty, eloquence and a quite extraordinary personal charm, Clodius had something of the make-up of a spoiled girl, a bad-tempered cat or a delinquent child. He may have hated Pompey simply because in his youth Pompey had been held to resemble Alexander the Great; and he may have attacked him for no better reason than that he had a reputation of power.

By the end of the year of his tribuneship, which was the year of my first campaigns in Gaul, Clodius was as thoroughly in command of the streets and the Forum of Rome as if he had been the leader of an occupying army. Indeed his workingmen's clubs and associations had all the elaborate organization of a military force. Even when, in the following year, he was out of office, he could still control the streets by calling out a sufficient number of his followers to deal with any particular occasion. A band of gladiators might be used to terrorize a jury in the law courts. Larger numbers would be required to enforce his will or guarantee his veto with regard to proposals made before the senate or the people's assembly. For instance in the January of the year when I was engaged with the Belgae, a large demonstration had been organized in the Forum in support of officially recalling Cicero from exile. Numbers of distinguished people took part and, so I was informed, in the course of the day numbers of them were wounded and some killed. Clodius's gangs, who broke up the demonstration before it had achieved anything, were responsible for the worst rioting that had taken place in Rome since the days of my childhood. I heard a further account of it later from Cicero's brother, Quintus, who had only escaped with his life because he had lain still among a number of dead bodies, pretending to be dead himself. It was, apparently, no exaggeration to say that the streets were running with blood and at the end of the day even some of those who had taken an active part in the violence were ashamed of what they had done. And Clodius, though his immediate object was secured, undoubtedly did himself harm by this revelation of his strength and his ruthlessness.

Many members of the senate began to regret the hostile attitude which they had adopted towards Pompey. They reflected that Pompey had never treated the nobility with contempt and had never glorified a state of chaos. He, if anyone, it was thought, could, if he were given the power, keep order in Rome. Cicero too now began to be revered as a symbol of lost and regretted respectability. The movement in favor of his recall grew in strength. Pompey strongly supported it and Crassus pretended to support it. I, when I was consulted, made it clear that, while I had nothing against Cicero and would welcome his friendship just as I admired his literary gifts, I still regarded it as important that his eloquence and prestige should not be put at the service of our enemies. As Pompey was prepared to guarantee that this would not happen, I made no objections to his recall. I would even have been prepared to use my influence with Clodius, if I had thought that on this issue I should have been able to use it effectively. As it was I knew that Clodius neither would nor, if he were to appear at all consistent in politics, could compromise on this point. It also seemed to me that it would be useful to us, in case Cicero failed to behave reasonably, to be able to threaten to support Clodius against him once again.

As I had expected, Clodius did his best to prevent the necessary legislation for Cicero's recall; but he was no longer a tribune and by the beginning of the summer he found that his command of the streets was disputed by a rival gang leader, Milo, who enjoyed the support of Pompey. Milo was much less intelligent than Clodius and never achieved any great popularity; but he was ruthless and, in ordinary street fighting, efficient. With his aid it was found possible to recall Cicero without any rioting on a very great scale.

Cicero returned to Italy in August. I was in the country of the Belgae at the time, but received regular accounts of every speech he made. I was amused to find that, at his first appearance before the people in Rome, he had compared himself to Marius, a fellow townsman of his, who, after great services to his country, had also been exiled. I cannot imagine two characters more different from each other than Cicero and my old uncle and have always wondered how this extraordinary comparison was received by Cicero's audience. In another speech, this time before the senate, Cicero made a violent attack on the consuls of the preceding year who had been in office at the time of his exile. One of these, Piso, was my father-in-law; the other, Gabinius, was an old friend of Pompey's; but we could hardly take exception to Cicero's invective. He had reason for it; it left us personally untouched; and it was in magnificent Latin. Next he showed his gratitude to Pompey by proposing for him one of those exceptional commands which Pompey always enjoyed and always exercised efficiently. One of the results of the chaotic conditions which, for at least a year, had prevailed in Rome was that the normal imports of grain had either not arrived or had been bought up by speculators. There was a real danger of famine and a consequent risk that, under the leadership of Clodius, the people might get completely out of hand. On such occasions the very name of Pompey was enough to restore confidence. People could still remember how once before, in his short and brilliant campaign against the pirates, he had brought prosperity in a moment and freed the whole Mediterranean from fear. Now, on the motion of Cicero, he was put in sole charge of Rome's food supply for a period of five years, with overriding powers over all transport and all areas where food was produced.

Pompey evidently carried out this commission with all his old energy and efficiency. No doubt glad to be away from Rome and from those political disturbances with which he was so ill equipped to deal, he sailed to Africa, Sicily and Sardinia, infecting his subordinates with his own enthusiasm and tolerating no obstruction or inefficiency on the part of producers and merchants.

Many of his voyages were made in wintry stormy weather and
people used to quote with admiration the remark he made to one
sea captain who told him that to sail on a particular occasion
would mean certain death. "I have to sail," Pompey replied,
"I do not have to live." Pompey was always rather fond of making
this kind of terse and exaggerated remark. He was more effective
with such sayings than in a set speech; but some of the remarks he
made about me just before the outbreak of the civil war were
singularly ill chosen.

I myself, of course, had no objection to the new powers and new
honors which were given to Pompey. I would not have objected
if these powers had been increased; and in fact Pompey, though
he was careful not to commit himself openly, did want still more
power. At this time King Ptolemy of Egypt was in Rome. He had
been driven out of Alexandria by his subjects and had come to
ask to be reinstated with the help of a Roman army. It was known
that Ptolemy himself hoped that Pompey would be entrusted with
this task, and Pompey would certainly have welcomed the appointment, if it had not been for certain difficulties. In the first
place there were many others who hankered after so lucrative an
opportunity — for Ptolemy was prepared to pay enormous sums
for his kingdom; and Pompey, having just begun to become, as it
were, respectable again, did not wish to give anyone an excuse for
turning against him. There was also still a strong feeling in Rome
against any step which might lead to the annexation of Egypt.
Much earlier in our political careers Crassus and I had come up
against this difficulty. We had both seen the geographical and
economic importance of Egypt and had twice unsuccessfully attempted to secure for ourselves some measure of control over the
area. At that time Crassus was chiefly interested in making himself
as strong as, or stronger than, Pompey. Now when he saw that
Pompey, not content with the wide powers he had already, was
intriguing, though clumsily enough, to get the Egyptian appointment, he completely lost his head and, forgetting that everything
depended on our existing alliance being maintained, began to attack Pompey with all the bitterness that had accumulated through

years of jealousy and short periods of self-restraint. Crassus approached Clodius directly and Clodius, who must have reorganized his gangs so that he was once more the master of the streets, made it impossible for Pompey to appear publicly in Rome. Wherever he went he would be followed by a crowd, led either by Clodius himself or by some trusted lieutenant. If he attempted to speak, he would be shouted down; if he kept silent, he would be assailed with insults and accusations of every kind of natural or unnatural vice. These meetings usually ended with Clodius or some other gang leader shouting out "Who is it who wants to go to Egypt?" to which the crowd would reply: "Pompey!" "And whom are we going to send?" "Crassus."

So, after the first months of the winter in which he had so efficiently dealt with the danger of famine, Pompey found himself as uncomfortable in Rome as ever. Clodius, of course, maintained that the shortage of food had been an artificial one, created by agents of Pompey so as to give Cicero an opportunity of proposing fresh powers for his reactionary friend; and Clodius was widely believed. Pompey retorted by attacking Crassus, but Crassus was too clever to give him any good reason for bringing a definite accusation against him. In his ineffective rage Pompey actually claimed that Crassus had hired someone to assassinate him. No one believed this story except possibly Pompey himself, and the fact that he was disbelieved made him more angry and more apprehensive than ever. I was informed that at this time he was approached by numbers of people who attempted to convince him that all his troubles could be traced back to his connection with me. He had lost the confidence of the senate, they would say, because he had been associated with my dictatorial conduct as consul; and now he was losing favor with the people through the agency of Clodius, who owed his power to my influence and to Crassus's money. If only, they continued, he would now make a clean break with me, the senate would welcome him with open arms; he would enjoy the position to which he was entitled, that of Rome's greatest general, and, with the senate behind him, would have no difficulty in eliminating Clodius from public life.

It was suggested that it might also be necessary to eliminate me.
Indeed Domitius Ahenobarbus, who had announced his intention
to stand for the consulship in the following year, was known to be
in favor of annulling the legislation of my consulship and recalling
me from my command in Gaul. Pompey was not expected, even
by my greatest enemies, to go quite so far as this; but it was
pointed out to him that he should do something to make it clear
that his alliance with me was at an end. It was proposed that he
should divorce Julia and take another wife.

If it had not been for this last proposition it is possible that
Pompey, although he was by nature an honorable man, might
have listened to the general argument, false as it was. But he was
devoted to Julia and Julia was able to convince him that, just as I
was being loyal to him, so it was his duty to remain loyal to me.
Moreover, though he had no very clear ideas and no very sharp
memory where politics were concerned, he had not yet forgotten
that the senate had refused to recognize his superior merits long
before he became allied with me and that, had it not been for me
and the land law which I passed, he would still have been unable
to satisfy the demands of his veterans. It is true also that Pompey
still regarded me, in spite of my recent successes in the field, as no
better than an amateur soldier. In the end, I fear, it was jealousy
as much as policy which made him turn against me. Now he could
see in me nothing of which to be jealous.

Nevertheless, during the winter and early spring that followed
the Belgic campaign, I was increasingly worried by the general
trend of affairs in Rome, and it was because of this anxiety that I
stayed later than usual on the Roman side of the Alps. I was
particularly careful to get reliable information with regard to
Cicero. He, I considered, was the one statesman who, under
certain conditions, could be really dangerous to us. I was
not afraid of the extremist minority. Cato was abroad; Domitius
Ahenobarbus was an inefficient blusterer. But Cicero had the
eloquence to confuse facts and was capable of making almost anything appear respectable. What Cicero would call a moderate
government or, in his own phrase, a "union of all the good" would

be (as I remembered from the time of Catiline) a mere disguise for some form of reaction that might well be chiefly interested in securing my death or exile. So I continued to follow Cicero's speeches carefully and noted that he was becoming, as the months went by, more outspoken. In March he made, as might be expected, another oratorical attack on Clodius, but also attacked, very brilliantly, my rather disreputable friend Vatinius, who had proposed the law that gave me my exceptional command in Gaul. And in early April it became clear that he was, with considerable senatorial backing, going to attack my land law. It was at this point that I recognized a real danger. Cicero's amendments to my legislation were so designed that, while Pompey would retain all the advantages which I had given him, all the rest of the law would be revised in the interests of certain big landowners. I could see that Cicero had succumbed, as usual, to the flattery of a few old families. Whether consciously or not, he was working so as to divide me from Pompey. I came to the conclusion that the alliance on which the whole of my future rested was endangered and I acted immediately. I, because of my office, could not leave my province; but I urgently requested Crassus to come to me at Ravenna and then, with him, I went on to meet Pompey at Luca.

A Successful Conference

MY TWO YEARS' ABSENCE FROM THE CENTER OF THE POLITICAL world in Rome enabled me, perhaps, to see our situation with more detachment and greater accuracy than did either of my colleagues. And I had other advantages too. I disliked neither of them, while each of them disliked the other. Consequently I was able to act as a kind of umpire between them. They were rightly unsuspicious of me and indeed I had no designs for securing for myself any position of pre-eminence. But I could speak with more authority now than I had been able to do at the time when, just before my first consulship, I had organized this coalition. Then I had no money and no army. Now I was already beginning to lend and to give rather than to borrow and, of the three of us, I was the only one with an army. As we had all grown up in a period of history full of the evidence (which in quieter and more ordered periods is suppressed) that the last word in politics is war, the very existence of my army, even though it was known that I had no intention of using it in a civil war, added height to my stature and force to my arguments.

First with Crassus at Ravenna, then with Pompey at Luca I developed what should have been an obvious train of thought. I pointed out that, whether we liked each other or not, the fact remained that our enemies were the same — namely a small group in the senate led by doctrinaires like Cato, disappointed and ambitious men like Bibulus (who particularly hated me) and ordinary reactionaries like Domitius Ahenobarbus. Such people were powerless to harm us so long as we acted together. If, however, any of us were to appear antagonistic to the other two, this small group could become powerful and would use its power against all three of us. The obvious line of attack on us was to the effect that we were subverting the Constitution. And on this point we were, to some extent, vulnerable. It was true that the legislation of my consulship had been carried out by means of direct appeals to the people and in opposition to my colleague Bibulus and a large number of the senate. And it was not inconceivable even now that a majority of the senate might be induced to declare all this legislation null and void. If that were to happen I should lose my command in Gaul and would face trial and probably exile if I returned to Rome; Pompey woud find himself unable to fulfill his promises to his veterans, and Crassus, instead of holding a position of real strength, would be reduced again to the level of the rest of the senate.

Moreover, if our opponents could be said to have a policy at all, this policy, which they called "liberty," meant nothing but restriction and inefficiency. If they had their will, great commands such as those which Pompey had exercised in the East and that which I was now exercising in Gaul, would be either prohibited or so hedged with restrictions as to be valueless. It would become once again the rule that small armies and provinces would be allotted to the usual members of the nobility, who would employ their years of office in making money for themselves without any thought for the future. This system of "liberty" for the few and the inefficient had been antiquated even in Sulla's time. Moreover the Roman people and half the senate already recognized this fact. The great majority were, whether consciously or half-consciously, on the side of those who, like ourselves, saw the future in larger and more generous terms, who recognized that a great empire could not be administered by relays of incompetent politicians and who saw that our strength and even our security depended on a more or less uniform direction of policy and on the exercise, by the right people, of more or less unrestricted power. Our opponents in every way shrank from the demands of the age and of the future. They represented a force of contraction rather than of that expansion which was militarily, economically and politically necessary for us. I could imagine that by the time that Gaul, Britain, the two Spains and the East as far as India had been integrated with our Italian empire there might be some reason in pausing and in consolidating positions already won. But I knew then, just as I know now, that my own genius, which urges me continually to advance, is adapted to the needs of our time and, if I live, is certain to prevail.

I summed up my argument by pointing out that there were two alternatives before us: either we could, in alliance, continue to dominate the central machinery of government and in this way secure for ourselves those wide and exceptional powers which we wanted to exercise and believed ought to be exercised; or we could acquiesce in a state of affairs under which no single one of us would be strong enough to make head against the combination of our enemies. I had little difficulty in convincing both Crassus and Pompey that my analysis of the situation was correct; but I was glad that I had had a day or two alone with Crassus before both of us held our meetings with Pompey. In the course of those few days I succeeded in persuading Crassus to make a handsome apology to Pompey for the hostility which he had shown to him in Rome and I also made sure that he would support all the suggestions for the future which I proposed to make. Crassus, to do him justice, had in the past made several efforts to establish friendly relations with Pompey, while Pompey, who expected to be admired, was not in the habit of making efforts of this kind at all. Now Crassus was more anxious than he had ever been for Pompey's support, since I had suggested to him that this could bring him the one thing which all his life he had most wanted — military command in a great war.

The proposals which I put forward in secret conferences at Luca were simple, but very far-reaching. It was suggested that Pompey and Crassus should together stand for the consulship for the following year. We would arrange matters so that the elections would be held late and I should therefore be able to send back large numbers of my soldiers on winter leave to vote in Rome. Once they were elected, legislation was to be brought forward by which Pompey and Crassus would each be given, at the end of their year of office, provinces and armies for periods of five years; and my own command in Gaul would also be extended for another five-year period. Pompey was to receive the provinces of Spain and, in addition, was to have the right to appoint subordinate commanders for his legions there, while he himself remained in Italy, still in control of the food supply. Crassus was to govern the province of Syria, from which he proposed to invade Parthia and, if all went successfully, India as well. In this way the world would be, as it were, divided among the three of us and each of us would have his own reason to be contented with his share. Pompey would not only have large armies once again under his control, but would also be nearer to Rome than either of us and so, in theory at least, better placed to exercise his influence. Crassus would have perhaps the most spectacular role to play. Since the wars of Lucullus and Pompey it had become generally believed that conquests in the East were lucrative. Crassus, without having yet reckoned with Parthia, was already beginning to collect information about the wealth of India. As for me, though it might appear that I had had the worst of the bargain — with the probability of hard fighting in difficult country — I was well satisfied. I too might achieve something spectacular if my planned expedition to the unknown island of Britain turned out successfully; and, with the continuity of my command, I should, I hoped, be able to bring into existence this new province of Gaul as painlessly and efficiently as possible. Meanwhile I should be training what would certainly be the finest and most devoted army in the world.

The results of our deliberations at Luca were kept secret until the time came for our plans to be carried out; but the mere fact of our meeting there at all was enough to transform the whole political situation in Rome. People recognized that our alliance was intact and that our combined power was overwhelming. To this little town in the Apennines came no less than a hundred and twenty senators, all anxious to secure some favor from us or at least to show that they would be willing, for a consideration, to work for us. We could now afford to ignore our open enemies; but both Pompey and I wrote in the politest possible terms to Cicero. It was not necessary to threaten him. He withdrew all opposition to the disputed provisions of my land law and later in the year made a fine speech before the senate in justification of the continuance of my command in Gaul. Indeed for the next few years I corresponded frequently with him, often on literary subjects, and was also in touch with him through his brother Quintus to whom I gave a responsible position on my staff in Gaul and who behaved admirably in that capacity. But unfortunately it is never possible altogether to trust Cicero.

So, in a very few days, we agreed upon arrangements which seemed useful at the time and very promising for the future. The jealousy of Crassus for Pompey, which had always been the greatest weakness of our alliance, appeared to have ended. Even the vexed question of Egypt had been easily settled as soon as we had agreed upon a plan by which both Pompey and Crassus would be occupied elsewhere. We decided that, during their consulship, King Ptolemy should be restored by Gabinius, a friend both of Pompey and myself, who at that time would be governor of Syria. It was understood that we should share the large reward offered by the king for his rehabilitation. Indeed at this moment there seemed to be nothing that could divide us. Each of us had a sphere of influence large enough to give scope to his energies, and the success of each one of us could do nothing but good to the other two. I believed, and Pompey, who knew the East well, agreed with me that Crassus's expedition was likely to be successful. If so it would result in a great influx of wealth into Rome. I too, I hoped, should be able to contribute something from my conquests and I was already thinking of some of those architectural improvements to the city which I am still carrying

out. Meanwhile Pompey's new theater, the most magnificent building in Rome, was almost completed and would be dedicated in
the course of his consulship. This had been constructed from the
spoils of the East and we imagined that Crassus, when he returned
victorious, would also wish to commemorate himself and our
alliance by some other great building project.

Indeed we seemed likely to make a new Rome, a more beautiful and more prosperous city, peaceful and grateful to us. I myself proposed, after the end of my governorship in Gaul, to stand
again for the consulship, again with the backing of Pompey and
Crassus, and I hoped that, when elected, I should be able to carry
through calmly and without opposition all those necessary reforms
to which even now I am only beginning to set my hand. In particular I felt more closely bound to Pompey than ever. He hoped that
my daughter Julia would bear him a child and, whether because of
this or because Julia had managed to impart to him some of her
own affection for me, I found him friendly, charming and reasonable. The future seemed to me more assured than I had ever
known it before. How wrong I was proved to be!

I could have imagined that not every one of my bright antici-
pations would come true, but could scarcely have foreseen such
total disappointment as that which followed. I expected for myself
some hard fighting in Gaul, but never expected so hard or continuous a struggle or such narrow escapes from annihilation. I
thought it possible that Crassus, though he was a good general,
might not adapt himself at his age (he was nearly seventy) to the
conditions of the East: I did not think it possible that he would
lose seven eagles, ten thousand prisoners and twenty thousand
dead. I could not have known that Julia would die in childbirth
or that Pompey would join my enemies.

We were cheerful and confident when we parted from each
other at Luca. Crassus was going back to Rome; Pompey was
on his way to Sardinia where he had work to do in connection
with the grain supply; I had received dispatches which warned
me of trouble among the Gallic tribes on the western Atlantic
coast. Young Publius Crassus was in command there. I had al-

ready promised to send him with a large contingent of Gallic cavalry to serve with his father when the time came for the campaign in Parthia. I took to him from his father, I remember, many affectionate messages and, as I set out for Gaul, I felt myself some stirrings of affection for old Crassus who had supported me with his money and his influence in the difficult and perhaps disreputable period of my youth. I was never to meet Crassus again and, as for Pompey the Great, I was destined to see of him nothing else except, eight years later, his shamefully severed head and the ring he used to wear, on which was engraved a lion holding a sword between his paws.

Chapter 8

Success in the West — Consulship
of Pompey and Crassus

IN GAUL I NOW ENJOYED NEARLY THREE YEARS OF UNINTERRUPTED success. It is true that the two expeditions to Britain were somewhat disappointing in their material results, but they, and the crossing of the Rhine, brought immense prestige to me and to my army. Towards the end of this period there were signs of trouble to come; yet no one, I think, could have reasonably predicted how serious this trouble would be. Indeed the great Gallic revolt might never have broken out at all if it had not been for the successful treachery of one obscure Gaul and the unpardonable folly of one of my own officers.

In these years and afterwards it was always necessary to keep a watch on the Belgae and on the German frontier, since the Belgae resented the growing importance of the Aedui, the Remi and other tribes which I favored and it was always possible, when any revolt was planned, to hire German troops from across the Rhine. Indeed in the end I was forced to adopt this expedient myself. Usually Labienus was in command of that section of the army which had to be held in reserve so as to be able to deal with sudden emergencies at times when I was occupied either in the far west or in Britain; I had the utmost confidence in Labienus and I do not think that he ever made a mistake.

By this time it was evident to the Gauls that our armies had come to stay. This was a fact which certainly aroused resentment, but I did my best to mollify the hard feelings of this nation of warriors by showing them the great advantages which could come to them as the result of a closer association with us. For the time being I did nothing to disturb their tribal laws, traditions or religion; indeed I was most careful to treat their magistrates with courtesy and even with a show of deference. On the other hand I took exceptionally severe measures in cases where we became the victims of treachery or where a definite undertaking was deliberately broken.

I was confronted with one such case as soon as I reached Gaul after my meeting with Pompey and Crassus. I found that in the far west the Veneti and other tribes of the Atlantic coast were in open revolt and had, contrary to all rules of civilized behavior, seized our envoys, some of whom were high-ranking officers. The Veneti were the greatest sea power in Gaul. They could produce a fleet of more than two hundred ships and these vessels of theirs were much better adapted to local conditions than were any ships which, at this time, we knew how to build. Knowing that it would be necessary to defeat these people on the sea, I had given orders for the construction of a fleet on the Loire before the campaigning season began. While this fleet was being built I marched myself against the strongholds held by the Veneti on land. This proved to be one of the hardest and most unrewarding campaigns which I have ever undertaken. We found ourselves involved in a kind of amphibious operation for which we had imperfect equipment and no training. The fortresses of the Veneti were, as a rule, situated on promontories or long spits of land; at high tide they would be surrounded by water and at low tide would often be equally well defended by shifting sands and estuaries. Sometimes, after incredible exertions from our men, we succeeded in building dikes to keep the sea out and siege terraces which could bring us up to the level of the town walls. We would then find all this labor in vain, since the enemy, who had command of the sea, would merely wait for the next high tide and then, taking all their pos-

sessions with them, would go aboard their ships and move on
to the next stronghold along the coast. The few losses which we
inflicted on them were out of all proportion to the effort expended
and it became clear to me that we could only bring this campaign
to a successful conclusion by destroying their sea power. As they
were fine and experienced sailors, with an expert knowledge of
their own difficult coast and even of the opposite coast of Britain,
it did not seem to me certain that our aim could be achieved. Yet
failure would be disastrous. If it were once shown that we could
be successfully defied, revolts would break out all over the
country. To survive we had to be thought invincible.

I had given the command of our fleet to young Decimus Brutus
and ordered him to sail as soon as possible. On his arrival in
enemy waters he was faced with a fleet of two hundred and twenty
enemy ships and, as he told me afterwards, neither he nor his
naval advisers had any very clear idea of how the action was to
be fought. The ships of the Veneti were too stoutly built to be
sunk by ramming and they were not easy to board, since they
towered above our ships, thus giving their men every advantage
as regards the discharge of arrows, javelins and other missiles. Our
ships, being propelled by oars, were more easy to maneuver; but
when there was any wind the enemy could outsail us and, if the
weather was really stormy, they could run easily and fearlessly
into shallow water where our ships dared not venture. The Veneti
also had all the advantages which come from superior training.
We had enlisted the best crews available from the Province and
from Gallic tribes which were friendly to us; but our crews lacked
experience of these Atlantic waters, with their exceptionally great
variations of tide, nor did they have that long tradition of seaman-
ship on which the Veneti rightly prided themselves.

Our one solid advantage lay in the actual fighting qualities of
the troops which we carried on board. It was therefore necessary,
if we were to be victorious, for this sea battle to be transformed, so
far as possible, into a land battle. In other words our only hope
was in immobilizing the ships of the Veneti and in capturing them
by boarding them. This, in theory, was obvious; in fact, however,

with a stiff breeze blowing, it was hard to see how exactly we could achieve our aim.

The battle was fought in a wide open bay. It began two hours before noon and lasted till sunset. Around this bay were rocky cliffs and on the hills behind these were, I remember, long alignments of gigantic monoliths which formed some sort of temple or holy place. People used to come here from all directions to celebrate a great midsummer festival, though this year the presence of our army had of course forced them to cancel their ceremony. This was a good thing, as in these remote parts the religious rites were more savage than in the rest of Gaul. Human sacrifice was still common, although some of the more civilized Druids (old Diviciacus, for instance) would patriotically maintain that it was rarer than in fact was the case. On the whole the Druids do not make use of temples or religious buildings and it may be that these impressive monolithic constructions (the stones are usually arranged either in straight lines or in circles) are the work of tribes who inhabited this country before the Druids and the Celts arrived. Or it may be that the Druidic religion is the primitive and original religion, which was taken over by the Celts. It bears certainly some traces of having been a rather more elaborate and philosophical creed than one would expect to find among a race of warriors who have only recently become at all civilized. It would seem, for example, that the Druidic belief in the immortality and transmigration of the soul must either have been derived from Pythagoras — which is unlikely, since Greek colonization was confined to the Mediterranean coast of Gaul — or else must be part of a very ancient body of religious doctrine which was already in existence during the lifetime of Pythagoras and into which Pythagoras breathed, for a short time, a little new life.

It is most interesting to observe the strange fervor with which, at various times and among various people, this doctrine of immortality has been either accepted or rejected. Among the Druids it is the main principle of education; it will be justified logically, often by means of the same sort of argument (again possibly Pythagorean in origin) which Plato puts into the mouth of Socrates; but it will be also commended on practical grounds, as being a belief which makes people happy and generous in this life (since they have all eternity before them) and, in particular, brave in battle (since, strictly speaking, it is impossible for one to lose one's life, whereas, by cowardice, it is certainly possible to lose one's honor). Yet on the other side we find that great scientist and helper of mankind, Epicurus, who claims to be conferring one of his chief benefits upon us by proving that, after the physical dissolution of the body, there is not the remotest possibility that the soul can survive. Personally I follow his arguments with pleasure and greatly admire his dexterity. His atomic theory seems to me the most intellectually satisfying of all philosophic theories which attempt what is perhaps the impossible task of explaining everything. But I am not emotionally disturbed or practically affected by the views of either Epicurus or the Druids about death. I cannot fully understand the feverish enthusiasm of our great poet Lucretius, as he celebrates the certainty of his own perpetual extinction; and on those occasions when I have risked death in battle, it has never occurred to me to imagine that I have, in fact, another life waiting for me. I think that on the whole conduct is not greatly influenced by metaphysical beliefs; it is more often the case that metaphysical beliefs are chosen or adapted to suit what seem to be, at any particular time, the demands of conduct. And in the supreme ecstasy of battle, when everything depends on the presence or absence of a good courage, I do not believe that any part at all is played by theories that concern the afterlife. At the moment of conflict those who have held such theories have forgotten them, and those who have never considered the subject are not likely to consider it then.

Certainly in this naval battle off the Atlantic coast there was little to choose between the two sides so far as courage was concerned. Each side too had that confidence which comes from experience and is a more valuable aid to courage than any theorizing. The Veneti knew that they were the better sailors and we knew that no equal number of Gauls could stand up to us in hand-to-hand fighting. All who were engaged had every encouragement to distinguish themselves. The Romans were fighting under the eyes of their commander in chief and of their comrades in the legions who thronged the cliffs and looked down on the battle as though it were some performance in a theater; and the Veneti had aboard their ships most of their tribal council and the pick of their fighting men. Moreover they had concentrated for this battle every single one of their ships which was fit for service. They intended this day to be decisive.

It was clear from the beginning that the usual methods of naval warfare would be of no service to us. In the early stages of the battle a few of our ships did attempt to ram enemy vessels. They invariably retired with their rams broken and often with their oars snapped off. Attempts to run alongside and board were usually foiled by the skill of the enemy pilots and the great variations in speed of which their ships were capable. Their leather sails looked clumsy, but they were remarkably effective; and, so long as their ships could keep at a certain distance from ours, their troops, standing above us, were able to inflict casualties on our men while suffering very little themselves. It was evident to me at once that, unless we could devise some means to immobilize, as it were, the whole action, the battle would be lost. In fact the battle was won in the first place by the use of a quite simple expedient and, in the second place, by luck.

Later I was unable to discover who it was who had first suggested that our ships should be equipped with long poles to which sharp sickle-shaped hooks were attached. It may have been a device thought out by some of our own soldiers or centurions; or the idea may have come from a Gallic pilot or seaman. Certainly Decimus Brutus deserves credit for having seen the possibilities of this invention even before it had been tried in action. Our men used these hooks to seize hold of and then cut through or snap the halyards of the enemy. As a result the yards would be brought down and the enemy ship would be left helpless and unable to move in any direction. It could then be attacked and boarded by two or three of ours at once; and, when it came to close fighting, our men had little difficulty in beating down whatever opposition they encountered.

We from the cliffs saw this maneuver repeated over and over again and realized that it was now only a question of time before the enemy would have to give up the struggle. I was delighted at the thought of a victory which would restore altogether the prestige which we had lost by our inconclusive operations on land; yet I was still apprehensive about the future. Presumably the Veneti would not wait until all their ships were destroyed. They would take advantage of the wind and run away from us, with the majority of their fleet intact. And, if we could not bring it to battle again, they would soon, as the winter approached, be once more in command of the sea. Indeed, just as I had expected, their commanders, having no answer to the tactics which we were employing, gave the order to retire. They put their ships before the wind and it seemed that we should have to be content with a victory in which, though we had gained honor, we had only inflicted trifling losses. However just at this moment a sudden dead calm fell upon the sea. There was no need for us any longer to use our instruments to cut the halyards of the enemy; nature herself had made their vessels motionless. What followed was rather a massacre than a battle. Even when one particular enemy ship put up a strong resistance, we, with the aid of oars, were able to bring greatly superior numbers against it; and so we went on, capturing ship after helpless ship until the sun set and our own fleet had to sail into harbor. We cheered them all the way in, since we knew that this victory had ended the campaign.

Not more than ten or twelve ships of the enemy escaped in the darkness. The Veneti had lost all power to defend themselves and the survivors surrendered unconditionally. This revolt of theirs had been begun by an act of treachery, had been very difficult to deal with and could have had most dangerous consequences. I therefore acted with unusual severity. All surviving members of the tribal council were put to death and the rest of the population were sold as slaves.

This was much the most important operation carried out that year, and by the time that the Veneti had been subdued not much of the campaigning season was left. Meanwhile my generals Sabinus and young Publius Crassus had fought most successfully with the northern allies of the Veneti and with the tribes of Aquitania. I used the last weeks of the autumn in a short expedition against the tribes occupying the coast immediately opposite Britain. I was already planning the invasion of that island.

For the winter I quartered the legions in the recently pacified country between the Seine and the Loire. I myself returned as usual to northern Italy and, in fulfillment of the promises I had made at Luca, gave leave to a number of my troops so that they could vote at the consular elections in Rome. Pompey and Crassus were, of course, elected, though not without some disturbance. By this time Cato had returned from his appointment in Cyprus. His work of administration there had been carried out well and he was careful to advertise the fact that no fault could be found with his accounts. This, no doubt, helped to reinforce his conviction that he was the only man alive who possessed perfect integrity. His sister, Portia, was married to my inveterate enemy, Domitius Ahenobarbus, who was not a very brave man and would, in all likelihood, have withdrawn his candidature for the consulship when it was known that Pompey and Crassus were to be his rivals. But Cato, who disliked Pompey almost as much as he disliked me, brought all his powers of persuasion to bear upon his brother-in-law and finally induced him, in the name of freedom and virtue, to stand for the consulship in opposition to his more powerful rivals. The result was that, on the election morning, Domitius was driven out of the Forum, narrowly escaping with his life. Indeed our control of the electoral machinery on this occasion was almost complete. Cato himself, who had a considerable following in Rome and had added to his reputation by his settlement of Cyprus, failed to get elected to the praetorship. He was defeated by my own nominee, Vatinius. In whatever disturbances there were, our party always had the upper hand.

Indeed our position of power was now even more secure than it had been at the time of my consulship. Yet in the course of these elections there occurred one sad happening, the results of which were not immediately apparent. Pompey himself was on one occasion close to the scene of some street fighting; swords were drawn and some of the blood that was shed stained the toga which he was wearing. He sent a slave to his house with the stained garment and with instructions to bring him another toga to wear. Unfortunately the slave, in his excitement, could only point to the blood and talk about the fighting, instead of stating immediately that his master, Pompey, had not even been scratched. It seems that my daughter Julia, seeing the blood on the toga, imagined that her husband must have been killed or wounded. She fainted away and the disturbance to her whole system resulted in a miscarriage. I am told that, though she made a superficial recovery and indeed soon became pregnant again, she never entirely regained her health. In fact she had now less than two more years to live. It is useless to speculate on what would have been her effect on history if she had lived longer. Still I believe that her wise influence would have saved the lives of thousands of men now dead, including that of her husband. And as for me, I did not need a civil war to become great.

Certainly in the early months of the year of Pompey's and Crassus's consulship I had no reason to take a serious view of Julia's illness and I could observe that all our arrangements for the future were being carried out smoothly. The provinces and powers desired by Pompey and Crassus were, in spite of Cato's noisy opposition, duly allotted to them; and, as we had agreed, my own command was extended for another period of five years. Quite quietly we arranged for the settlement of Egypt. On Pompey's instructions Gabinius marched from Syria with his army, restored King Ptolemy to the throne and received from him large sums of money on account with the promises of much larger sums in the future. These measures were carried out without any authorization from the senate and they naturally aroused the anger of Cato and his party. This party, however, was now too weak to cause us any anxiety. Cicero, who had been approached both by Pompey and by friends of mine, had wisely recognized that he would be safer and more influential if he supported us than if he opposed us. We were scrupulously polite to him and he was grateful. In the following year he actually spoke in the law courts in favor of our friends Gabinius and Vatinius, both of whom he had been for some years in the habit of persistently attacking as his bitterest enemies. I myself received a number of letters from Cicero during these years, all very friendly in tone.

It began to seem, in fact, that our irreconcilable enemies were losing all influence and that our own alliance was growing stronger every day. Now, towards the close of his life, Crassus for the first time appeared to be getting on well with Pompey. This may have been simply because his mind was now set, not on Roman politics at all, but on the distant East towards which he proposed to march even before the year of his consulship was over. Meanwhile Pompey himself seemed to have become more popular than ever. In the summer of this year took place the dedication of his new theater — the finest building that had ever been erected in Rome — and at the same time games were held and entertainments provided for days on end. Nothing so magnificent had been seen before. Nearly everyone who wrote to me from Rome alluded to the five hundred lions and four hundred panthers that had been killed, to the six hundred mules that formed part of the scenery for a production of the tragedy of Clytemnestra and to the strange behavior of the crowd who, when a number of elephants were wounded and began to trumpet, appeared for once to sympathize with the sufferings of the wild animals.

Chapter 9

Massacre of Germans — Landing
in Britain

WHILE POMPEY AND CRASSUS WERE ENJOYING THEIR SUCCESSES in Rome, I, during the same year, had added to my reputation in Gaul. I had intended to devote the greater part of the campaigning season to my project of invading Britain, but was unfortunately prevented from starting on the expedition until so late in the year that there was not enough time to achieve much. However, the very fact that the expedition was undertaken at all produced a tremendous impression at Rome.

In fact the campaign which I fought against the Germans earlier in the year and which delayed my departure for Britain was, from a military point of view, the more important of the two operations. An enormous host (their numbers were estimated at four hundred and thirty thousand) had crossed the Rhine not far from the sea, had already occupied the lands of some of the Gallic tribesmen and were gradually spreading westward. This was a dangerous enough situation in itself, but it was made much more dangerous by the fact that among many of the Gallic tribes the anti-Roman party was actively intriguing with the Germans, promising them help and encouraging them to advance. Those who were intriguing in this way were, of course, acting mainly in their own private political interests; but they represented themselves as patriots who were attempting to secure German help in the great enterprise of driving the Romans from Gaul. I myself was well aware of what was going on, but for the time being found it advisable to dissemble. In addressing a council of the Gallic chiefs, many of whom I knew to be traitorously in communication with the enemy, I merely reiterated the sentiments I had expressed at the time when we took the field against Ariovistus, representing myself as the protector of Gaul against foreign invasion. In order to carry out this role at all convincingly it was necessary for me to have cavalry contingents from the tribes. I took the contingents, but was uneasily conscious that, while some of them were completely reliable, others were halfhearted and some were secretly on the side of the enemy.

We moved fast and it was probably fortunate for us that when we made contact with the Germans we found that most of their cavalry had gone off on a plundering expedition and were not expected back for some days. Quite obviously in order to gain time, the enemy began to negotiate with me; but they made a serious mistake. Seeing a good opportunity, they made, during a period of truce, a treacherous attack on our cavalry with the small cavalry force of their own which had remained with their army. It was true that our men were not expecting any attack; but even so the fact that eight hundred Germans succeeded in routing five thousand of my Gauls is a sufficient indication that at least some of these Gauls were ready to co-operate with the enemy. However this success of the Germans led to their destruction. Next day all the German chieftains came to my camp, ostensibly to apologize for this unprovoked attack, but in fact, of course, to gain time in which the rest of their cavalry could arrive. But I now had the legitimate excuse which I wanted. I arrested the whole deputation and marched directly on the German camp. What followed was an interesting example of the importance of leadership in war. This vast host, deprived of its leaders, proved quite incapable of using the great strength which it in fact possessed. First, at the sight of the legions, the women and children began aimlessly to run from the shelter of the camp. I sent out my cavalry to cut them down and then the men, seeing their own people being massacred, began to run too. We drove them to the point where the river Moselle joins the Rhine and went on killing them throughout the day. I have never seen so many dead bodies. We did not suffer a single fatal casualty and only had a few wounded.

After the destruction of these Germans I offered their leaders, whom I had held under arrest in camp, leave to depart. But they were overwhelmed by the catastrophe which had fallen upon their tribe; they had no confidence in the Gauls who had originally invited them into the country and they were afraid of being killed or tortured by those other Gauls whose property they had carried off in the course of their invasion. So they elected to stay with me. I allowed them to retain their liberty and found them useful subsequently in some of my dealings with various German tribes. I had already formed a high opinion of the German cavalryman (who is also trained to fight on foot) and I could imagine that an occasion might arrive when I could use some German horse in my own army. I had already received deputations from one powerful German tribe, the Ubii, from across the Rhine and it had occurred to me that, after the incorporation of Gaul and perhaps Britain in our empire, I might turn my attention to Germany and might find that these Ubii could play the same part there as the Aedui had played in Gaul.

These plans of mine were necessarily disrupted by the great Gallic revolt and by the civil war; and now both honor and efficiency demand that I should march against Parthia. It seems, however, that if I continue to live I must continue to conquer and I may well, when the Parthian war is over, bring an army back to the West by way of the Black Sea, the Danube and Germany. All this, however, is in the uncertain future. And in those days when I was planning the invasion of Britain I was more concerned with keeping the Germans out of Gaul than with subduing their own country. I did, indeed, advance beyond the Rhine directly after we had destroyed those great hordes which had crossed the river; but this was rather a demonstration of our potential strength than a deliberate use of it for attaining any territorial aim. It was, never-theless, a most exciting operation and I still feel some satisfaction at the thought of the dramatic quality of this year in which for the first time in history a bridge was built over the Rhine and a well-equipped army was transported across the Ocean to Britain. Our Rhine bridge was one of the most impressive feats of en-gineering which I can remember in any of our campaigns. The bridge was finished and the army had marched across within ten days from the time that we began to cut the timber.

There was no doubt whatever that the Germans now felt a re-spect for us very different from the attitude which I had observed in Ariovistus before his defeat. A number of tribes sent deputa-tions and promised to deliver hostages, while the warriors of the strongest German nation, the Suebi, withdrew into the depths of their forests. We spent nearly three weeks in Germany, burning the crops and houses of those tribes which had not made terms with us or were enemies of other tribes which had asked for our pro-tection. I was tempted to go farther into this unexplored country, which contains animals that are quite unknown in the rest of Europe and whose inhabitants, though savage and treacherous, make good soldiers and are, I should say, capable of becoming civilized. But I recognized the fact that, for the time being, we should regard the Rhine as our frontier and I was, of course, at-tracted too by Britain, an island of which we knew even less than we did of Germany but where I expected to find a more cultured race of people than the Germans and also more wealth.

In fact I must own that both of our two expeditions to Britain were very diappointing in their results, except as propaganda for myself and the army. We found very little of the precious metals and none of the pearls which we had hoped to find; the fighting was not easy; and we suffered severe losses of material through a combination of high tides and storms. On the other hand the in-vasion of a land so utterly remote appealed in a quite extraordi-nary way to the imaginations of people in Rome. Cicero, for ex-ample, not only hoped that his brother Quintus, who was now on my staff, would bring a fortune back with him from Britain, but also expected to hear tales of marvels. He would probably have believed us if we had told him that we had discovered the end of the world or the very place where Odysseus, according to Homer, summoned up to the air the souls of Achilles and of Agamemnon. He seriously contemplated writing a poem, possibly an epic, to celebrate my achievements in these campaigns. This would have been, so far as the theme is concerned, an agreeable change from Cicero's usual subject of his own consulship. But I really did not give him sufficient material. Certainly I myself would have explored the country further, if I had had the time and the opportunity. I still know nothing of the tribes that live in the extreme North where, they tell me, there is perpetual daylight throughout the summer and at midwinter the sun never rises at all. Indeed I might have made many more discoveries at the frontiers of our empire if, for reasons which affected my own survival, I had not been forced to attend to what was happening at the center.

As it is I seem to have been for long in the position of one who, far from being able to rest at all, has never even been able to finish one task satisfactorily before some other task, still more urgent, has been forced upon his attention. At some times I seem to see myself running a race, as in a dream, ever faster and faster towards a receding goal; and at other times I still appear to run and still outstrip my competitors but feel, again as one feels in dreams, some hampering and compulsive weight upon legs that must go on moving, however tiredly, and must never admit reluctance.

The first expedition, in the year of the consulship of Pompey and Crassus, was on a small scale. I only took with me the Tenth and Seventh Legions and about five hundred cavalry, and I did not intend to accomplish anything more than a preliminary reconnaissance. I had hoped indeed to be able to make an unopposed landing and to accept the submission and alliance of the coastal tribes. With this end in view I had sent on ahead a Gaul, Commius, who knew Britain and whom I trusted. I believe too that at this time Commius deserved my trust. I had recently used my influence to have him made king of his tribe, the Atrebates, and he had, I think, some hopes that I might help him to carve out another kingdom for himself in Britain. He was a brave, intelligent and ambitious man. It was a pity that Labienus did not like him and did not know how to handle him. Certainly on this occasion he risked his life for me. In spite of having arrived as my envoy he was seized and held captive by the natives as soon as he landed, and would probably have been put to death by them if they had succeeded in preventing the landing of the main army. As it was we had some fairly stiff fighting before we could get a foothold on the beach. The Britons, with their painted faces and bodies, were at first an alarming sight and it took some time before our men were able to make full use of their superior training and arms. I was impressed too by the British use of armed chariots, a weapon which has become obsolete in Gaul but which, in the right conditions, can be very effective.

After we had defeated the Britons on the beach, the nearest tribes made their submission and restored Commius to us safe and sound. But then everything went wrong. The transports with our cavalry failed to arrive; our fleet was badly damaged in a storm; continuous rain and high winds made all military operations difficult; the Britons, seeing our difficulties, attacked us again and, though we could always defeat them in battle, we could never follow up our successes, since the only cavalry available to us were about thirty horsemen who were the personal retainers of Commius. Indeed I was glad to get back to Gaul with the army intact and with a fleet that, under difficult conditions, had been made once again seaworthy. Next year, with a bigger expeditionary force, I hoped to achieve more important results. Yet in Rome the campaigns of this year received a most honorable recognition. Only Cato objected to the honors that were voted to me. He actually had the effrontery to propose that I should be handed over to the Germans as one who had offended against international law by detaining their envoys. But even my enemies were not much impressed by this ignorant and spiteful intervention and the senate decreed for me a thanksgiving service of no less than twenty

days. For this great mark of distinction I was largely indebted to
Pompey. I think that by the time my dispatches reached Rome
Crassus had already set out for the East. His departure for what
was obviously going to be an aggressive war was bitterly opposed
by a large section of public opinion and some tribunes even attempted to forbid him to leave the city. I was told that on this
rather awkward occasion Pompey did everything possible to
help his colleague. He accompanied him as far as the gates and by
his cheerful bearing made it plain to everyone that he expected
Crassus to return victorious and that he fully supported him in his
undertaking.

I, for my part, had given young Publius Crassus the opportunity
to raise a force of a thousand picked Gallic cavalry. He took
them back to Italy with him and went on to join his father in Syria
in the following year. He was the most promising of my younger
commanders and I was sorry to see him go. I had hoped too to
find him very useful to me politically in Rome. He had married
Cornelia, the beautiful and intelligent daughter of Scipio, and he
was an ardent admirer of Cicero, who, since he has always enjoyed
admiration to an almost indecent extent, was very fond of the
young man himself. I wished Cicero, who was already on friendly
terms with me, to become an even firmer friend and I was anxious
too that Scipio and others who thought like him should become
dissociated from Cato, Bibulus and the extremists. Young Publius
had great tact and great charm. He was devoted both to me and
to his father. Indeed at this time there was no other young man
for whom one could so confidently have predicted a brilliant
career.

I talked much of him, I remember, and, of course, of his admired Cicero when I was traveling from northern Italy back
again into Gaul in the spring of the year when we invaded Britain
for the second time. My traveling companion was Cicero's brother,
Quintus, who, like everybody else on my staff, was looking
forward eagerly to the British expedition. We used to discuss both
politics and war, but most of our conversation during these days
was on literary subjects. I have always been able to write or dictate

easily when traveling either on horseback or in a carriage; in fact I find rapid movement particularly stimulating to the mind. On this journey I wrote my essay "On Analogy" and dedicated it to Quintus's brother who, though he himself employs a style that is most unlike mine, has always been generous enough to see some merits in my own method of writing. Quintus too enjoyed this little essay of mine and he, though a bad poet, is not at all a bad critic.

I remember discussing with him also the great poem of Lucretius which, about this time, had been sent to his brother for criticism and revision. Lucretius himself had just died — some say as a result of an unhappy love affair, and this explanation seems quite credible if one thinks of those fine but feverish passages in his poem which describe the passion of love. In these passages and others Lucretius seems to show a peculiar tension which proceeds, I think, from a state of mind which may be called, to use a Greek word, "schizophrenia." Half of his nature rejects what the other half affirms. He heaps scorn and lavishes pity on those who are foolish enough to believe in the existence of supernatural powers or who seek from love anything more than a transitory physical satisfaction, or who devote their lives to the combinations of politics or the glories of war. Yet in the depths of his own nature he is more prone than most people to superstitious terrors; clearly he wants to find in love some kind of ecstatic security which transcends and outlasts sensation (and this, according to his master Epicurus, is an impossibility); moreover he is a Roman and a patrician — born, therefore, into politics and war. In his poem he is really attempting, with the utmost passion, to convince not others, but himself. He is not expounding, but fighting. Hence his vigor and his extraordinary emotional and intellectual strength.

It has often seemed to me a strange paradox that, whereas in the life of a man of action what is most necessary of all is an unswerving conviction of the justice and rectitude of one's own aims and methods, there are poets and thinkers who not only thrive on uncertainty and indecision but actually derive an additional strength from what, in a man of action, would be halfheartedness. Perhaps there is a sense in which one may say that poetry does more justice to reality than does the simple and effective prose of action. For instance one may, from a practical and human point of view, deplore the misery and indecision of Catullus (who also, I think, died this year) in his feelings about Clodia; yet, from another point of view, one must admit that these feelings have a certain validity; such a woman can indeed inspire both love and hatred simultaneously and Catullus, in representing such an unfortunate situation, is representing truth. And even I am moved when I read in Lucretius of the perfect and supposedly admirable detachment of the philosopher — of that place high up in the mountains from which a man can look down upon a plain where legions are marching and counter-marching, masses of men equipped and directed towards a purpose; yet all that the remote onlooker perceives is a little movement and a distant gleam. There is truth in this picture; but if I were to allow my mind to dwell on this truth, I should become wholly ineffective; and if more than a few thinkers were permitted to indulge in the luxury of such quietism there would soon be an end of thought, of Lucretius and of civilization, all of which are created and sustained by wholehearted action directed, often ruthlessly, towards definite and necessary ends. Yet here again there is a paradox. Mere ruthlessness and mere determination are certainly not everything we look for in a man of action. They are often not even effective. Both Marius in his old age and Sulla throughout his life were utterly ruthless. Sulla moreover had a very clear idea of what he wanted to do. But his idea was wrong in the sense that it was inhuman; while Marius, through what may be described as an excess of humanity, had no idea at all.

It seems to me that some reflection, some notion of the ways in which action is limited and determined by humanity, is an advantage to a practical statesman or commander. He too should perhaps suffer to some extent from the schizophrenia which we notice in poets. He should be aware that nothing is finally settled by the winning of a battle or by the passing of a law. But, while recognizing this fact, he must be absolutely determined that the battle shall be won or the piece of legislation carried. Otherwise nothing will be settled at all. He must act as if he believed action to be final, though really he believes it only to be necessary.

He must believe too in his own freedom, even though he knows how limited this freedom is. Yet his belief is justified, since from time to time, and as the result of infinite effort as well as of genius, an opportunity may occur of exercising true freedom, of creating something that would not have come into existence had it not been for the deliberate use of one's own will. Such opportunities are extremely rare. As a rule the active man can, in a sense, be more accurately described as passive; and the more deeply he is involved in events, the more he is subjected to their pressure. He may start with a clear idea both of his aims and of himself; but the means used to be effective (and if he is not effective, he is nothing) will force him to adapt his aims to possibilities and to alter his own notion of himself simply because he has been unable to act as he would have wished. I, for example, have always prided myself on my loyalty to my friends and on the mercy which I have shown to my enemies. I think I may say that I have succeeded in being consistently loyal to my friends and that I have been more merciful to my enemies than I would have been had I strictly considered the demands of my own safety. I am conscious that there are now in Rome many people whom I have forgiven and who would, if they saw the chance, repay my forgiveness by striking me down. But it is decorous to take such risks. I would rather be Caesar than a man constantly in fear and constantly guarding against his suspicions. Yet, though everything in my nature urges me towards magnanimity, the exigencies of war and rebellion have forced me on occasions to act as savagely as ever Sulla did, though I may honestly say, I think, that my most savage reprisals have nearly always been taken against whole tribes and peoples rather than against individuals.

At this time when we were preparing for the second invasion of Britain I still hoped that in Gaul matters would go smoothly. I had been given in the previous year the great honor of the

twenty days' thanksgiving service. Most people in Rome assumed
that I would now proceed from success to success and that, from
an orderly and pacified province, more and more wealth would
find its way to Italy. On the whole I shared the general opinion,
though both I and Labienus were well aware that there was still
unrest in Gaul. That great slaughter of the Germans at the con-
fluence of the Rhine and Moselle had not had exactly the desired
effect. It had certainly impressed upon the Gauls an idea of our
strength and of the ruthlessness with which we would proceed
against treachery; but it had also caused a different kind of alarm.
At the time when I first arrived in Gaul our army was certainly
regarded as formidable, but most Gauls (even really intelligent
men like Diviciacus) thought of it more as a useful ally in inter-
tribal politics than as an absolutely dominating power. It was
now clear that we intended to control the whole country and
even to extend our influence into Britain and Germany. Yet still,
with all the reputation which we had acquired, our numbers were,
when compared with the forces available to the Gauls, very inconsiderable. It began to become clear to those Gauls who resented our presence and our authority that, if they were ever to re-
assert that independence which they were gradually losing, they
would have to act quickly and to act, so far as possible, as a
united country. It was this kind of general movement which
Labienus and I most feared.

Patriotism is a powerful motive among the Gauls and we knew
that if any leader could be found who could represent himself
as fighting for the freedom of the whole country, it would be hard
even for friends of ours (like Commius, for example) to resist the
national impulse. Labienus was in favor of getting rid of a number
of those Gauls who seemed to be potential rebels and of putting
men whom we knew to be reliable in positions of authority in
every state. He was, with considerable reason, particularly anxious to arrest and execute Dumnorix, the Aeduan, who, as we all
knew, still headed the anti-Roman party in his state and still had a
powerful following of his own. In my view, however, such measures would merely precipitate a revolt. Wherever possible I was

already arranging for pro-Roman Gauls to become kings and chief magistrates of their tribes; but this had to be done with tact. It would do more harm than good if we raised to authority men who were known to have acquired it only through us. And as for putting to death anyone who was not openly in revolt, that seemed to me dishonorable in itself and also, at this juncture, impolitic. I still hoped that Gaul would be won, at least partly, by conciliation; and, in spite of the struggle that lay ahead, events have proved me right.

I did, however, agree with Labienus that it would be unwise to leave behind in Gaul anyone capable of starting a movement against us while I, with the bulk of the army, was in Britain. I therefore asked a number of Gallic chieftains to come with me to Britain as commanders of the cavalry detachments furnished by their states. Some of these chieftains were, I knew, perfectly loyal; others (Dumnorix, the Aeduan, for example) were suspect. And indeed reports soon reached me that Dumnorix was beginning to spread the most extraordinary stories about me. He was assuring his compatriots that I had asked them to accompany me to Britain so that I should have a good opportunity of murdering them all. And he was putting himself forward as a leader, if the rest would follow him, of a movement to drive every Roman out of Gaul. Towards me personally he behaved more or less correctly and even began to attempt to ingratiate himself. He promised that, if I would secure for him a position of power in his tribe (perhaps the kingship), he would work loyally in my interests and he constantly begged me to leave him behind on the continent so that he would be able to co-operate with Labienus during my absence. But neither I nor Labienus was decieved. I was determined to have Dumnorix with me and remained wholly unaffected when he told me first that he had a morbid horror of seasickness, and then that he had religious responsibilities which made it impossible for him to leave Gaul. As it was we had to wait, all ready to embark, for nearly four weeks until we got the right wind for sailing. Finally the weather changed and I gave the orders for infantry and cavalry to go aboard the transports. It

was at this moment that Dumnorix, with a band of his own retainers, slipped out of camp and made off for his own country.
This was the first occasion when my authority had been flouted by
a subordinate and an ally. I fully realized the significance of the
event. Putting off everything else, I sent a strong detachment of
cavalry in pursuit of Dumnorix with orders to bring him back,
dead or alive. He was soon overtaken, but refused to surrender. It
must be owned that he died bravely, fighting to the last and shouting out over and over again that he was a free man and a citizen of
a free state.

    We were then able to set sail, but it seemed to me that this ex-
pedition was starting under bad auspices.

Chapter 10

Signs of Danger

INDEED IT SEEMS TO ME NOW THAT FROM THIS TIME MY DIFFICUL-ties continued to increase and new dangers began to beset me on every side. I was no longer pursuing an uninterrupted career of conquest, but was soon fighting desperately to retain what I had won and then struggling still more desperately for my life and my honor. The whole structure of security, both military and political, which I had raised for myself through the years began to slip, to break and to collapse. Even fortune seemed, not once but persistently, to turn against me; for how could I have calculated or imagined so many setbacks coming in the order and with the impact that they did? At the time of the second invasion of Britain it appeared that, because of my alliance with Pompey and Crassus, all my interests were safeguarded and guaranteed in Rome; that Gaul was subjugated and that my own future was secured. I had already planned that after the end of my governor-ship in Gaul I should return to Rome to be elected consul and to celebrate the triumph earned by my army and myself. I was aim-ing at no revolution and, for once in my life, I could consider myself safe. But before long I was left with nothing but my army and stood in danger of losing even the glory I had won in war.

When, after so much delay, we did set out for Britain, our

armament was certainly an impressive sight. The transports, the warships and the vessels chartered by private individuals came to a total of at least eight hundred. Five legions and two thousand cavalry were on board. But I can admit now, though I did not do so at the time, that even this expedition was a failure. It is my habit always to appear in front of the enemy before I am expected, but on both occasions when we invaded Britain we arrived late in the year and had not the time to achieve what I had planned. On this occasion we were still further delayed by yet another disaster to our fleet. Moreover the Britons fought well and their king, Cassivelaunus, showed a surprising military ability. He carefully avoided anything which could be called a regular engagement, but used his charioteers, cavalry and light troops very intelligently to interrupt our communications and to entice small detachments of our men away from the main body. The Britons, like many of the Spanish tribes, prefer to fight in rather open order and so never afforded the kind of target which we wanted. We could always advance, but these advances were never decisive and often in what we thought of as a pursuit we lost more men than we destroyed. Luckily I was able to use Commius as an intermediary in dealing with some of the British tribes who resented the authority of Cassivelaunus. It was rather through fear that his fellow countrymen would desert him than because we were in a position to destroy his army that Cassivelaunus in the end made what amounted to a token submission. He promised hostages and the payment of an annual tribute to Rome. These were undertakings which looked well when written down in my dispatches. In fact, though a few hostages were delivered, no tribute was ever paid. Before the campaign began I had contemplated the idea of spending the winter in Britain, thinking that in this way I might consolidate the conquest of the island and at the same time enrich the army and myself. Now however I realized that the operation would take longer than I had imagined. I was also constantly receiving dispatches from Labienus which warned me of a growing feeling of unrest in Gaul. It seemed best therefore to bring the army back to the continent before the dangerous period of the autumn gales. We were short of ships and the transports were badly overcrowded; but the operation was carried out easily and without any losses at all.

While in Britain I had received the news of the death of my mother Aurelia. This was in the course of nature and, though I mourned for her, I could at least enjoy the satisfaction of knowing that she had lived to see her son as Chief Pontiff, as consul and as a commander in the field who had received greater honors than any living general except for Pompey. I had every reason then to believe that she died happy and I think now that she would have wished to die when she did rather than have lived to see the desperate struggle of the future. But now on my return to Gaul I was met by letters which told me of another death, a death that was premature, most affecting to my own feelings and most dangerous in its possible effects. My only daughter Julia, the wife of Pompey, had died in childbirth. The son she had borne had only survived her by a few hours. No death has ever affected me so deeply as this death of my daughter. Pompey also, from his letters, appeared inconsolable, and at this time of our bereavement I felt for Pompey more affection than I had ever felt before.

It did not immediately occur to me that now he had ceased to be connected with me as a son-in-law he would become increasingly detached from me in politics and in personal feeling, though, when some of my friends mentioned the possibility of such an estrangement, I could see that this was something to be feared. Indeed it may well have been the fear of just this disastrous division which led the people of Rome to insist upon burying the body of my daughter and Pompey's wife in the Field of Mars with every possible honor. Public opinion, though often blind or misguided, does sometimes show a peculiar prescience. The people of Rome admired Julia for herself and honored her because of her connection with Pompey and with me; but also, I think, they felt, however dimly, that they had lost by her death a certain security. For if Pompey and I were to pursue different policies, the whole fabric of their world would be torn from top to bottom.

I myself at this time felt no such apprehensions. But I could have given way to my natural grief if I had had the time to relax a moment from my duties as commander of an army. As it was I was soon convinced by Labienus that there was a serious danger of large-scale revolts in Gaul and both he and I were fully occupied in planning what seemed to us the most appropriate measures for dealing with a situation in which there were many unpredictable elements. On the surface everything seemed calm. I had summoned a meeting of Gallic chiefs at Samarobriva. There were very few absentees and the congratulations which I received on my successful campaign in Britain appeared to be sincere. Some of the chieftains did indeed speak to me of the burden likely to be imposed upon Gaul this winter by the quartering of the legions and, as was natural enough, everyone found reasons to show why it would be better for the legions to spend the winter in the territory of some tribe other than his own. In fact the harvest had been bad this year throughout Gaul and it seemed to me that it would really be difficult for any one state to support the whole of our army for the whole time before the next campaigning season. As I also had unmistakable evidence that intrigues were being carried on against us in a number of different states, particularly in the Belgic territory of the north and east, it seemed to me that it would be a good thing to have troops available for action in a number of districts at the same time. By distributing the legions in a number of camps I should be able both to spare any one tribe too great a burden for its resources and also to increase our security in the event of an uprising.

The dispersal was not, or should not have been, too wide for safety. One legion was some distance from the rest, but it was in a perfectly quiet area. The other seven legions were all quartered separately in Belgic territory and were all within a hundred miles of one another. Labienus with his legion was on the Rhine in what seemed to us the most exposed and dangerous position. One of the other legions, which consisted largely of recruits, was strengthened by the addition of five extra cohorts. This force was under the command of Sabinus and Cotta, both commanders who had proved themselves efficient in the past. I took, indeed, every reasonable precaution. The army appeared secure and I could see nothing to prevent me from carrying out my usual winter visit to my other provinces on the Italian side of the Alps. However I delayed my departure a little longer than usual and waited at Samarobriva until I received messages from each legionary commander telling me that his legion had fortified its camp and was satisfactorily placed with regard to supplies.

I had expected trouble in the North, but I now received news of an anti-Roman outbreak in central Gaul. Here in densely wooded country (though there are some important towns) live the Carnutes. They claim to inhabit the very center of the whole of Gaul and in their secret forest fastnesses the Druids hold each year ceremonies of a peculiar sanctity. I had found them a difficult tribe to deal with until I had succeeded in having one of my own nominees, Tasgetius, appointed to the kingship. I was now informed that Tasgetius had been murdered by his countrymen and I at once transferred one of the legions from the country of the Belgae into the country of the Carnutes. I ordered its commander to arrest all who were implicated in the murder and to spend the winter among the Carnutes, requisitioning their food and generally indicating to the tribesmen that any act of rebellion would entail disagreeable consequences for themselves. I was myself very anxious to return to Northern Italy so that I could the better keep in touch with the rather disturbing political situation in Rome, and I was therefore extremely annoyed at finding that my departure was still further delayed by this affair. I was wrong. In fact one may say that this murder of Tasgetius was for me and for the army in Gaul the greatest possible stroke of luck. It is appalling to think of what the consequences might have been if I had left Gaul at the time when I intended to leave. Even where I was, on the spot, vital news reached me so late that it was only just possible to act in time.

I was almost on the point of departure when a messenger, a Gaul, reached me from the camp of Quintus Cicero. He informed me that, for the last ten days, Cicero and his legion had been attacked by a force of sixty thousand Gauls; he described the siege

towers and lines of entrenchments made by the enemy who had
worked under the instruction of Roman prisoners; he told me
that messenger after messenger from Cicero had been intercepted
by the Gauls and tortured to death under the eyes of our besieged
men; at the time when he left, he said, there was scarcely one
among the defenders still unwounded; they were still holding out,
but how much longer they would be able to do so was most uncertain. And he added a report which, though I was inclined to
discount it at the time, still lay rankling in my mind like some
sensitive spot which at any moment will break into a searing pain.
It was widely rumored, he said, that somewhere near the German
frontier an entire Roman legion and its commander had been
destroyed. This I could not believe; yet the thought that such a
thing might be possible filled me with horror. I was horrified too
when I reflected that for so long a time I had been entirely unaware of the danger to which Cicero was exposed.

Cicero's camp was in the country of the Nervii. It was obvious
that I must reach him with the least possible delay and it seemed
to me that I must take the risk of marching to his relief with a
comparatively small force, since it would take too long to bring together the whole army. I had one legion with me at Samarobriva
with which I proposed to set out at once, and I sent messengers to
the commanders of the two other legions nearest to Cicero's camp,
asking them to march immediately and to join me on my way. One
of these commanders was Labienus and from him, soon after I set
out, I received a reply which disturbed me more than any news
has ever disturbed me before or since. He informed me that I
had lost a legion and five cohorts almost to a man. This was the
force that had been spending the winter at Aduatuca under the
command of two experienced officers, Sabinus and Cotta. Somehow or other, according to Labienus, they had been induced to
leave their camp and had been surprised and destroyed by the
Gallic tribe of the Eburones. Only a few stragglers had escaped
and succeeded in reaching Labienus's quarters with the news. The
result of this disaster had been that the tribes nearest to Labienus
had surrounded him and were preparing to attack his camp. He

told me that he felt confident he could hold out, but thought it most dangerous to leave his fortifications to attempt to join me.

I now saw before me the terrible possibility of total failure. I had already lost one Roman army and, for all I knew, Cicero's army too by this time might have been overwhelmed. I was well aware of how quickly and completely the feelings and resolutions of the Gauls are apt to change and I knew that a general rising throughout the country would confront my scattered legions with greater force than they would be able to sustain. I saw that Labienus had, as usual, assessed the position accurately. It would be most unwise for him to leave his camp, and by remaining where he was he was immobilizing large enemy forces which might be used against me or against Cicero. Nevertheless I was now left with the absurdly small force of two legions with which to face an army of at least sixty thousand Gauls who would be elated by their previous success and would be receiving every day more reinforcements from their neighbors.

With these two legions I moved fast into the country of the Nervii. Cicero and his men still held out and, as I drew near, the Gauls, who were informed of how few we were, broke off the siege and came against us in full force. I was able to trap them in a position where their numbers and their confidence were of no advantage to them. We won a great victory and in doing so saved both Cicero and ourselves. But I had not sufficient troops to follow up this victory so as to make it decisive, and, though we were safe for the time being, I felt the whole of Gaul poised above us like a breaking wave. I gave up all thought of returning to Northern Italy for the winter. It was important, I knew, for me at this critical time to be able to communicate quickly with my friends in Rome; but more important than any politics was the existence of my army. My place was with my legions and I must stay with them.

Everything that I saw and heard confirmed me in the belief that we had only narrowly escaped a complete disaster and that enormous efforts would be required to make good the ground that we had already lost. I found that Cicero and his legion had fought magnificently and I was proud indeed of the courage and resource which they had displayed. But I was alarmed for the future when I saw with my own eyes the great fieldworks, towers, mantlets and all the other apparatus of siegecraft which the Gauls had built. Only a year or two before these people had regarded such devices of ours as miraculous. Well-fortified towns had surrendered at the mere sight of a tower moving up to the walls on wheels. But now our methods of warfare had ceased to be mysterious. And the Gauls had discovered not only that we could be imitated, but also that we could be disgracefully defeated.

From the accounts of prisoners I was now able to form an accurate idea of the appalling calamity which had overtaken the army of Sabienus and Cotta. What had happened was this. One camp had been suddenly attacked by the tribe of the Eburones in full force. This was not one of the great or influential tribes, but it was led by a chieftain of unusual intelligence and ambition. Indeed I shall always remember the name of Ambiorix and I have given his people, or what remains of them, every reason to remember me. It appears that the sudden attack of Ambiorix caused our men more surprise than damage. It was beaten off after some fairly severe fighting. What most impressed our officers, and particularly Sabinus, was that it should have taken place at all; for it seemed incredible that this obscure tribe should have ventured to challenge the power of Rome. But one must allow for the incredible in warfare. It is often the only way to victory. So, after his army had failed in their open attack. Ambiorix made use of his failure in order to prepare the way for success. He cleverly succeeded in persuading Sabinus that he had not intended to make the attack at all. It was his tribe, he said, who had forced him to take this action, because there had been a general agreement among all the Gauls to attack at this time every Roman camp in their country. He, Ambiorix, was personally still most grateful to me for the favors I had bestowed on him and he wished, if at all possible, to show his gratitude. He was therefore willing to allow our army to march out of his territory and join up with Labienus or with Cicero (the two nearest camps). Only he advised Sabinus to take advantage of this offer quickly. Large forces of Germans had been called in by the Gauls; these had already crossed the Rhine and would soon be in action. Moreover he could not guarantee that his own tribe would not take courage again if time were allowed to elapse.

Sabinus believed this story. It appeared to him that, unless there were really a combined movement of the Gauls and Germans against us, Ambiorix would never have dared to behave as he had behaved. He therefore proposed to act just as this treacherous barbarian wished. His fellow commander, Cotta, who unfortunately was junior to him in rank, took up a different and a proper attitude. He insisted on two points only — that it would be wrong to leave camp without orders and that in warfare one does not take the advice of an enemy. But, without organizing mutiny in the army, Cotta would have been unable to get his own way. Perhaps he was actually tempted to take this step, since certainly most of the centurions would have been on his side. As it happened he behaved correctly, if fatally, and allowed himself to be overruled. The army set out next day. It was ambushed and destroyed. Cotta fought bravely to the end and died fighting. Sabinus, till he was treacherously stabbed in the back, continued to attempt to negotiate. It seemed that throughout the whole action Ambiorix's men had shown both discipline and courage. After capturing all the weapons and all the baggage of our army they had swept on to make their attack on the camp of Cicero, and Ambiorix had attempted to make use of the same stratagem which he had employed successfully against Sabinus, urging Cicero to retreat while there was still time. But Cicero, though a much less experienced commander than Sabinus, had behaved with a quite admirable resolution. He was prepared, he said, to negotiate with Ambiorix, but only if he first laid down his arms. This is the kind of attitude which impresses barbarians and confirms the courage of one's own men. Yet, though I admired the conduct of Cicero and of his legion, I had to admit that the native troops had almost proved too much for them, and I observed that although our men were rightly proud of their own achievements, they, and indeed everyone else in the army, were profoundly disturbed by the fate of Sabinus, Cotta and their troops. In the speeches which I made at this time to my soldiers I was careful to emphasize the fact that the disaster had taken place not through any superior fighting abilities shown by the enemy, but owing to the criminal incompetence of one commanding officer; and I succeeded in infecting others with my own determination that this disgrace should be fully and decisively revenged. Nevertheless I was myself filled with apprehension when I thought of the skill with which these Gauls were now beginning to imitate our methods, of the discipline which they seemed to be acquiring and of their enormous numbers.

My anxiety continued throughout the whole of that winter. True that the defeat which we had inflicted on Ambiorix and his allies had eased the situation somewhat. The troops which had gathered to attack Labienus had dispersed as soon as it was known that I was still in Gaul myself and ready to reinforce any legion that was threatened. Later Labienus won a brilliant victory on his own which was enough to guarantee his safety at least until the spring. Still scarcely a day passed during these winter months without some news of anti-Roman agitation in one tribe or another. I had to devote nearly all my attention to the politics of Gaul just at the moment when I should have been intervening actively in the politics of Rome. Above all I had to be sure that next year we should be able to take the offensive rather than await developments which would certainly be directed against us. I sent some of my best officers into Northern Italy with instructions to raise recruits and I wrote to Pompey, asking him to release for service with me some of the troops which he was recruiting for his own command in Spain. Pompey acted like a patriot and like a friend. I secured from him an entire legion. My own officers raised two others. Thus by the beginning of the campaigning season we were able to take the field with ten legions, thus having been reinforced by twice the number of cohorts that had been lost by Sabinus. The size of these reinforcements and the speed with which they had been concentrated served as an indication to our enemies that we contemplated no relaxation or retreat but rather the tightening of our hold on what we possessed already.

Chapter 11

Gathering Storm

THE NEXT YEAR IN GAUL WAS A YEAR OF REPRESSION AND OF punishment. The measures I took were successful in so far as they checked for the time being the outbreak of that general revolt which I feared. But the main objects which I had set myself were not achieved. The Gauls were not terrorized into submission: Ambiorix was neither captured nor killed. In every campaign that I undertook I gained the advantage of surprise and yet the results were not commensurate with the effort expended. I was constantly impeded both in Gaul and in the wider field of Roman politics by unforeseen and unforeseeable occurrences. It began to look as though I should have to fight not only against the combination of men but against fate.

When I look back on the events of this year I see in my mind's eye little except pictures of savagery, ruin and devastation. I see the smoke of burning towns and villages and houses, long processions of prisoners, and I can still see the bleeding lump of flesh that was Acco, the chief of the Senones. There was not only a frantic hurry but also a kind of squalor about all our proceedings this year except perhaps for the display of our army across the Rhine, which was certainly a grand and dignified spectacle. This time the bridge was constructed even more quickly than on the previous occasion and a still larger army marched across it into

Germany. I had hoped to bring to battle the great German tribe of the Suebi, but their leaders wisely withdrew their army into the interior of the country where I could not follow them without taking great risks and wasting more time than I had to spare. Nevertheless, although we got less booty and fewer prisoners than I had hoped, this expedition had most important results. The German tribes who had been in friendly relations with us for the past two years renewed their offers of help and I was able to make arrangements for the recruiting of a considerable number of German cavalrymen and for having them trained in the way I wanted. This force was to prove absolutely decisive in the campaigns of the following year.

The treacherous and guilty tribe of the Eburones lived (I am correct in using the past tense) in the glens and mountains of the Ardennes. North of them, in the flat marshy lands along the west, were the Menapii and to their south were the powerful tribe of the Treveri who had been defeated by Labienus in the previous winter but since then had joined with Ambiorix of the Eburones and others in an anti-Roman league. Before crossing the Rhine we had, in two sharp campaigns, crushed both the Menapii and the Treveri. We now turned in overwhelming force against the Eburones. In the first cavalry raid of the campaign we very nearly succeeded in capturing Ambiorix himself. As it was he escaped with a small bodyguard of not more than four horsemen and for the rest of that year was continuously on the run. There was no attempt at any organized resistance to us. Indeed Ambiorix had ordered his people to scatter in every direction, for each man to shift for himself. I had decided, if possible, to exterminate the whole tribe and to leave Ambiorix, if in the end he survived, with either no subjects at all or with a very few who would execrate his name for having involved them in the loss of all their possessions and all hope for the future. We destroyed every town and village in the country, all the crops and nearly every individual homestead. We drove off all the cattle and hunted down the men, the women and the children who had taken refuge in the mountain glens or the marshy land to the north. Though we were never confronted by any considerable force, small detachments of Eburones would sometimes get together and, fighting desperately, would inflict some casualties on our foraging parties or succeed in cutting off individuals who had strayed too far from the column. Partly in order to avoid such annoying losses and partly in order to advertise as widely as possible the way in which we were prepared to treat rebels and traitors, I invited anyone who chose from the neighboring tribes to come and join in plundering and destroying the Eburones. There were plenty of volunteers. Yet by the end of the summer Ambiorix himself was still at large and in his devastated territories there still remained a few wretches in existence. I would have preferred to have made a cleaner end of this business.

At the close of the campaigning season I convened the Gallic council in a town of the Remi. I wished at this council to do everything I could to confirm the allegiance of our friends and to intimidate our enemies. The news that was reaching me from Italy had made me determined to spend the winter on the Italian side of the Alps where I could communicate quickly with my friends and agents in Rome. I wished to be sure of the safety of my army in my absence and, before leaving, I distributed gifts and honors among the leading men of the Aedui, the Remi and those other tribes in whom I had the most confidence. I also inflicted an exemplary and cruel punishment on the chief of the Senones, Acco, who early in the year had attempted to raise his people against us but had been surprised and overwhelmed by our legions before he had even completed the organization of his revolt. I had him killed in the savage military fashion of our ancestors. In the presence of our army and of leading Gauls from every state he was stripped naked, his head was tied firmly in the fork of an upright piece of wood and he was beaten to death with rods. There was little left of him when the flogging was over but, to complete the traditional procedure, the head was finally severed from the body. This disgusting spectacle was greatly enjoyed by the army who had been longing for some notable execution to crown, as it were, their year of revenge. Many of the Gauls too congratulated me on having so clearly demonstrated to the whole country that, while I would reward my friends, I would behave implacably towards traitors.

I believed indeed myself that this demonstration was necessary; but I was well aware that, though I had increased our security for the moment, I had also made enemies of some whom I would have wished to have on my side. It was now clear to everyone in Gaul that our orders were to be obeyed throughout the country. We might give to one tribe or another the title of "Friends and Allies" and I was certainly careful to interfere as little as possible with the political and religious organization of each tribe. Yet still each tribe had to conform to my will. They could only be friends if they were subjects. This fact was made clear for all to see by the execution of Acco and I knew that some of the best and proudest of the Gauls would never forgive me for this necessary act. I remember noticing at the time of the execution the face of Commius whom I had made King of the Atrebates, who had been of the greatest help to me in Britain and elsewhere and whose power I would gladly have increased still further. As the blows fell upon the bleeding back of one who was, like himself, a chieftain and a warrior, Commius, I could see, was passing through a total revulsion of feeling. Afterwards I took particular care to speak affably to him and to encourage him in his private ambitions; but he could no longer address me with the ease and frankness which I had admired in the past. Before I left the army I instructed Labienus to have him watched.

It was the end of my sixth campaigning season in Gaul. I knew that during these years I had accomplished much more than I could have imagined possible at the time when I went first to Geneva to fight the Helvetii. I had explored Britain and penetrated Germany. I had added to our empire what might become the strongest and greatest of our provinces. And I had an army which in its experience, fighting qualities and loyalty was the best beyond comparison in the world. But I was well aware that our position in Gaul was still not securely established. One other disaster like that which had befallen the army of Sabinus might mean an ignominious end to all my ambition and achievement. Also I

could see that in Rome the whole basis of my political authority
was in danger of crumbling. One of my partners was dead and
disgraced; the other was in process of being alienated from me.

I think that it was at the end of July, when I was still occupied
with the extermination of the Eburones, that I received the news
of how my old friend Crassus and his brilliant son Publius had lost
their lives and their army in the deserts of Mesopotamia. This was
the greatest military disaster which we have suffered since the
time of Hannibal. I hope to avenge it myself and when I set out,
tomorrow or the next day, for Parthia, I shall have no reason to
suppose that I shall not be setting out on another career of victory
and of conquest. Yet I am sobered by the reflection that this,
after all, is what Crassus himself must have supposed at a time
when he was so near to death. Certainly neither I nor Pompey
imagined at the time that so overwhelming a defeat was possible.
It was a defeat which, from a military point of view, could have
been most dangerous. Fortunately for us the Parthians are incapable of keeping a large army in the field for long and do not
appear to have any commander or ruler with more than local
and transitory ambition. Had they possessed any general or
statesman with the will to exploit their success, they could have
overrun Syria, Asia and Egypt without much difficulty. As it happened, young Cassius, the friend of Brutus, acted very efficiently
with the few troops still left to us in the East. Later my old colleague and enemy Bibulus was sent out to take command. This
was already a sign that no very serious danger was expected.
Otherwise there would have been a demand that either Pompey
or I should take on the responsibility; for Bibulus, though energetic enough, was never a skillful commander.

At the time when the news was first heard of the disaster in
Parthia, no one thought of entrusting Bibulus with an army, nor
indeed would I have felt any apprehension at the idea of this
particular enemy of mine being given additional power. I still
felt secure. Yet as I began to reflect on the political implications
of the disaster which had overtaken Crassus, I could see clearly
that they all tended in a direction that was contrary to my own

interests. It was natural enough that, after the spectacular failure of Crassus, public opinion in Rome should turn against the whole idea of great and hazardous foreign conquests whether in the East or elsewhere. Those who had initiated this modern policy of military conquest were Pompey, Crassus and myself; the policy had been opposed by Bibulus, Cato and their group. Consequently one might expect, at least for the moment, a strengthening of this group and some attacks on Pompey and myself, the survivors of the original triumvirate. But in fact public opinion does not often proceed along rational lines. What was remembered about Pompey was not his recent approval of a venture which had turned out disastrously, but the great personal successes which he had enjoyed in the East. To the average man Pompey remained the invariably fortunate and never defeated soldier. He had to exist as a symbol of Roman stability and a reassurance for Roman doubt. It was also known that, except for a few short periods of time, he and Crassus had always been on bad terms. All this was enough, since public opinion is seldom influenced by reason, to exculpate Pompey from any share in what now appeared to be the mistaken policies of Crassus. It was also important that Pompey, with an army under his authority, was at the gates of Rome.

As for me, who had also approved of the eastern adventure of Crassus, I was less fortunately situated. I had always been more closely associated with Crassus than Pompey had been; my reputation was rather that of one who would act brilliantly and unexpectedly than of one who, like Pompey, could be relied upon quietly and inevitably to succeed; moreover, I had myself lost a legion and five cohorts. It was therefore natural, if not logical, that the defeat and disgrace of Crassus should be widely attributed to something described as "Caesarism" than to any of its real causes. I found too that whereas a year ago my more ardent supporters in Rome would proudly refer to me as "Rome's only general," they would now hesitate to use the phrase since it would be generally accepted as being only applicable to Pompey.

Though I recognized this shift in feeling, I was not at the time very seriously disturbed by it. I intended, after two or three years, to stand again for the consulship and knew that, when I came to do so, I should, so far as anything is foreseeable, have further victories to my credit. Moreover, though my position with regard to the senate might be less strong than it was, I could always depend on the support of the Roman people at election time. I was fully aware that it was of the utmost importance for me to remain on good terms with Pompey, and I could see easily enough that my enemies would attempt to alienate Pompey from me; but I did not believe that they would succeed in doing this. Not that I had any illusions about Pompey's character. I recognized that with him vanity was perhaps the strongest of all feelings; but I knew too that he was loyal and patriotic, as he had shown by sending me one of his own legions in the previous year. I fancied too that he would remember the many political discussions which we had had together in the past when I had always succeeded in convincing him that our interests and our enemies were the same. Both he and I had always been obstructed by the same narrow group of reactionary politicians; nor was there any reason for rivalry between the two of us; the world was big enough to contain us both. On these facts I had often insisted and so, I knew, had Julia. I thought that Pompey had grasped them and I overlooked what I am afraid is the true verdict of moralists — that one weakness, which may appear inconsiderable, can be enough to overthrow and corrupt a whole character which would otherwise have been strong, stable and consistent.

The fact was that Pompey could not endure the notion of an equal. He was, till the very end, too proud openly to admit that I came into this category, yet he strongly feared that I might actually become a superior. These underlying and secretive thoughts and intuitions oppressed his spirit and warped his judgment. In his own conception of himself there was no room for treachery or for meanness and it would be both treacherous and mean to turn against me, who from the beginning had supported him, who had been his father-in-law and who entertained absolutely no designs against him. Therefore he had to be convinced that in following his unworthy motives he was really conforming to

some higher dictates of morality. He had to believe or affect to believe that I was a revolutionary, while he stood for legality and for
the Constitution. It was an absurd pretense. I had never held any
office in the state before the year when I was legally entitled to do
so, while Pompey, from his earliest youth, had been privileged to
evade the laws. He had triumphed when a mere youth and become
consul without having had a single one of the necessary qualifica-
tions. His greatest commands had come to him by a vote of the
people in opposition to the will of the senate. Indeed I could
claim with some show of reason that my own career, when compared with his, was of a peculiarly conventional and law-abiding
character. Such a claim would not have been, perhaps, entirely
justified. There has always been something spectacular about my
actions and, unlike Pompey, I have always had a clear idea of the
direction in which I am going. In so far as I have ideas I may be
described as more revolutionary than he was. But my ideas have
never led me in the direction of civil war, and now, when I think of
the ghastly battlefields of Pharsalus, of Thapsus and of Munda,
where so many Romans died and so many were embittered for
life, I feel indeed the guilt that anyone must feel who has been
implicated, however unwillingly, in a disgraceful action; but there
is a sense in which it is true to say that this is what they willed —
Pompey, Bibulus, Cato, Ahenobarbus — and this is what I would
have given anything, except my honor, to have avoided.

In the winter after the defeat and death of Crassus I had no
such apprehensions of the future. It did not seem to me possible
that Pompey and I could be opposed to each other in civil war and
at the head of more legions than have ever been mobilized in our
history. It may be that my own vice is to be too trusting where
my friends are concerned.

This winter the situation in Rome was more chaotic and disturbed than it has ever been in peacetime. I watched it from my
province in Northern Italy and often wished that the laws would
permit me to cross the provincial boundary and intervene personally in the affairs of the capital. In fact it was lucky for me that
I had to stay in the north, since, as things turned out, I should

soon have to hurry back to Gaul to meet the most serious danger of the whole war. Meanwhile there was no one in Rome capable of exercising authority except for Pompey, and Pompey was deliberately refraining from using the authority which he had. He was waiting for the moment when, as had so often happened in the past, the situation would become intolerable and there would be a general demand for him to come forward and, with the aid of exceptional powers, to deal with it.

The elections this year were constantly being postponed, partly because of instances of quite unexampled bribery (in which two of my own protégés were implicated), partly because of the unrestrained intimidation practiced by Clodius, who was standing for the praetorship, and Milo who, with strong senatorial backing, was standing for the consulship. Both Clodius and Milo were expert gang leaders and blood was shed every day in clashes between the two of them. Each, given the opportunity, would have killed the other in cold blood. This opportunity, about midwinter, came to Milo who took advantage of it. Clodius was surprised with a smaller escort than usual. His supporters were overwhelmed by Milo's gladiators and Clodius himself was first wounded and then, in circumstances that could not conceivably justify a plea of self-defense, murdered. Clodius had many enemies in the senate and it appears that directly after the murder many of these (notably Cicero) imagined that Milo's violent and successful use of Clodius's own methods would bring peace and stability to the Republic. They were very soon disillusioned. Clodius remained the favorite of the people of Rome. Indeed no one in our time except myself has been able to hold their affections so long and so firmly. Even today, when I am regarded rather as an autocrat than as a popular leader, I can imagine that, if it should happen that I were murdered as Clodius was, my funeral, like his, would be the occasion for a tremendous outbreak of spontaneous indignation — though in the event of my assassination I cannot imagine how order in the state could be restored so easily and quickly as Pompey restored it after Clodius's funeral. The people had taken control of the streets and of the ceremony itself. None of Clodius's enemies

dared show his face on that day and the senate house was burned
as a pyre for the dead body. It was a not inappropriate gesture,
and one that was peculiarly alarming to Cicero.

After the rioting was over it became clear to people of all parties
that, if life were to continue, order must be restored. There was a
strong demand that Pompey should be made Dictator. He had an
army; he had been attacked by Clodius but had avoided giving
any open support to Milo; he was by nature a traditionalist and
had also, by accident, acquired something of the reputation of a
popular leader; he was, finally, the man to whom Rome always
did turn in time of trouble. Some of my own friends, remembering
that I also had an army, suggested to me that we should agitate in
favor of a proposal for making Pompey and myself joint consuls.
If Pompey had agreed to such a proposition, no one, I think, could
have successfully opposed it, and it would have had the very great
advantage of reasserting the alliance between us. In fact, if I had
been able to work for one more year in collaboration with Pompey, it may be that the civil war and all its infinite damage would
have been avoided. But I myself was in no position to support the
proposal suggested by my friends. Though I certainly did not
realize yet how serious would be the rebellion in Gaul that was
just about to break out, I was well enough informed to know that
my presence with my army was absolutely necessary unless we
were to risk losing all our conquests.

I therefore saw to it that Pompey was informed that I would
support any movement made to grant him exceptional powers. I
insisted, however, that in the course of the use of these powers he
should see that Milo was brought to justice. I was informed by my
friend Balbus who, as usual, was acting for me in Rome, that Pompey would have Milo brought to trial and condemned. But, so
Balbus told me, Pompey's attitude towards me still left something
to be desired. He had given the impression that, in his view, I
should be content with my command in Gaul and should not
attempt to influence the politics of Rome. Moreover he rejected
another proposal which I made to him about this time and which
was designed to bring us closer together. I suggested that he should

once again take a wife from my family and I offered him Octavia, the young daughter of my niece Atia, an intelligent and good-looking girl (so I was informed — I had not seen her since her childhood). In order to make the alliance still stronger I indicated that I was willing to divorce my wife, Calpurnia, and to marry Pompey's daughter by his wife Mucia. I could remember this daughter as a child, since I had myself been the lover of Mucia, when Pompey was in the East. Indeed I had been sorry for Mucia when Pompey divorced her. I did not know at the time that his next wife would be my own daughter Julia. Now it seemed to me an appropriate thing that, just as Pompey had once been my son-in-law so I should become a son-in-law of his, and for the sake of so firm an alliance I was ready to go against some natural feelings of my own (I was and still remain fond of Calpurnia). But Pompey's reply to my offers was, though polite enough, negative. His daughter was already engaged to Faustus Sulla, the son of the Dictator, and this fact provided Pompey with a reasonable excuse for declining my proposal. Pompey himself could never live long without a wife, and in choosing a wife his affections nearly always played a considerable part. He had become genuinely fond of Cornelia, the widow of young Publius Crassus who had died with his squadron of Gallic cavalry in Parthia. Cornelia was a gracious and remarkably intelligent woman, a good wife for anyone. I was not surprised when, towards the end of the year, Pompey married her; but I recognized that this marriage might draw Pompey still further away from me. Cornelia's father was Metellus Scipio, a stupid man and one who was by nature jealous of anything superior to himself. Later in the following year, Pompey, who, supported by such unlikely people as Cato and Bibulus, had been created sole consul with the right to appoint a colleague, adopted his father-in-law as fellow consul. Scipio would scarcely have got elected in any other way as he too had been implicated in the bribery scandals of the preceding year.

I myself was not sorry to find that Pompey had been given the exceptional powers which he desired and I was not surprised at the energy he showed in the use of them. There were indeed some thoroughly unjust prosecutions, but on the whole the year of Pompey's consulship was a year of good government in which the ordinary decencies of civil life were protected. Milo was duly brought to trial and Cicero, very bravely in the circumstances, undertook to defend him. I believe, however, that at the last moment, when he found himself surrounded both by Clodius's friends and Pompey's soldiers, Cicero's nerve failed him and that the speech which he actually delivered was a very different affair from the version published later, which is indeed a fine piece of writing. But I myself had little time to study the events that took place this year in Rome, since I was more than fully occupied in Gaul. I did, however while I was still in Northern Italy, make one necessary arrangement for my own political future. I secured the support of the tribunes for a law (which was passed in the year of Pompey's consulship) authorizing me to stand for the consulship without having to appear in person at Rome. I had not yet made up my mind in which of the next years I should come forward as a candidate, but I wished to be sure that, if elected, I could proceed directly from my command in Gaul to the consulship in Rome. This was a precaution absolutely necessary for my personal safety. I knew that, if I had to return to Rome as an ordinary citizen to sue for the consulship in the ordinary way, I should be exposed to the attacks of my enemies who, in spite of all that I had achieved, would not scruple to fabricate some sort of charge against me and, by the use of every kind of legal obstruction, would attempt to prevent my candidature and check my career. I could deal with such attacks, no doubt, but only by means of rather unconstitutional methods and these I did not want to pursue. I was therefore relieved when this law, the law of the Ten Tribunes, was passed. It seemed to guarantee my future and I thought that, so long as I could survive what I could already see were the tremendous difficulties and dangers of this year in Gaul, I should have nothing else to fear.

Pompey had not long been in office when I received from Labienus news which left me in no doubt that, so far as Gaul was concerned, all my worst apprehensions were being realized.

Chapter 12

The Great Gallic Revolt

QUITE EARLY IN THE YEAR LABIENUS HAD SENT ME SOME INFORMA-tion which, though I had been partly expecting it, still distressed me profoundly. He had secured ample evidence to prove that Commius, the King of the Atrebates, was taking a prominent part in forming a league of all Gaul with the aim of asserting the national independence and driving every Roman from the country. I knew that Commius was able and ambitious. I had treated him as a friend and had done all I could to reward his valuable services to me. If now he had turned against me, this could not have been be-cause of thwarted ambition or any personal complaint. Clearly he was being carried away by some kind of patriotic impulse, and others, who had much less reason to be grateful to me than he had, would feel the force of this same impulse much more strongly. Labienus had attempted to deal with Commius in a clumsy, treacherous and inefficient way. Indeed this was the only occasion in all the Gallic wars when I deplored his judgment.

I myself have always and for every reason both of policy and of honor been opposed to the idea of the assassination of an enemy, and I should have imagined that on this subject Labienus knew my mind. He chose, however, to send to Commius, who did not know that he was under suspicion, a high-ranking officer with a party of centurions who were instructed to strike down the Gallic chief as soon as he was engaged in conversation. Roman centurions are not often employed as assassins and on this occasion the men executed their task inefficiently. Commius was wounded, but escaped. He was now, of course, a quite irreconcilable enemy and the story of the attempt on his life very naturally was a factor in bringing over many other Gauls of importance into the party opposed to us. This party was moreover greatly encouraged by the news from Italy. It was assumed that the disorders in Rome which followed the murder of Clodius would continue indefinitely and that I myself would be delayed in Northern Italy until late in the spring. Once before the Gauls had surprised a Roman army without its commander in chief. Now an even more favorable opportunity seemed to have presented itself. If I could be cut off from my legions, the legions themselves would be immobilized, revolt would spread throughout the whole country, and our men would be destroyed either by starvation or by the overwhelming military force that could be brought against them.

Stated thus briefly the Gallic plan may appear vague, leaving too much to chance, indeed a product of wishful thinking. In fact it had been worked out in considerable detail and was put into practice with resolution and intelligence. The signal for the general revolt was given by the Carnutes in central Gaul who, at their town of Cenabum, massacred every Roman trader and official who had come there for the winter. Reports of this crime spread quickly. For example, by the evening of the day of the massacre the news was known a hundred and fifty miles farther south, in the country of the Arverni. The Arverni were then and still remain one of the most powerful tribes of Gaul. The anti-Roman party among them was led by the young Vercingetorix, whose father had been King with authority extending widely over the whole country. Vercingetorix quickly seized power in his own state and soon secured the support of nearly every tribe in central, southern and western Gaul. In the north too the movement was spreading. Some of the Belgic tribes had been so weakened and terrorized by our operations of the previous year that they remained for the moment inactive. Others were ready enough for war and their efforts were being concerted by several chieftains of ability, among whom was Commius.

Our own dispositions were as follows: Labienus was in the country of the Senones with four legions. To the southeast and not far away were two other legions among the Lingones; two more were farther off in quarters among the Treveri. It was exceedingly difficult for Labienus to know what to do and in fact he behaved correctly, I think, in making no move at all. Our legions were safe enough where they were, while any mistaken or premature advance or withdrawal might lead to difficulties. This was a situation which demanded the presence of the commander in chief and I was cut off from my armies by mountains which at this time of the year are usually regarded as impassable, and, after the mountains, by miles of hostile territory. It appeared that of the more important tribes only the Aedui and the Remi could be depended upon and, knowing the Gauls as I did, I was prepared to find that even these tribes had been somehow or other, by bribery, promises or flattery, induced to join the national movement. The revolt had deprived me of nearly all my Gallic cavalry and I was now particularly glad that I had taken steps to secure some squadrons of German horse for my service. As it was the enemy appeared to hold the initiative everywhere. Their large forces, mainly of cavalry, could be concentrated quickly wherever their leadership might decide. We, at this early season of the year, were severely handicapped by lack of supplies as well as by the uncertainty and difficulty of the routes.

I found that Vercingetorix was very cleverly threatening us in two directions at once. His two threats were directed at the two most sensitive of our positions, and the fact that he had unhesitatingly adopted this strategy made me realize at once that I was now opposed by a leader of outstanding ability. There was a kind of historical lucidity about the way his mind worked. He had seen that we had only secured a foothold in Gaul at all because of our conquest of the original Province — the coastal plain and valley of the Rhone bounded by the Alps and the Cevennes. It was from this small and already Italianized base that we had moved northwards, first gradually and tentatively, then, in the six years of my proconsulship, with such speed that we had overrun the whole country

from the Mediterranean to the Atlantic and the Rhine. And he had
perceived that we had been able to make this advance with some
show of legality and some certainty of material support entirely
because of the friendly relationships which I had cultivated with
the Aedui. For long in the past the Aedui and the Arverni had disputed the supremacy of Gaul. Now, through Roman influence,
the Aedui had attained a position that was probably more important than would be justified by the numbers and resources of the
tribe. Yet I knew that, in spite of all that we had done, Dumnorix
had not been the only Aeduan who had resented our authority; and
Vercingetorix must have been aware that, if he could detach the
Aedui from us, not only would our armies be left isolated in the
middle of Gaul, but every tribe in the whole country would join
the movement against us.

Vercingetorix had reason to believe that his own country was,
for the moment, secure. Between the Province and the territory of
the Arverni rose the great mountain mass of the Cevennes, now
covered with snow. Not a single track across these mountains was
regarded as passable. He had therefore felt that he could leave his
home country undefended and had marched northwards in the direction of the Aeduan frontier. Clearly his motive was first to bring
in the few tribes in that area which still remained loyal to us and
then to tamper with the loyalty of the Aedui themselves. At the
same time he had organized a powerful force from the tribes to the
southwest. This force was advancing directly on our Province
through the gap between the Cevennes and the Pyrenees. I had
never expected such daring strategy from any Gaul and had left
the Province inadequately defended.

The danger, or dangers, were very obvious and pressing. I had
to rejoin my army, safeguard the Province, and protect the Aedui,
and I could not do all these things at once. It remained to do them
as quickly as possible. Till I had done all of them I could not regain
the initiative.

It seemed to me that I should deal first with the danger that was
most pressing. If the Province were overrun, I should lose not only
a most valuable base but the whole of my reputation as a general.

I could imagine the panic there would be in Rome at the news of the loss or even of the invasion of this rich area, so long pacified, and of the interruption of our land communications with Spain. Almost certainly there would be a move to have me superseded and no doubt it would be suggested that Pompey should fulfill his customary role of restoring what would appear to be a desperate situation. I did not want to be classed with Crassus as a military failure and I did not want Pompey to take from me the credit for the conquest of Gaul as he had taken from Lucullus the credit for the conquest of the East. So, with a small escort of cavalry, I set out for the Province, traveling rapidly along the coast road through Marseilles to Narbonne. Here I found the population in a state that was very near to panic. In a few days I was able to reassure them. I concentrated every available man in the threatened area, quickly constructed a line of fortified posts along the frontier to the west and north of Narbonne and saw to it that each of these posts was in charge of an enthusiastic and reliable officer. The enemy showed some intelligence in not venturing to attack these lines. Had they done so they would have suffered very severe casualties. As it was they fell back in the directions of Aquitania and the Loire. The Province was never seriously threatened again. My first aim had been secured.

I now called upon my troops for a very considerable effort. I proposed to cross the Cevennes into the country of the Arverni which had been, I knew, left virtually undefended. It was generally agreed that at this time of the year not even a small party traveling light could cross these mountains, let alone a military force with its baggage and equipment. I have noticed however that people are apt to describe as "impossible" things which they either do not want to do or else have never seriously attempted. Our crossing of the Cevennes was difficult but it took place. Often the soldiers had to shovel away snow to a depth of six feet; the cold was intense; we were short of food, since we were traveling as light as possible. In the end, however, we emerged into the warmer country beyond the mountains and here found all the food and plunder that we could desire. The Arverni were taken completely by surprise since they too had entertained the common notion of "impossibility." Nearly all their fighting men had gone north with Vercingetorix and so our small force of cavalry from the Province was able to range safely all over the country, doing damage unopposed.

I anticipated that Vercingetorix would soon receive greatly exaggerated accounts of our activities and would be forced to turn southwards again to defend his own people. I wished him to believe that I myself was remaining with the force that was engaged in ravaging his country and I allowed even my own officers to assume when I left them that I was only going to be away for a few days. As it was I recrossed the Cevennes with a very few picked horsemen and then went northwards, riding by day and night. On the way I picked up a contingent of German cavalry and with these as escort crossed the country of the Aedui and had reached my two legions among the Lingones before anyone had the slightest suspicion that I was in the neighborhood. I was quickly joined by the other two legions who had been among the Treveri and at the head of these four legions I marched to join Labienus in the country of the Senones. By this time Vercingetorix had discovered that I was no longer with the small raiding force that now withdrew again to the Province.

So far, it may be said, I had some reason to be satisfied with myself. I had saved the Province; I had reached and united my army; and I was now in a position, I considered, to meet any force that the Gauls might bring against me. Yet there were many other considerations which could have caused me to fall into the deepest despondency. I reflected that I had had to hurry like a fugitive, guarded only by a small body of mercenaries, through a country which in my dispatches to Rome I had declared to be subjugated and loyal. I had not even dared to entrust myself to our oldest friends, the Aedui. Other old friends, such as Commius, were plainly turning their backs on all the hopes I had held out to them and on all the personal affection which I had offered them. They preferred a national movement which was dedicated to the destruction of everything which I had achieved since I first came to Gaul. If this movement were successful, Gaul would be once more exposed to attack from across the Rhine, and the people of Gaul (I knew them) would very soon relapse into that state of political inefficiency and disorder from which I had attempted to raise them. And I myself, if defeated in war or forced to withdraw through lack of supplies, would be utterly discredited both as a general and as a politician. So far from attaining my second consulship, at which I aimed in a few years' time, I should be at the mercy of my many enemies who, by legal proceedings, would certainly drive me into exile, poverty and obscurity.

I saw that, once again, I had to fight for my life, for my honor, for the honor of my army and for the future towards which I was so strongly impelled. I saw too that I was likely to be confronted not only by very great numbers of the enemy but by a military skill very much greater than any which I had encountered before. Many of the Gauls now in command of national armies pledged to destroy the Romans had been trained in military science by me personally or by the best officers in my legions. These men knew our methods; they were able to construct fortified camps and even to engage in siege operations. And in particular, I reflected, they were perfectly well aware of the importance to us of supplies and the difficulties which in the early part of the year we were bound to encounter if they could cut us off from the sources on which we had been used to depend. They knew my weakness in cavalry and they knew that if I were forced to disperse the legionaries over a wide area in order to bring in food and plunder, they themselves, with their greatly superior numbers of cavalry, would be able to do us far more damage than they could hope to do in a pitched battle.

Their leader, Vercingetorix, had already shown himself to be not only a daring soldier but a clever and far-seeing commander. He was also, as I discovered, an admirable diplomatist and was taking all the most appropriate measures, using both bribery and threats, to bring every state of Gaul (and in particular the Aedui) into the national movement. He was able to show more continuous energy than any Gaul I have known and he was ruthless to those who failed him in courage or obedience. Those few Gauls who at this time came to us with news of his movements or who appeared to

be in any way willing to collaborate with us were, nearly all of
them, victims of his displeasure and living monuments of his ferocity. Some had their eyes gouged out, others had had their ears,
legs or hands lopped off. It was a savage way of treating the recalci-
trant, but it was effective. The orders of Vercingetorix were
obeyed. I myself had sometimes to imitate his methods and indeed
from the beginning of this struggle, on which everything depended,
I allowed my soldiers greater license than hitherto. They would be,
I knew, for most of this campaigning season under an almost intolerable strain, and it seemed to me proper that they should enjoy in-
tervals of relaxation in which they could indulge those passions of
greed, cruelty and lust which are common to most men and which
are felt with particular force after long periods of severe discipline,
hardship and danger.

Paradoxically an army exists to create or to maintain order and,
when its task is easy, it will be itself (unless its commander is incompetent or licentious) an example of order and of restraint. But
when it finds its very identity and existence threatened by danger,
when it is exposed to the unknown and to the treacherous, even its
good qualities may lead it to excess. I myself am an admirer of all
the decencies; but, when fighting for one's life, it is neither usual
nor safe to preserve them. So, faced with this mortal danger in
Gaul, I was prepared to be at least as ruthless as my enemy,
though I was never myself swept away by an unreasoning impulse
of savagery. My acts of barbarity were deliberate and I was ready
at any time, if I could see therein a real possibility of advantage, to
behave with mercy and with moderation.

All through this year Vercingetorix was constantly facing me
with new problems and, if I won a victory, he would as often as
not contrive to turn it to his own advantage. I had hoped that, when
he received the news that I had succeeded in crossing Gaul and
rejoining my legions, he would lead his army against us, taking advantage of the high morale and genuine enthusiasm which he had
certainly aroused. But he was too intelligent to act impulsively, as
most Gauls do. Instead of coming anywhere near us, he returned
from his own country in the direction of the Aeduan frontier.

Here he brought over to his own side the large and powerful tribe of the Bituriges and then began to attack a town of the Boii, who, ever since I had spared them after the battle with the Helvetii, had remained loyal to us. Vercingetorix had again very cleverly placed me in a dilemma. He knew that at this time of the year (it was still winter) Roman armies never took the field. The routes were difficult and supplies almost unobtainable. If I marched to the relief of the Boii, I should involve myself and my army in very serious difficulties. If, on the other hand, I were to allow my friends and allies to be destroyed without raising a finger to help them, my credit with the Gauls would be gone and I should soon have no friends or allies left. I decided that I must face all risks rather than allow it to be supposed that I was incapable of helping my friends.

I set out with eight legions for the country of the Bituriges and of the Boii. We were immediately faced by difficulties of supply. A few tribes did obey my instructions and sent convoys to us, but these convoys were in most cases intercepted by bands of partisans who, either as nationalists or as plain robbers, had sprung up all over the country. We were forced to live at the expense of the local population and in many cases had every justification for doing so. On our route, for instance, lay Cenabum, the town of the Carnutes which, by the massacre of our merchants and officials, had given the signal for the general revolt. We reached the place before the people had had any opportunity to organize a defense. The inhabitants no doubt imagined what was in store for them and attempted to escape by night across a bridge which connected their town with the other side of the Loire. But I had foreseen this move and kept two legions under arms throughout the hours of darkness. They broke into the town as soon as news was received of the attempted flight. These night assaults are usually more terrible and savage than anything which takes place by day. Certainly, in the narrow streets among the burning buildings, very few of the inhabitants of Cenabum were able to escape. The whole town was destroyed and I gave all the booty it contained and all the prisoners to the soldiers. Before this time there had been some grumbling about the early start of the campaigning season and the shortage of supplies. For the rest of the year the men bore almost incredible hardships without complaint.

After the sack of Cenabum other towns on our route were glad to capitulate, to hand in their arms and to give me, what I most needed, their horses. Vercingetorix was now in the same difficulty as that in which previously he had placed me. If he were to keep his alliance together he would have at least to make some show of an appearance in the field. He therefore left the Boii alone and attempted to relieve one of the towns which I was besieging. In a short cavalry engagement his advanced troops easily routed what was left to me of my Gallic cavalry, but when I saw my own Gauls turn and run, I sent into the battle the four hundred German horsemen whom I had kept with me from the start of the campaign. It was a critical moment. Vercingetorix was in any case greatly superior to me in cavalry; but my difficulties would be much increased if it were to be shown that his superiority was absolute, that I was incapable of ever challenging him at all except in a pitched battle of infantry — a battle which he would, of course, avoid. Fortunately my Germans did all that could have been expected of them. They were picked troops and they charged with a kind of fury which is characteristic of their nation. It must have been a bitter moment for Vercingetorix when he saw his own cavalry forced back. He had hoped to find me entirely deficient in this arm so that he would be able to control every part of the surface of Gaul except that on which my legions might be at any one time standing. Now he saw that he could not depend on the complete supremacy for which he had hoped. It remained true, however, that numerically his superiority was enormous. My four hundred Germans could not be everywhere and, though I could use them tactically for a particular purpose, they could neither guard my lines of communication nor guarantee me my supplies.

Vercingetorix seems to have made a correct assessment of the situation immediately. At a council of war he put before the Gauls a most daring and original plan which, if it had been fully carried out, might conceivably have forced me to retire behind the Alps, at least for the time being, thus losing all the profit and all the prestige of my former victories. He proposed that not only every storehouse and barn, but every town along our line of march should be set on fire. In this way, he explained, our armies would be entirely deprived of supplies. We should either die of starvation or be forced to disperse our forces so widely that we should become an easy prey to the enemy, who had superior numbers and greater mobility. The Gauls, showing a kind of determination which I should never have expected from them, approved this plan. I can still remember my own feelings of dismay when, a day or two after our cavalry victory, I saw in every direction around us great pillars of smoke climbing into the air. The Bituriges, who occupy a most fertile part of Gaul and who are among the most prosperous people in the whole country, were deliberately destroying everything within our reach which could be of use to us. Vercingetorix's logic was correct and had prevailed; for it was true enough that they could rebuild their towns and villages, but they would never, if Roman armies remained among them, recover their liberty.

I myself was at this time marching towards Avaricum, the largest and richest town of the Bituriges, indeed probably the finest city in the whole of Gaul. By capturing this place I hoped not only to bring back the whole of this part of the country to its allegiance, but also to secure sufficient supplies to tide us over our immediate difficulties. Later I discovered that Vercingetorix had wanted to destroy even this great and famous town. The Bituriges however had implored him to spare it and had pointed out that it was excellently situated and provided for defense. Vercingetorix had reluctantly given way to their entreaties and I am by no means sure that he was wrong. The place was indeed extremely difficult to capture and it was defended with a resolution and an ingenuity which caused me not only surprise but alarm. My soldiers had never suffered such hardships as they suffered in these late cold winter days during the siege of Avaricum. I myself scarcely slept at all during this time, since both by day and night work was going on continuously on the siege towers and terraces, while patrols had to be constantly vigilant to guard against an attack by Vercingetorix's main army which was never far from us and which succeeded easily in cutting off the very few convoys of supplies which, in response to my urgent requests, were sent to us from the Aedui and the Boii.

Once Vercingetorix actually offered battle and my men clamored to be led against him. They were cold, exhausted and desperate and wished by fighting to escape from the weary work of each day and to finish things off in victory. I led out the army to the position which Vercingetorix had chosen and then, in spite of a clamor among my troops which almost amounted to mutiny, I led it back again. My men were perfectly prepared to charge through a marsh and uphill on the other side; but I saw not only the difficulty of the position but also the great skill with which Vercingetorix had disposed his troops, ready to attack from the flank any group of our men which might attempt the crossing of the marsh. I have taken more risks in battle than most commanders; but this was a risk which I would not take. Defeat here would have meant irreparable disaster, while victory would not necessarily have ended the war. My own troops were furious with me, as they always have been when they have imagined that I lacked confidence in them. But I explained the situation to them afterwards and I even suggested (knowing that my suggestion would be rejected) that, since I was exposing them to such tremendous hardships, we should abandon the siege of Avaricum. They made it clear to me that they would prefer to die of starvation and exposure rather than fail to finish off what they had begun and show the Gauls what the consequences were of butchering our civilians and defying a Roman army.

This was one of the most difficult siege operations in which I have ever been engaged. Had it lasted much longer the whole war might have been lost, for, by the time that we were ready for the final assault, our men were half-starved and, though they retained an extraordinary resolution and ferocity, I could see that their physical powers were beginning to fail them. It was on a rainy day and at a time when the enemy were not expecting an attack that I gave the signal for the assault. Our men went into battle like wild beasts, yet they followed my instructions to the letter, occupying the whole circuit of the walls before they descended into the town where, at first, the enemy were prepared to fight it out with them.

But, when the enemy saw themselves almost completely surrounded, they panicked, threw away their arms and attempted to
get away while there was still time. But for them the time had run
out. There had been forty thousand people in Avaricum and of
these not more than eight hundred got away. The rest — men,
women and children — were killed by our troops who were so embittered by their sufferings that they did not even think of making
money for themselves by taking prisoners. We found plenty of
food in Avaricum, but the disposal of the dead bodies presented us
with quite a serious problem.

Chapter 13

A Moment of Decision

I HAD HOPED THAT THE NEWS OF OUR SUCCESS AT AVARICUM AND of the massacre of its inhabitants might have the effect of detaching from Vercingetorix some of his supporters and so making my task easier. I found that, on the contrary, this victory of ours had merely added to Vercingetorix's prestige. It was remembered that he himself had been in favor of destroying and abandoning Avaricum. Our success there was considered a proof of his wisdom rather than of our superior ability. Moreover throughout this time his agents had been busy all over Gaul. Commius was organizing a league of the Belgic tribes; the tribes around Paris were already in arms; movements of troops were reported from the Atlantic coast and from Aquitania. I was particularly worried about the loyalty of the Aedui, who had failed to give me the support I had required during the siege of Avaricum and whose leading men were, I knew, constantly being urged or bribed to join the national revolt by friends of their own in the service of Vercingetorix.

I was very greatly handicapped at this time by my concern about the Aedui. Almost directly after the capture of Avaricum I found myself compelled, instead of following up my victory, to use up valuable time by going in person to the country of this tribe in order to settle a controversy about the chief magistracy. While I was there I became uneasily aware that there was not a single

Aeduan and perhaps not a single Gaul whom I could trust. Old Diviciacus had died and those who had shared his views were few and lacking in influence. Of the two possible candidates for the chief magistracy neither seemed to me reliable, and I had to content myself with giving my support to the one who had the better legal claim and demanding from him cavalry, infantry and supplies for my army. I left the country of the Aedui full of apprehension and before long my worst apprehensions were realized.

I now took a calculated risk which was, I think, in the circumstances justified but which nearly resulted in disaster. It seemed to me that, with so much of the north of Gaul in arms, the situation might become desperate if the existing rebel armies around Paris were reinforced by the Belgic armies which Commius and others were raising. And at the same time I had to deal with Vercingetorix and the Arverni and, most important, keep open my communications with the Province. In every part of the country the enemy enjoyed enormous numerical superiority, but still it seemed necessary to divide my army in two. I sent Labienus north to the neighborhood of Paris with four legions, while I myself, with six legions, marched directly on Gergovia, the capital of the Arverni. I wished first to make an end of Vercingetorix (thus safeguarding the Province) and then to march northwards to join Labienus in subjugating the rest of the country.

On the march to Gergovia, Vercingetorix used his cavalry cleverly to intercept our supplies and confronted me with a number of difficulties, which I surmounted. When we reached the great block of hills on which Gergovia stands, I could see at once that the place could never be carried by assault and determined to invest it. But Vercingetorix made the best possible use not only of the excellent position which he had to defend but also of the great numbers of fighting men whom he had at his disposal. It soon became clear to me that six legions were not enough for carrying out the prodigious siegeworks that would be required. Meanwhile my agents informed me that the Aedui were on the point of revolt. I could not afford to spend the rest of the summer tied down to an inconclusive siege operation and I could see that, serious as would be the

consequences to my prestige, I should have to withdraw. Before
doing so, however, I planned an operation against the town which,
though it ended unfortunately, might, if luck had been rather more
on my side, be now remembered as one of the most brilliant of my
successes.

My aim was to inflict a defeat upon the Gauls, so that my sub-
sequent withdrawal from the position would appear more dignified
than otherwise. But I had not excluded the possibility that, if all
went well, we might actually succeed in capturing the town. By
means of various stratagems, which included the dressing up of all
my muleteers as regular soldiers, I succeeded in inducing Vercingetorix to concentrate nearly all his forces on one weak sector of
his defenses where he assumed that I was about to make an attack.
Meanwhile I had kept most of the legions under cover at the opposite side of the town. They suddenly went into action, overran all
the Gallic camps and defenses below the actual city walls of Gergovia and inflicted considerable losses on the enemy whom they
had surprised. This sector of the fortifications was virtually undefended, since Vercingetorix had withdrawn his men to the other
side of the town. But there were crowds of women on the walls who,
so I was informed, behaved in a rather extraordinary manner. They
had no doubt heard of the massacre at Avaricum and had some
reason for alarm; but their hysteria took a curious form. While
screaming and crying with terror, many of them bared their breasts
provocatively and some were actually lowered down from the wall
so that they could offer themselves to as many of the legionaries as
cared to enjoy them. But the soldiers were, on the whole, more interested just then in the prospect of glory and of booty than in the
gratification of their lusts. They too remembered what had happened at Avaricum and believed themselves invincible. A few of
them did get to the top of the wall and, if they had had another
half-hour to deal with the weak opposition which they encountered, it is probable that we should have captured the town and
destroyed Vercingetorix there and then.

As it was Vercingetorix reacted very quickly. I was soon informed that the main body of his troops was hurrying towards the

threatened sector and I realized that we should have to be content with what we had achieved already. I sounded the signal for retreat and stood by with the Tenth Legion and some cohorts of the Thirteenth so as to be ready to support the men of the other legions if they had any difficulty in the withdrawal. It appears that some of the legionaries failed to hear the trumpet signal and others refused to obey the orders of their officers, so confident were they that the town was already in their hands. Had this initiative of theirs proved successful, I should have been forced to commend them for it; as it was, their disobedience brought its own punishment. They were soon, on very unfavorable ground, surrounded by greatly superior numbers and they had the utmost difficulty in fighting their way back downhill to the protection of the legions under my command. In this battle I lost seven hundred men killed and among these were no less than forty-six centurions. It was the only time that troops under my personal command were defeated in Gaul and these were the highest casualties that I ever suffered in this country.

I knew how the Gallic victory would be exaggerated not only in Gaul itself but in Rome, where my enemies would soon be proposing that I should be recalled before I, like Crassus, had lost whole legions of Romans to the enemy. But what mattered at the moment was the morale of my army. I addressed the troops and pointed out to them that their losses had been due not to any superior quality in the enemy but to their own lack of discipline. I congratulated them on the fine spirit which they had shown in the first stages of the battle and reminded them that no soldiers, however good, can fight both against superior numbers and difficult ground. They were aware, I said, that it was just for this reason that I had not, in spite of their protests, led them against Vercingetorix's army at Avaricum. The troops were, I could see, shaken by the defeat, but many of them were passionately eager to avenge it. Choosing a particularly strong position I drew them up in order of battle, thus challenging Vercingetorix to bring his whole force against us and try conclusions. As I had anticipated, Vercingetorix was much too intelligent to do so.

He had already won a resounding success, which his propagand-
ists would advertise all over Gaul; he must have guessed that I
should be forced to fall back and he naturally preferred to attack
my army when it was at a disadvantage on the march rather than
to fight on ground specially selected by myself. As the expected
news arrived from the Aedui, he must have believed that he
had already won the war. And indeed an impartial observer
might now have considered the odds to be in his favor.

Even before the battle of Gergovia a powerful group of Aeduan
nobles had attempted to bring the whole country into the war
against us. I had succeeded in frustrating them for the moment,
but had no illusions about what was likely to happen unless I
could soon win some striking success. My attempt to do so had
ended disastrously and now the inevitable took place. The Aedui
with all their dependent tribes joined the national movement.
Their leaders acted energetically. Two Aeduans who had served
in my army and had been treated by me with the greatest distinction quickly seized a strongly fortified position in their country
on the Loire where I had concentrated all the hostages from all
over Gaul, great quantities of military stores, most of my personal
luggage and most of the horses which I had been buying up for
later use. They massacred all Romans in the town, carried off the
hostages and destroyed all the property that they could not take
with them. Meanwhile strong detachments of the Aeduan army
were posted along the Loire to prevent my crossing it and all
bridges were destroyed. The river itself was swollen by melting
snow and was, so I was informed, impossible to ford. And beyond
the river, far to the north, was Labienus with his four legions, engaged, as I was, with greatly superior enemy forces.

This was a most disquieting moment. Some of my officers were
so impressed by the difficulties of our position that they considered
that our one hope of safety was to retreat southwards to the
Province. I rejected this plan without any hesitation at all. Labienus
and his four legions were in the North; and it is not my way to fail
to come to the assistance of my friends and my soldiers. And what
sort of figure should I have cut, crossing the difficult passes of the

Cevennes in full retreat at the head of six legions? As so often, it seemed to me that our best chance lay in moving faster than the enemy would imagine possible. So we marched north by day and night towards the Loire and reached the river long before any considerable concentration of the Aedui could be got together. We found something in the nature of a ford and I used the cavalry as a kind of human and animal dam to break the force of the current. While they formed a line across the river upstream, the infantry, holding their arms above their heads, crossed below them, with the water never reaching higher than their shoulders. We crossed the river without losing a single man and then marched on to join forces with Labienus, who had himself had very great difficulties to contend with. The news of our defeat at Gergovia and of the revolt of the Aedui had soon reached the tribes against which he was operating. Indeed it was generally believed that I had been unable to cross the Loire and was in full retreat towards the Province, abandoning the northern army to its fate. Labienus knew me better, but he had found himself surrounded by enemies whose numbers and confidence were increasing daily. He had shown very great skill in extricating himself from a most difficult position, had won a great battle and was able to join me north of the Loire with all his forces intact.

All my ten legions were now together again. I was ready enough to meet in pitched battle any number of men whom the Gauls might bring against me. But I was well aware that the Gauls were unlikely to make the mistake of doing what I wished them to do. The initiative had once again passed to Vercingetorix and he made very clever use of it. His position among his own people was now stronger than ever. Immediately after joining him the Aedui, on the grounds of their strength and influence, had claimed the right to be the leaders in the war. But at a national assembly (held, incidentally, along the lines which I myself had laid down as being appropriate for the government of the country) Vercingetorix, by an overwhelming vote, had been confirmed in his supreme command. The Aedui who, under my protection, had been used to consider themselves the leading power in Gaul, were disgruntled, but had to obey with what grace they could manage to show. As for Vercingetorix, he made full use of his extremely strong position. All roads were in his hands. I was cut off from both Italy and the Province. Letters from Rome did continue to reach me by devious routes, but they were infrequent and arrived late. They were also depressing. It appeared that my enemies were confidently prophesying that, even if I avoided disaster, I should be forced to retire ignominiously, with nothing left to show of all the conquests that had already been advertised. They were now all the more loudly demanding that I should be recalled. Some indeed had already suggested that the situation could only be restored by the intervention of Rome's greatest general, Pompey. This, I knew, was the kind of language which Pompey liked to hear. I realized that for the rest of this summer my survival not only as a commander but as a politician would be at stake. And what particularly depressed me was the knowledge that in fact the situation was just as bad as my enemies were pretending it to be. For the time being, moving about in the territories of the two remaining states that were loyal, the Remi and the Lingones, I was safe; but I was short of cavalry, short of provisions and unable to dictate the course of the war so long as Vercingetorix kept to his policy of intercepting my supplies and avoiding a general action. I spent some weeks within reach of the Rhine and paid out enormous sums in order to secure German mercenary cavalry. Without them it would have been dangerous for me to move at all, and Vercingetorix was compelling me to move by organizing a number of attacks all along the frontiers of the Province. He knew that if the Province were once overrun I should be finally discredited and that he would be able to make, in return for its evacuation, any terms he liked with the senate in Rome.

So, before I had raised all the squadrons of cavalry which I could have wished, I began to move south towards the country of the Sequani and the scenes of my first battles. I had to be in a position to defend the Province and, for the first time, I was doing what the enemy wished me to do rather than forcing my own will upon his.

Certainly I had no intention, when we made this move, of abandoning all my conquests — if this could possibly be avoided. I still hoped for some chance of being able once more to seize the initiative. But to the Gauls it may well have seemed that we now regarded our position as utterly hopeless and were evacuating their country, anxious only to save our own skins. Vercingetorix himself must have been thinking along these lines. Otherwise he would not have made what proved to be, for him, the fatal mistake of launching his entire cavalry force upon us while we were on the march. Instead of continuing to pursue his successful policy of using his cavalry to intercept our supplies and to cut off stragglers, he became, it seems, overconfident and determined to win the supreme glory of annihilating our entire army. No doubt he had heard of how the Parthian cavalry had destroyed the legions of Crassus. Why should he and his Gauls not destroy us? Indeed in some circumstances his plan might have been successful. As it was, he was misinformed about my own cavalry strength and he had not allowed for the fact that my soldiers were very different material from the inexperienced troops which Crassus had commanded.

We did indeed have a hard fight for it. The Gauls were full of confidence and, as I discovered afterwards, they had all sworn an oath that none of them would ever visit wife or children again unless he had ridden twice through our column. If this oath was kept, the women of Gaul must have been for some years sadly neglected. Their warrior husbands attacked us in three divisions — from in front and from each flank. They had expected, no doubt, to cut their way through a long and straggling column of marching men, but they were greatly deceived in their expectations. The legionaries quickly formed a hollow square with the baggage in the center. My own cavalry, which consisted of some Gallic detachments from the northeastern tribes and a good number of Germans, met the huge enemy force most gallantly. They were much encouraged by the fact that they could depend upon infantry support, while Vercingetorix's huge infantry army, drawn up ready for battle a little distance away, played no part in the

action at all. Wherever I saw that our cavalry was in difficulties,
I sent out a few cohorts at the double. Except in fighting which
lasts for many hours and results in exhaustion, no cavalry is a
match for first-class infantry. So time and time again our cohorts
prevented the dense masses of Gallic horsemen from routing our
men. Finally some of my Germans on the right managed to fight
their way to the top of some rising ground. From here they drove
the enemy downhill right up to the lines of Vercingetorix's infantry. I saw then that the battle was won, and sure enough it was not
long before the other two divisions of the enemy broke and fled.

It was a moment, for me and the army, of extraordinary exultation. Such moments remind me of what I have seen sometimes in
the boxing ring, when two opponents appear to be evenly matched
or perhaps one (the eventual loser) may seem stronger than the
other. One of these has only to turn his eyes aside, to lose concentration and resolution for the barest fraction of a second, and he
has lost everything. The other is instantly aware that he can win
and he does win. So I felt as I watched the rout of Vercingetorix's
cavalry. I saw that he had betrayed an absolutely fatal weakness
and my great anxiety came to an end. Instead of thinking how I
could preserve the Province and salvage some of my own reputation, I concentrated my mind entirely on the total destruction of
the enemy in the field. Had Vercingetorix stood his ground that
day with his infantry I should have led the legions against him at
once and should have been perfectly confident as to the result of
the engagement. As it was Vercingetorix saw the situation as
plainly as I did. He immediately withdrew and for the rest of that
day we followed him, killing about three thousand of his rear
guard.

Next day he fell back on the fortified city of Alesia, once more
confronting me with a difficult problem, but this time a problem
which I fancied that I could solve. The position was immensely
strong, but I had ten legions with me and determined to invest it.
Our siegeworks were rather more than ten miles in circumference and in the early stages of their construction Vercingetorix

made one more attempt to drive us back by engaging us with his cavalry. It was again largely owing to the courage and tenacity of my Germans that we won another victory. But our lines were still not completed and Vercingetorix still had some freedom of action. What I feared most was that he would escape himself with his cavalry, abandoning his infantry and the town to their fate. This, strategically speaking, would have been the right course for him to pursue; but either he was too honorable to abandon his army in this way or else he felt confident that the measures which he did take would be successful. He remained in the town himself with eighty thousand picked men and sent out all the rest one night through a gap in our entrenchments. They were instructed to return to their own tribes and to raise for the war every man in Gaul who was capable of bearing arms. The plan was that a vast relieving army should then march to Alesia. We, instead of being the besiegers, would become the besieged and, caught between the army of Vercingetorix in the town and the relieving army from outside, would be, it was hoped, annihilated.

I was aware that, even allowing for difficulties in supply, the Gauls could bring against me an army of about half a million men. I knew that they had good commanders apart from Vercingetorix himself — Commius, for instance, and several of the Aedui who had served under me. But somehow I felt confident that, if we showed sufficient resolution and worked hard enough, we were on the eve of the greatest of our triumphs. My confidence was shared by the whole army. I have seldom or never known a time when officers and men worked so hard and so cheerfully. And indeed the work performed was prodigious. We now built an outer ring of fortifications more than fourteen miles in circumference facing the great plain over which we expected, after a time, every day to see advancing the great host of relieving Gauls. Thus we had two lines to hold, one facing inwards and one outwards. Each was immensely strong and the ground in front of each was covered with all kinds of traps and obstacles. Mamurra, my chief of engineers, showed extraordinary ingenuity in the plan-

ning of these defenses and the soldiers delighted in carrying out his
ideas and finding nicknames for the various new gadgets which
he was always inventing.

The Gauls are not, as a rule, good organizers. Fortunately they
gave us sufficient time to complete our preparations and meanwhile the garrison of Alesia itself had begun to run short of food.
Vercingetorix dealt with this difficulty with his usual ruthlessness.
One day we saw the gates of the town opened and a long procession moving slowly and, it appeared, reluctantly through them.
These were the old men, the women, the children — everyone in
fact who was unfit for war. I watched them descend the hill and
approach our lines. There they stood with hands outstretched,
begging to be taken as slaves so long as they were given something
to eat. I gave the strictest orders that none of these — not even the
good-looking women and boys — were to be admitted to our lines.
We also had to be careful of our supplies of food. Moreover it
would have an adverse effect, I considered, on the morale of the
garrison if they were to see their friends and relatives starving before their eyes. And this indeed was what happened. For some
days these wretched people kept up their hopeless supplications;
then, as their weakness increased, they withdrew either in groups
or singly, most of them seeking, as animals do, some rather se-
cluded spot in which to die. They were at least spared what might
have been an even harder and more indecorous fate. For, as I
was informed later, it had actually been proposed inside the
town that these noncombatants should be, as need arose, slaugh-
tered like animals so that their flesh could be used to keep up the
strength of the fighting men. So desperate and unyielding was the
spirit of these Gallic patriots.

I think that nearly all of these outcasts had died of starvation before, at long last, the great relieving army appeared. The Gauls
had kept their force within manageable proportions. There were
eight thousand cavalry and about a quarter of a million infantry.
This huge army was well led by Commius and by good Arvernian
and Aeduan officers. In all they made, in conjunction with the defenders of the town, three full-scale attacks on us. The details of

these attacks still stand out vividly in my mind. I remember how
on the first day our German cavalry once again, and after many
hours of continuous fighting, just managed to turn the scale in our
favor. I remember the night attack on our entrenchments which
followed, and the splendid courage and resource shown by our
men, particularly perhaps by Trebonius and by Mark Antony,
who, when sober, is an excellent soldier. But in particular I remember how close and how finely poised was the decision in the
last day's fighting. In this battle nearly every man in my army
must have been engaged, since I was constantly sending reinforcements from more or less quiet sectors of our defenses to sectors where we were seriously threatened. The Gauls fought desperately and there were moments when our men very nearly began
to waver. These critical moments passed. At one point Labienus
restored the situation, at another I myself led into the fight the
last of our reserves and succeeded in finally beating back the attack that was launched on us by Vercingetorix from the town. I
then rode on, taking with me all the troops I could gather together, to that part of the front where Labienus was still holding
out, meanwhile sending the cavalry through our outer lines to attack the Gauls from the rear. The soldiers saw that the battle was
won and fought with a redoubled ferocity. So long as we had
strength we killed and killed. What was left of the great relieving
army next day dispersed. And on the following day Vercingetorix
and the garrison of Alesia surrendered.

I set aside the prisoners from the Arverni and the Aedui. These
tribes had done me most harm and had behaved most treacherously. But in war as in politics justice has often to make way for
convenience. These two powerful tribes had either to be exterminated or conciliated. It was in accordance both with my own
nature and with the interests of the country to adopt the latter of
these policies. So, after making suitable arrangements for the de-
livery of hostages, I restored some twenty thousand of their men
to these two tribes and by so doing secured our interests for the
future. All the other prisoners were distributed as booty among my
soldiers. Each man got at least one Gaul either to use as a personal

servant or to sell in the market. I spared most of the chieftains, since I knew that it was only through their agency that I could re-establish my authority over the country. As for Vercingetorix himself, he was a fine and resourceful soldier, but he was an irreconcilable enemy. I kept him in chains until he could be shown in my triumph, after which he would be strangled, as Jugurtha and other great enemies of the Roman people had been strangled before.

When my dispatches announcing these campaigns were received in Rome, there was a considerable alteration of feeling and of speculation. The senate decreed in my honor a thanksgiving ceremony which was to last for twenty days.

Chapter 14

Gaul Pacified

OUR VICTORY AT ALESIA WAS DECISIVE, BUT GAUL WAS STILL FAR from quiet and once more I was compelled to spend the winter north of the Alps, although, as I was constantly being informed by Balbus and other friends in Rome, my personal interests made it urgent for me to give the most serious attention to politics at home. But I put Gaul first. Even in the depths of the winter I was engaged in various punitive or precautionary operations, taking out the legions as it were in relays, so that while some were resting others were on active service. When I was not engaged in these operations I was endlessly busy with the affairs of the various tribes and by the end of the winter had certainly made our position secure in the greater part of the country, although I knew that in the next campaigning season there would still be some hard fighting to do. The main opposition was in the north, where Commius and others had organized a very powerful combination of Belgic tribes; and in the southwest also there were large and dangerous concentrations of rebels who still refused to submit. It was known that my command in Gaul could not legally last for more than two more years and the Gallic patriots imagined that, if they could hold out for that time, they would be safe enough in dealing with any successor who might be appointed to me. But I was determined that my conquests should be secure and I was confident that, now that we had crushed the power of the Arverni and the Aedui, no other combination of tribes could succeed.

I attempted by every means within my power to gain the good will of those who had been already subdued and, with regard to all the tribes of central and eastern Gaul, my efforts were entirely successful. They had learned their lesson and now the able and ambitious among them saw (as I had hoped they would see from the beginning) that their best opportunities for distinguishing themselves and doing good to their countrymen were in taking service with me. I had frequent conversations with chieftains from all over the country and could see that they were beginning to realize that Rome could offer them a future much more splendid than their past and that that condition of constant internecine warfare, instability and inefficiency to which they had been used scarcely deserved the name of "liberty." I wished that I could approach Commius with these arguments, since he was one of the most intelligent Gauls I have known; but I knew that he, largely because of Labienus's clumsy attempt to assassinate him, was irreconcilable. We marched against him and the Belgic league which he had helped to organize early in the spring and we encountered a desperate and skilled resistance, though I had as many as seven legions operating in this area. In the end we were successful and practically wiped out the large and powerful tribe of the Bellovaci, who had formed the main military strength of the league. Commius, as always, escaped. He, alone among the chieftains who survived, sent no offer of peace or submission.

The only rebels still in the field were in the southwest and my generals dealt very ably with them until the last remnants of their defeated armies took refuge in what was regarded as the impregnable fortress of Uxellodunum. It seemed to me essential that this final center of resistance should not be allowed to exist and so I came south myself in order to supervise the very difficult operations which were required. This was my last military action against the Gauls, and the Gauls in this case were a band of desperate men who had been filled with a fanatical hatred of us, who were plentifully supplied with provisions and occupied a citadel which

it was quite impossible to take by assault. In the end, after long
and arduous mining operations, we cut them off from their water
supply. They assumed that a miracle had taken place, some sign
of divine displeasure, and surrendered. Most of them were crimi-
nals and I determined to make an example of them all. Every man
who had borne arms had his hands cut off and was then released.
It was a savage punishment and one not at all in accordance with
my nature, which is inclined to be merciful; but I was justly, I
think, infuriated by the inability of these people to follow the logic
of events. I wanted an end of fighting and a period, short though it
must be, in which I could establish real peace and order and give
my soldiers some of the rest which they had earned.

It has been calculated that, during our campaigns in Gaul, we
killed one million men and took another million slaves. These
figures are, I should say, more or less accurate and deserve to be
set against the seven hundred dead, which were the most I lost in
any battle. It should also be remembered that from the time of the
surrender of Uxellodunum to the present day there has been peace
and order throughout Gaul. The country enjoys greater prosperity
than it has ever enjoyed. Today in its flourishing cities my statue
is worshiped with divine honors. If some of the worshipers raise in
my honor arms which have been truncated of their hands, these
will soon in the natural course of events have disappeared and will
be replaced by others who will be grateful, I hope, for comfort and
for culture and will have no recollection at all of the miseries of
their forebears or of the hardships suffered by my legions.

All through this year's campaigns and all through the winter
and summer that followed them I had to give much time and attention to the political situation in Rome. Here my enemies were
stronger than they had been and I had no doubt that they were
planning, if they could, to eliminate me from public life. But I
was used to this sort of opposition in politics and I fancied that,
with the prestige of my Gallic victories and by the mere existence
of my army, I should have no difficulty in attaining what I wished
— which was simply the consulship at the end of my command in
Gaul. There was one factor in the situation which caused me anx-

iety, and this was the ambiguous attitude of Pompey. At the time of my first consulship he had needed my help very badly. Most of the senate had been opposed to him and indeed the more reactionary members had long held the absurd view that he was a dangerous revolutionary. Recently they had become aware that in fact he was by nature one of them. After all he had begun his career as Sulla's favorite young officer. He only differed from the average conservative senator in having very much greater ability and a quite extraordinary vanity. So long as his ability could be used and his vanity gratified, he would be happier as a bulwark of the Constitution than in any other role.

In the last few years this had been just the role which he had successfully adopted. His admirable efficiency with regard to securing Rome's grain supplies, the rough and ready, but none the less effective, methods by which he had restored order after the murder of Clodius — all this had greatly added to his prestige and corroborated the opinion which he held of himself, which was that he was indispensable and incomparable. In the earlier days, when he had been married to my daughter Julia, he and I had got on well together. I was careful to feed his vanity and he was shrewd enough to accept my guidance in the intricacies of political life. I had not yet won anything much of a military reputation; I owed more money than anyone else in Rome; I had very great influence with the people, a rather brilliant reputation in social life, but, in most people's view, no other assets. Certainly Pompey could have had no reason to be jealous of me and, though he was aware that I was helping him politically, he was convinced, with some reason, that he was giving me much more help than I was giving him.

But in the last eight years the whole situation had altered. Both Pompey and I had become, in different ways, stronger. Pompey still had his great reputation as a soldier and he was now also a power in politics. All his old enemies in the senate looked up to him and were eager to gain his support. He also enjoyed, as he had so frequently enjoyed throughout his life, various extralegal powers. While remaining in Italy, he kept under his personal command seven legions in Spain and he could, as he had shown in that consulship of his which had amounted to a dictatorship, use troops to intimidate the law courts and insure the conviction of those whom he wished to be convicted. Meanwhile I, because of my long absence from Rome, had not quite the authority in city politics which I had once possessed, although I was still sufficiently popular and had no doubt that when I stood for the consulship I should be elected. And, both in reputation and in actual power, I was altogether a different person from that untried general and practiced politician who had fought with the Helvetii. My achievements had not been, perhaps, quite so spectacular as those of Pompey in the East, but they had been spectacular enough. I had been up against greater difficulties than any which Pompey had ever had to face (except perhaps in his not very glorious campaign against Sertorius) and I knew that, though Pompey had good troops and officers in Spain, my army was the best in the world. I had no intention of using this army in a civil war; but I knew from experience that the mere possession of an army was, in our times, a necessary safeguard.

The plans made against me during these years by my enemies were easy enough to follow and I was informed of them regularly in letters from Balbus and others. I must own that I was profoundly irritated to find these enemies so utterly irreconcilable. During the last eight years I had given none of them any reason to hate me and had indeed gone out of my way to conciliate some of them. While they had been living easily in Rome, I had been spending sleepless nights and hard days in the conquest and defense of empire. Certainly I had enriched myself and won glory in the process. But from the height and discipline of my experience I looked with anger and contempt at those in Rome who, I was told, were in the habit of speaking of me as an amateur general, interested chiefly in the profits of the slave market, and of my men as pleasure-loving and rapacious. Such talk might well come from the kind of person whom I remembered among those cowardly officers who had asked for leave rather than march against Ariovistus. By this time there were few or none of such people in my army. And then there were other, and precisely opposite, stories which were told about me by my enemies in Rome. According to this version my soldiers had been exposed by me to such long marches, such endless digging of entrenchments, such unremitting labor that they were ready to mutiny. They were longing for another general to be appointed to succeed me and they would most certainly desert me to a man if there were any question of an armed conflict between me and Pompey. I was told that Pompey himself was inclined to believe this story, especially if it were embellished with the addition that my army would greatly prefer to serve under his leadership than under mine.

I have always, of course, been used to the vagaries of public opinion and the dishonest use of political propaganda. I and my party, for instance, used to make effective and very unfair attacks on Lucullus for our own political ends. But there was at least some truth in the things we said then, as indeed was proved by the fact that in the end Lucullus had not been able to control his army. But in these attacks which were being made on me there was no truth whatever. I had to recognize that in Rome there was a small body of people who, whatever I might do and however I might attempt to conciliate them, would never be satisfied until I was dead or in exile. There are no doubt today some of these people left, though today there is no possibility of arranging for my exile. Often I asked myself how it had come about that I, who have always had more devoted friends than anyone in Rome, could have acquired so bitter a circle of enemies. And indeed it was not easy, nor is it now, to find an explanation. I knew, for example, that these people would never forgive me for my somewhat high-handed procedure during my first consulship. Yet it would be generally agreed that the laws I passed were good and necessary; they had benefited many people and had harmed no one, except perhaps one or two very big and inefficient landlords, such as Domitius Ahenobarbus who, I was informed, was particularly anxious to be appointed as my successor in Gaul. Moreover every action that I took during my first consulship had been taken with the support of Pompey; yet Pompey was now the model of republican respectability, while I, who in the interim had been fully occupied in fighting Rome's battles abroad, was described by Pompey's friends as an irresponsible demagogue, almost another Catiline.

I was sometimes amused and sometimes embittered by the reports which reached me of the malignant gossip and intrigues of these enemies of mine. Yet still I scarcely took them seriously, since it seemed to me that in the past I had dealt easily enough with much more dangerous political combinations. Now the main issue was a clear one. My enemies could indeed ruin me if they could contrive to get me to Rome without my army as a private individual before I was elected consul for the second time. They would accuse me of some crime or other (possibly going back even to my first consulship) and, if meantime they had secured the support of Pompey who, at the gates of Rome, still retained his military command, they could be fairly sure that I would be convicted and thus driven out of political life for the future. But in order to frustrate this plot, all I had to do was to retain my command until I became elected consul, when I should be automatically free from any risk of prosecution. And in the course of my consulship I should of course provide for my future safety. I had already secured, by means of the law passed by the ten tribunes, permission to stand for the consulship in my absence. All I required now was a small extension of the period of my command. This seemed a reasonable enough thing to ask for, considering the state of Gaul and the fact that Pompey's command in Spain had recently been extended considerably and for no good reason.

Yet in the year following the surrender of Vercingetorix, most of which I spent in finally pacifying Gaul, I found that opinion in the senate was hardening against me. One of the consuls for this year was Marcus Marcellus, who was a very bitter enemy. I might have had an even more bitter and much more able enemy as his colleague, for Cato had stood for election that year. But he had loudly advertised the fact that he was merely asking for the votes of his fellow citizens on his merits and that he did not intend to spend a single penny on his election expenses. As anyone might have foreseen, he failed to get elected. As it was, however, Marcellus did me what harm he could. In the early summer, when I was still fighting in Gaul, he attempted in the senate to raise the question of my recall and replacement. By the usual tactics of delay my supporters were able to put off this discussion till the autumn, by which time the war in Gaul was over and there was a strong feeling that my achievements should receive honor and gratitude rather than the implied disgrace which Marcellus was proposing. But it was agreed that the whole question of the Gallic provinces should be debated on the first of March in the following year.

I was still not in the least worried about the outcome of these maneuvers. I had fully earned the distinction of a triumph and a second consulship; I had no plans for the disruption of the Constitution; I was threatening no one. In these circumstances it did not seem to me credible that my enemies would proceed so far as to force me to fight for my honor and my life. The use in the senate of a tribunician veto would be enough, I considered, to frustrate any sudden stroke of malice and to gain for me the little delay which was all I wanted. Nevertheless I saw that my enemies had grown stronger in the last two years and realized that I should have to make use of all the money and influence which I possessed in order to be sure that their plans came to nothing. I wished that Clodius were still alive, since he would have helped me by violence. And I wished that Cicero were in Rome, since I felt sure that he could help me by moderation. He, however, had, much against his will, been appointed governor of Cilicia and was, I gathered, seriously perturbed in case he might have to face a Parthian invasion. I sent him from my staff his brother Quintus and gave him advice about the choosing of other competent officers, since it was difficult to imagine the great orator himself at the head of an army. In fact he did very well in his province. There was no Parthian invasion and in the following year he actually appeared in Rome to claim a triumph on the strength of having exterminated a band of robbers somewhere in the mountains. Then — though it was late in the day — he did attempt to make some of my opponents see some reason.

Most of all I wished for an opportunity to meet Pompey himself and I much resented that antiquated provision in our Consti-

tution which forbids a general to cross the frontier of Italy while
he retains control of his army. I also, as is natural, resented the
fact that this legal barrier did not operate in the case of Pompey,
who had seven legions in Spain, yet still remained near Rome.
Had I been able to meet him personally, I know that I should have
persuaded him to come to a working agreement with me. But this
was not to be. All my contact with Rome was through intermediar-
ies.

Of these I made the best use I could. One of those whom I
found most useful at this time was young Mark Antony. I soon became very fond of him and indeed remain so, in spite of the many
embarrassments which he has caused me. When he first came to
me, he had the reputation of being a brave soldier, but singularly
dissipated and perpetually in debt. This was not unlike the reputation which I myself enjoyed at his age, except that no one then
thought of me as a soldier. I soon found that Antony, though a
tremendous drunkard, was a very good soldier indeed. He is
tough, intelligent and has that easy kind of generosity which at-
tracts the devotion of one's subordinates. He had done admirably
in the war against Vercingetorix; I found great pleasure in his
company and was determined to help him in his military and
political career. In the year after the final subjugation of Gaul he
proposed to stand for the tribuneship and there also occurred an
opportunity for standing for an important priesthood. I used all my
influence for Antony in both these elections; but before then I
had, partly owing to his advice, secretly attached to myself a
friend of his in Rome who, until his tragic end, served me most
loyally. This was young Curio, who up to this time had always
professed himself a bitter enemy of mine — probably simply in
order to draw attention to himself, since he was just beginning
his career. He had been a great friend of Clodius, and had married Clodius's very formidable widow, who had, I think, advised
him that a good method of becoming known in politics was to begin, as her husband had done, by attacking every prominent figure
of the times.

Curio was as dissipated as Antony, as able and courageous, and even more deeply in debt. I paid his debts, which were not far short of what my own had been when Crassus first came to my relief, and I helped to secure his election to the tribuneship for the year in which it had been decided that the senate should debate the question of appointing someone to take over my provinces. It had been arranged that the agreement between Curio and myself was to be kept secret for as long as possible. He was to continue to make attacks on me, but he was to attack Pompey also and was to insist, in the interests of peace, that if I were asked to give up my army, then Pompey should be asked to give up his too. I knew that Pompey would never do this.

Curio began his year of office as tribune in the December of the year in which, by the capture of Uxellodunum, we had completed the repression of the Gallic revolt. I could rely on him to look after my interests in the senate for that year, and for the following year I hoped that Antony would be elected tribune. Before he laid down his office I myself, if all went well, should have been elected consul.

I spent the winter after Uxellodunum with the legions in Gaul and by the spring could feel reasonably certain that the whole country would now remain at peace. The Gauls had made a supreme effort and were exhausted. The loss of manpower and of property had been enormous. I found them glad to accept the advantages of our superior organization in rebuilding their economy and I fixed the tribute to be paid to Rome at a very modest figure, knowing that it would take many years before the country had completely recovered. But we had now no dangerous enemy in Gaul. Even Commius had submitted. On one occasion when I was in the south he had applied to Antony, promising to refrain from all anti-Roman activities and only asking that he should be allowed to keep his oath, which was never to come again into the presence of a Roman. Antony good-naturedly and rightly (since the time of repression had passed) accepted this offer of submission. Later, so I have been told, Commius left Gaul and went to Britain where he has succeeded in founding a kingdom for himself. I should like to see him again, but I doubt whether I shall have the time or find it useful to revisit that rather disappointing island.

I was busy enough in the following year too with the affairs of Gaul. Indeed I was so busy with these and with the political situation in Rome that I neglected to finish my "Commentaries" on the Gallic War. I had managed to complete the record up to the defeat of Vercingetorix at Alesia and had written the last book or two very rapidly so that they could be published in Rome as soon as possible. I was gratified to find that they were greatly admired for their style by the best critics, including Cicero, whose good opinion is certainly worth having. I am not entirely dissatisfied with these productions myself. The great hurry in which they were written seems to have communicated a kind of urgency to the story, at least in some passages. The account given is basically true, though perhaps I have disguised the fact that, at the very beginning, we were very nearly defeated by the Helvetii. I took care to point out at the time of publication that these are not finished literary works, but are rather intended as notes which may be of service to future historians. They also had, of course, a more limited and immediate object, which was to prepare the way for my consulship by allowing the literate classes in Rome to see clearly and distinctly what I and my army had been doing. But I doubt whether, from this point of view, they were of much service to me. Opinion had set and hardened. My friends were the same as ever (some of them being rather embarrassing to me politically), while no argument or demonstration could now convince my enemies of anything which they did not want to believe.

I suppose that one of the weaknesses of my character is in the fact that I find both hatred and jealousy difficult to understand, though I have certainly had plenty of reason to observe their effects. Even today I may well have bitter and unrelenting enemies and these may be numbered among those whose injuries to me I have forgiven or whose help I have rewarded. Certainly during this last year of mine in Gaul I had no conception of how determined to destroy me were my enemies in Rome and it was only at the last moment that I took precautions to save myself.

One of the consuls for this year, another Marcellus, was married to my great-niece, Octavia. He had always disliked me, and, ever since I had made the suggestion that Octavia should leave him and marry Pompey, he had thrown in his lot entirely with my enemies. The other consul I had bribed to remain inactive. Curio throughout the year (or rather until the ninth of December, when his term of office ended) had served my interests admirably. He had vetoed all proposals to appoint a successor to me and had stood out firmly against all the attempts made by Marcellus to intimidate him. I was not even seriously disturbed by a senatorial decree which cost me two of my legions. There was some evidence for suspecting the danger of a Parthian attack in the East and, to meet this danger, both Pompey and I were asked to contribute one legion. Pompey decided to contribute the legion which he had lent to me some years earlier and I also sent back to Italy one legion of my own. I wrongly presumed that these legions would either be sent immediately to the East, or else that my legion would be returned to me.

In the summer I made a quick visit to Cisalpine Gaul where I was given a magnificent reception by the cities. Much of the material for my legions had come from this area and the people knew that, if I were elected consul next year, I should attempt to secure for all of them the long overdue rights of Roman citizens. By this time I had heard that Antony had been successful in both of his elections. I should have him as tribune on my side to replace Curio, and he had also defeated my enemy Domitius Ahenobarbus in the election for the priesthood. On the other hand my own candidate for the consulship, an old officer of mine, had failed to get elected and both the consuls for the following year belonged to the party that was opposed to me. Still I had only to frustrate their efforts against me for a few months of their year of office, and I fancied that Antony could do this easily enough.

I went back again to the legions across the Alps and in country of the Treveri held what was intended to be a final review. For once these men had had an easy year; many of them were looking forward to their discharge after they had taken part in the triumph that would certainly be decreed to me. It was a most moving oc-

casion for all of us. I myself intended to spend the winter south of
the Alps and I sent the Thirteenth Legion down to Cisalpine Gaul
where I should rejoin it later. For my other eight legions I established winter quarters among the Belgae and the Aedui. Both for
security and convenience these were the best areas. I had heard
too of ridiculous rumors in Rome to the effect that I was concentrating my army in order to invade Italy. By having only one
legion with me in the southern province I hoped to show how
utterly unfounded such rumors were.

By the early winter I was established in Ravenna. I had been
in constant communication with Rome and could see that there,
from my own point of view, the position was worsening. But, if
necessary, I was prepared to make concessions much larger than
anyone expected. I let it be known that, if the senate wished to
replace me in Gaul, I should raise no objection; I should be content with two legions and the small province of Illyricum until the
time when I could be elected consul. It seemed to me that such
an offer as this would most certainly be accepted joyfully by all
parties. I was wrong. In the second fortnight of December, Curio
arrived unexpectedly at Ravenna. He brought me the most serious
news. Even now I believed that a civil war could be avoided, but
I realized at once that the time had come to take certain precautions. I sent messengers north with orders to the Eighth and
Twelfth Legions to leave their winter quarters and proceed in the
direction of Italy.

Book Two

Chapter 1

Civil War

HISTORIANS ARE APT TO DATE THE OUTBREAK OF THE CIVIL WAR from the time when I sent the first units of my army across the provincial boundary of the Rubicon into Italy. That is one way of looking at the matter. But from another point of view it may be said that the civil war has lasted all through my life. The contradictions in outlook, method and feeling which had existed at the time of Marius and Sulla still remained unresolved; and it was perhaps not an accident that in this greater struggle the protagonists, Pompey and myself, should have been in our very early days so implicated with these two examples of the past. Pompey had sprung to fame as the most brilliant of Sulla's young commanders; I had nearly lost my life and had almost despaired of ever making a name for myself, because I was the nephew of Marius. Since that time I had, with great difficulty and danger, revived, to some extent, the party of Marius. I was known in politics as a leader of the people and as an opponent of that artificial and repressive brand of traditionalism for which Sulla had stood, and which had been opposed in the past by several liberal-minded members of my own family. Pompey also had, on various occasions, opposed the Constitution of Sulla and got himself a name as a popular politician. But he had only done so when the Constitution appeared to operate against his own personal ambition at some particular moment. It was clear that in his view everyone except himself should be strictly bound by its provisions.

Now, at long last, the reactionaries in the senate, who, out of jealousy, had for so long been opposed to Pompey, had begun to realize that all he had ever asked for was to be their leader. It had naturally occurred to them that they could best make use of his leadership by setting him against me. Of course their views of me were as wrongheaded as had been their views of Pompey. I had indeed the support of the people and of many elements in the state which could be regarded as disreputable; but I possessed (and one would have thought they might have observed this) a certain sense of responsibility and efficiency. I was not, as they pretended, another Catiline. If I became consul I should take many measures which extreme conservatives might deplore (most of them, still fifty years behind the times, were averse even to granting the citizenship to the northern Italians), but I should not, for example, abolish all debts or indeed tolerate any kind of anarchy. The accusation of aiming at a monarchy had been made, and still was made, both against Pompey and me. It was not true in either of our cases, although now, as a result of the events of the last five years, I am beginning to wonder whether some such title as "King" may not be the most appropriate one for me. Certainly no such idea had ever occurred to me at the time of the outbreak of the civil war.

The facts of the situation, very broadly speaking, were, I consider, these. In the course of the last two generations our empire had become too big and too complicated an organization to be governed efficiently without conscious and far-ranging planning at the center. The small clique of hereditary nobility who had governed Rome for so long might, I suppose, under certain conditions have developed the qualities required by a changing world. But for the last two generations it had become increasingly evident that they neither would nor could develop these qualities. Where everything showed the necessity of expansion (in political, military and economic senses) their practices had been invariably restrictive. And they continued to justify their dangerous and disreputable actions by pretending that they were maintaining or interpreting a time-honored constitution. Even Cicero, who has always been unduly swayed by a respect for the "great families," had seen through this pretense, and had shown in a book which he published about this time that he realized the need for reorganization, for flexibility in policy and for justice. Yet for him, as for many others, the need remained theoretical. He could not translate his abstract words into more ordinary and necessary phrases — land settlement, foundation of colonies, broadening of the citizenship, security of frontiers, traffic organization in Rome, drainage and all those thousand evident and concrete needs of which I am aware and which I endeavor to meet. Nor, I think, does he see even now that I am at least as much of a constitutionalist as he is. This is perhaps partly because I have been brought up as an aristocrat and because my ancestors were kings and, according to the legend, gods. I remember being struck by the fact that even Catiline, who did, unlike myself, deserve the title of revolutionary and would, if he had been successful, certainly have put to death about half the senate (a thing that I could never contemplate), retained to the end, no doubt because he too came of a patrician family, a rather pathetic veneration for the forms. When his cause was quite hopeless he had himself proclaimed (illegally, of course) consul and went about attended by lictors. But my own respect for the Constitution is based rather more on reason than on sentiment.

I aim always at a world of tolerable and expansive freedom and I know that such a world cannot exist without order. Our political, military and religious institutions both symbolize and preserve order. People are most happy when they revere these institutions and obey what is enjoined by them. Yet in every generation these institutions, the framework of our lives and regulators of our needs and ambitions, are represented by real men of flesh and blood. Except in very dangerous and disturbed times these men need possess no very outstanding qualities of virtue or intelligence; it is sufficient that they should be respectable. And in times of crisis they must be willing to admit the necessity of change. For these institutions, which are so hallowed by time and so venerable, must be our guardians and our protectors; if they control our actions or repress our ambitions, this must be for our good. When those people who represent our institutions are clearly seen to be using the sanctified forms of government to repress legitimate initiative, to distort justice, to perpetuate inefficiency, then a situation arises which may be described as revolutionary, although even then, with a little wisdom, the horrors and convulsions of a revolution may be avoided.

I was anxious myself, during the weeks that preceded the civil war, to do and say anything that was at all likely to give the opportunity for a little wisdom to prevail. I had seen in my early youth one civil war and I knew well enough how this struggle between Marius and Sulla had resulted in waste, misery, the deterioration of character and a weakening of our whole nation which might have made survival impossible. I, and I think almost everyone in Italy, shrank from the idea of another civil war. I thought, and I still think, that Pompey himself must have shrunk from such a prospect; for he was, in his own way, a patriot and, even on the narrowest basic of selfish consideration, he should have realized that he was risking for no good reason all the power which he possessed and all the honor which he had won. It seems that his judgment, usually so sound in military affairs, must have been vitiated by false rumors designed to feed his vanity. He actually appears to have believed that the majority of my army would desert and go over to him and he no doubt considered that any attempt I might make to march on Rome would break down ignominiously like the attempts which had been made in our lifetime by Lepidus and by Catiline. As for me, I saw clearly enough the risks before me and the dangers to our empire and the world. I could, I suppose, have saved Italy from civil war, if I had consented meekly first to lay down my command, then to be condemned in a Roman court by an unjust verdict of my enemies. But in so doing I should have acted unlike myself, sacrificing my own honor and that of my army, failing to make good the promises I had made, and abjectly surrendering to just those forces which I knew to be bad, incompetent and ruthless — forces which I had consistently opposed ever since the time when as a boy alone I confronted Sulla.

I do not altogether like the notion of necessity in history, since I believe that all, or most of us, enjoy in our actions a certain measure of free will. Even now I am sure that the civil war could have been avoided and would have been avoided if I had been able to have one private conference with Pompey. And yet the very fact that the outbreak and continuance of this war was so unreasonable, so utterly opposed to the wishes of the majority of our people, sometimes makes me believe in its inevitability. Behind Pompey and behind me had gathered the same forces, good and bad, as had been behind Sulla and Marius. And somehow the situation had become, if not more clarified, more abstract. Pompey and I were not personal enemies, as Marius and Sulla had been. Indeed I had always supported Pompey in politics and he, by his influence, had made it possible for me to do as I wished to do in my first consulship and later. Each of us, certainly, could command personal loyalty among our own followers, but the quarrel was not quite one of persons. Pompey and his party claimed to be representing the traditional government of Rome against one who was a potential, indeed an actual, revolutionary. I also of course claimed to be acting legally and, with the aid of the tribunes, I had a reasonable argument to support my case. In fact, however, Pompey was, with his eyes fixed upon the past, representing a tradition which, in spite of animated and even convulsively strong performances, was almost dead; while I, still in some respects groping into the future, was representing something which, born from the past, will become the tradition by which in ages to come people will live. I myself shall have done something to shape this tradition; yet it can be looked upon as something necessary and something stronger than I. It will have to exist, if Rome herself is to exist. And if I were to die tomorrow in one of my epileptic attacks (these can occasionally prove fatal), or if I were to be assassinated and power were to go back again to those of my enemies who, through my forgiveness, have survived, this power could never be exercised again along the old lines, nor, I think, could ever be wielded again by the same sort of people. More wars still might be necessary and in the end the new system which I, partly from conscious will, partly from force of pressure, have initiated, would return and continue to develop.

In that December and those early days of January, before I led my men across the Rubicon, I was not thinking quite along these lines. Yet still I was aware of powers behind me whose representative I seemed to be. Certainly my personal honor and ambition were involved, yet with these, as I had found before in Gaul, were also involved the fortune of Rome, of the army, of the provinces. I was naturally aggrieved personally, since it seemed to me that the bitter attacks made on me every day by Marcellus, Cato, Lentulus and the rest were a poor reward for what I had achieved during my years abroad; yet I felt even more bitter in mind when I reflected that, if these people were to have their way, all that I had achieved already and all that I planned for the future would go for nothing. What angered me was not so much the personal animosity of my enemies as their total incapacity for forethought or for government.

Even though I knew them well enough I could still, up to the last moment, not believe that they would force me into war. Throughout that final December I offered concession after concession and gave, by means of my agents, assurances which must have been believed if there had been any disposition towards equity or reason. Friends meanwhile were warning me of various plots which were being made against me. It was said that a number of my officers had been bribed to work with my enemies and in particular I was informed that Labienus was in constant communication with Pompey and with those of Pompey's friends who were most determined to cause a breach between us. But I could not believe such stories. I had known Labienus since we were boys; it was because I had trusted him from the first that he had earned by his own merits such great wealth and great glory in all the Gallic wars. He had been on a different level from all my other generals and, whenever possible, I had given him an inde-

pendent command. In military matters we had always seen eye to
eye and on this basis at least our friendship had prospered.

In other ways there were certainly differences between us.
Labienus had a harsh, violent, vindictive disposition. He could be
generous to his friends, but would never forgive an enemy. I
knew that he had disapproved of the conciliatory measures
which I had been taking in Gaul throughout the last year. If he
had had his own way, everyone who had taken part in the revolt
(and that was practically the entire population) would have
been destroyed or reduced to slavery. I knew too that he was
jealous of the favors I had been showing to Antony, whom I
found a most agreeable companion as well as an able and energetic officer. The fact that Antony, who was in many ways a
particularly dissipated and pleasure-loving character, could also
be a good general did not fit in with Labienus's preconceived
ideas. But I did not fit in with his preconceived ideas either, yet
for all these years he had worked with me most loyally and successfully. He had never lost a battle and on the only occasions in
Gaul when we had suffered reverses, he had been nowhere near
the scene of action. It may have been that, looking back on his
long career of victory, he considered himself to be a better general
than I am; and indeed in many ways he was not far inferior. I
could understand it, if from time to time he said disparaging
things about me. He was a choleric man, proud and self-opinion-
ated and he was ill at ease when there was no fighting to do.
Throughout the last campaigning season I had spent all my energies on politics, whether in Gaul or Rome. We had marched the
legions from one district to another, merely to keep them fit and to
make our supply problem easier. And in my hours of relaxation I
had enjoyed the kind of intellectual and literary conversations
which have always delighted me and have never much pleased
Labienus.

I remember being particularly interested in the new school of
very young poets, several of whom came from my own province
of Cisalpine Gaul which had already produced Catullus. Young
Asinius Pollio had just joined my staff, after finishing his studies

in Rome, and he used to talk with the greatest enthusiasm of the new style of writing which, he claimed, was being developed by his friends there. One of these friends was a mere boy of eighteen, the son of a farmer near Mantua, called, I think, Virgil. According to Pollio this boy had an amazing aptitude for versification and was planning to write an epic on the subject of the early Kings of Alba who are, of course, my ancestors. This seemed to me a project worth encouraging, though at some later date Pollio has informed me that this Virgil has given up poetry and is devoting himself to philosophy. I must ask Pollio about him again some time. Nobody can write an epic in his extreme youth, and most intelligent youths end by getting tired of philosophy. But at the time of which I am thinking, these literary conversations which I had with Pollio and others used, for some reason, to infuriate Labienus. I suppose that he objected to any activity in which he could not himself take a leading part, and it was no doubt because I was interested in poetry that he used sometimes to refer to me as an amateur general. But I could never believe reports of his actual treachery.

It seemed to me that, in spite of certain differences in our temperaments, each of us owed the other gratitude. I thought too that Labienus realized well enough that my enemies were led by a narrow group of members of ancient families who would never receive among themselves as an equal one who, like Labienus, had no great connections in Rome. Both generosity and self-interest would, I considered, keep him attached to me; though by this time of my life I knew already that not many men are governed by generosity and not all by self-interest. However it is not in my nature to suspect my friends. I would rather be betrayed, as I was by Labienus, or even assassinated, as was Sertorius, than spend my life in taking precautions against those whom, if one has the feelings of a human being, it is both natural and agreeable to trust. Up to this moment Labienus is the only friend who has betrayed me; so I should count myself happy.

In that December and those days of January I discussed the worsening situation only with those of my most intimate circle.

Each day was critical and still it seemed to me that at any moment good sense could preserve us all from catastrophe. On the first of December Curio had very cleverly succeeded in getting a vote taken in the senate on the motion that both Pompey and I should lay down our commands simultaneously. This proposal was carried by three hundred and seventy votes to twenty-two. It was an interesting vote in many ways. It clearly indicated the fact that, out of the whole senate, only twenty-two members were my irreconcilable enemies; but it tended to disguise the fact that these twenty-two members had more energy and determination than the three hundred and seventy who on various grounds, whether of patriotism, friendship to me, laziness or self-interest, had voted against them. The twenty-two irreconcilables had made up their minds that at all costs I must be eliminated from political life. Even before this time they had been spreading rumors to the effect that I was already marching on Rome, in spite of the evident fact that at that moment such an operation was from a military point of view absolutely impossible. They knew that if Pompey either retired to his province of Spain (where he should have been long ago) or relinquished his command altogether, it would be impossible, considering my influence with the people, to arrange judicial proceedings in such a way that I would certainly be brought to trial and condemned. It was therefore necessary for Pompey to retain his command and to remain in Italy. So the opinion given by the great majority of the senate was simply ignored. On the following day the consul Marcellus (accompanied by his colleague who, being in my pay, was content simply to do and say nothing, and by the two men, both enemies of mine, who had been elected to take office as consuls for the next year) went to Pompey, who was waiting for them outside the city boundaries. Then, in direct contravention of the known wishes both of the senate and the people, Marcellus solemnly instructed Pompey to take command of all armed forces in Italy and to make what preparations he thought fit in order to defend the country. Pompey accepted the commission. He began at once to recall veterans and to make arrangements for further recruiting. Meanwhile he took

over the command of the two legions from my army which, in
obedience to the senate, I had sent back for service in Parthia
but which had evidently been kept in Italy just for this emergency.

This was the news which Curio, about the middle of the
month, brought to me at Ravenna and which made me realize for
the first time that it might be necessary to defend myself by force
of arms. Curio himself urged me to march on Rome immediately,
before Pompey and the senate could mobilize the forces available
to them. I had already, he considered, a legitimate reason for
such action. I should be defending the rights of the tribunes and
the expressed will of the senate. He pointed out, rightly enough,
that most of my victories had been won by concentrating my
forces much more quickly than the enemy had expected; and
here, he suggested, was an excellent opportunity of employing my
habitual technique. This advice however was, at this moment, too
impetuous. The general feeling in Italy and in the legions themselves was strongly opposed to the idea of civil war. If civil war
did break out, it was important that everyone should know (and
in particular that my own soldiers should know) that I had done
everything possible to avoid it. At this moment I had only one
legion on the Italian side of the Alps. Pompey had two legions in
the south and was already raising others. I was not afraid of these
numerical odds, since I could imagine the confusion and disorder
that must exist when an army is in process of formation, whereas I
knew that my own men were trained, disciplined and ready for
action. But for any action to be successful with our small force it
was essential that we should enjoy the good will of the civil population. I neither wished to be nor did I want anyone to imagine
that I could be another Sulla. If I had to fight, it must be made
clear that I had avoided fighting until the last moment compatible
with safety, and that I was ready, at any moment, to negotiate
peace. I only summoned two legions from Gaul and these were,
in the first place, rather to insure my own safety than to consolidate any advance I might make. I knew, in any case, that it
would take some time before they could reach me. I had already

sent my lieutenant, Hirtius, to Rome with a message for Pompey's father-in-law Scipio, telling him that I was prepared to resign my command of both Gauls and to keep merely the small province of Illyricum with only two legions, or even with only one, until the time when I could stand for election as consul. Further than this I could not go without abjectly surrendering myself into my enemies' hands.

Curio was, I think, impressed and also surprised by my attitude. Up to this time he had never known me well and he had been a violent, if theoretical, opponent until I had paid his debts for him. No doubt he still held the fashionable, but incorrect, view that I was a wholly unscrupulous and ambitious character who would use any means to gain his own ends. My real friends knew me better. I am a great respecter of all the decencies and am never unscrupulous unless it is absolutely necessary. In these few days Curio became a dear friend of mine and I was greatly moved by his passionate loyalty. I wish he were alive today.

Towards the end of December letters from Rome made it appear more and more likely that my worst fears would be fulfilled. Pompey was openly describing me as a rebel, or as an upstart whom he had raised to power himself and could as easily pull down again. When someone, not unreasonably, inquired of him whether he had in fact under arms sufficient forces to defend Italy, he had, in his old manner (which, though ridiculously arrogant, was often quite effective), replied: "Wherever in Italy I strike my foot, legions will spring from the ground." This, in fact, was not far from the truth, so long as he was allowed sufficient facilities for going about the country stamping his foot.

I made one more effort. In a letter to the senate I declared that I was willing to lay down my command if Pompey laid down his command at the same time. I demanded that a vote should be taken on this proposal. And, so that there should be no doubt in anyone's mind of my resolution, I declared that, if my terms were not accepted, I was ready to defend myself and the Republic. It was at the end of December that Curio, traveling by day and night, took this letter from Ravenna to Rome. He arrived on the

morning of the new year and had time to get to the senate house
before the new consuls began proceedings. His own term of office
was over, but he gave my letter to Antony who was now tribune
and Antony, supported by another tribune, Quintus Cassius,
handed the letter to the consuls and demanded that it should be
read.

It seems that now the entire senate was terrorized and brow-
beaten by three men. One was Pompey's father-in-law Scipio, a
man of no great ability, but incurably vain. When he spoke it was
believed that he was speaking in the name of Pompey himself
and he succeeded in frightening the senators by saying that, if
they failed to take strong measures against me now, Pompey
would withdraw his support and leave them all at my mercy.
Lentulus, one of the new consuls, was another who would tolerate
no thought of compromise. At first he refused permission to Antony to reveal the contents of my letter. He then characterized it
as a letter sent by one who was already, to all intents and purposes, a public enemy, and forbade all discussion of its contents.
He and Scipio were supported in all their intransigence by my old
enemy Cato, who had always disapproved of me on every ground,
moral and political. I think that what he objected to most about
me was the fact that I had for so long enjoyed a love affair with
his stepsister, Servilia, the mother of young Brutus who, though
for a time he was much influenced by his priggish uncle, is now, I
hope, one of my greatest friends. Cato, who has never believed
that anyone except himself is even moderately honest or well-intentioned, enjoyed the privilege of still being rude to Pompey as
well as violently opposed to me. He too rejected any possibility of
compromise. It was, he said, because of Pompey's own stupidity
and ambition that I had been allowed to become great; now it
was up to Pompey to behave for once like a good citizen and to
crush me under his foot.

Thus these men, with a small band of less eminent but equally
rabid supporters, carried everything before them. On every day
during this first week of January on which the senate were able to
meet, some measure was passed against me or against my friends.

No one during these debates mentioned the victories and sufferings of my army during the last nine years in Gaul, or the thanksgiving services which had been decreed in my honor. No one even bothered to investigate whether or not Pompey had at his disposal sufficient force to defend Italy against me in case of war. It was assumed that most of my army would desert and that Pompey, by stamping his foot, would perform an immediate miracle. So in a few days of confusion and miscalculation these bitter and irresponsible men brought war upon the world. A decision was made by which, unless I laid down my command before a certain date, I was to be declared a public enemy. The tribunes Antony and Quintus Cassius, who attempted to intervene, were expelled from the senate and their lives were threatened. Finally on January seventh was passed what is known as "the final decree" empowering the consuls to take what measures they think fit to secure the safety of the Republic. This is a decree against which, or against the misuse of which, I have agitated all my life. It has invariably resulted in putting power at the wrong moment into the wrong hands. It is an instrument of hysteria. Now mobilization began in earnest throughout Italy. Domitius Ahenobarbus, always one of my bitterest enemies, was appointed to take over my provinces and my army. Antony, Curio and Cassius fled from Rome, disguised as slaves, and hurried northwards towards Ravenna. They reached Rimini on December tenth. I instructed them to wait there, since I had decided to invade Italy. On the night of the eleventh I sent advanced detachments of the Thirteenth Legion across the Rubicon.

Chapter 2

Conquest of Italy

I DO NOT THINK THAT ANYONE IN RAVENNA, EXCEPT FOR MY closest friends, knew what my intentions were. I spent most of the day of January eleventh in public and in the evening entertained a number of guests to dinner. When I left this party I took every precaution to deceive onlookers about the direction in which I intended to go. They saw me drive out of the town by the road leading away from Rimini and may well have conjectured that I was on my way to some assignation with a lady (I have always, when time permitted, found the wives and daughters of these northern Italians most agreeable) rather than taking the first step in a terrible and destructive war. Soon I altered my course and was joined by various officers who had left the town at the same time as I, but by different routes. I took all these measures of secrecy because I wished to occupy Rimini without any opposition at all. I had decided to avoid as far as I possibly could all conflict with my fellow countrymen, to fight only if I must fight and to make it clear to all that I was at any time ready to negotiate on reasonable terms.

So, just before dawn, I and my small party reached the frontier of my province at the river Rubicon. Most of the cohorts were waiting here for me, though some bodies of picked men and centurions had already quietly entered Rimini and were prepared to

hold it for us, should this be necessary. At this point I did pause
for a short time and reflect deeply. Some of my friends were, I
think, surprised at what appeared to them to be my indecision.
My mind, however, was already made up. I knew that it was
necessary to go forward. And yet I was suddenly overcome by a
feeling of horror, as though I were contemplating an act of incest
with my own mother. For the glory of Rome and the good government of her people had always been dearer to me than my own
life. Yet now I was on the point of invading Roman soil, as Sulla
had done — that Sulla whom, of all characters in our history, I
most detest. It was true that, unlike Sulla, I had no wish to exterminate my enemies and that, if I were victorious, I should never
be revengeful. But, however honorable my intentions and however just my quarrel, I was still bringing war upon my own people.
Also, although the consuls, in acting as they had against me,
were making improper use of their powers, they were still legally
elected consuls and their chosen instrument, Pompey, was a national hero whose name and victories were known in each house-
hold of Italy. He, like I, could command affection and, from his
veterans, a kind of adoration.

Such is the complex of legality, honor and loyalty in a state
that these unjust and vindictive men who were enemies of mine,
backed by Pompey, who, in spite of his vanity and his political in-
eptitude, was a great patriot and a great general, could summon
to their side and represent much that was decent, normal and law-
abiding. Whereas I who in spite of my services to the Republic
was to be declared a public enemy was forced to commit that indecent gesture, first made in our history by Sulla, of stripping
away the modest and civilized veil of behavior and institution
with which we naturally like to surround our life, and of revealing
the naked fact of our savagery — that in the last resort everything depends on the power of physical coercion. Then too I was
appalled at what might be the extent of the operations now about
to begin, nor could I be by any means sure that I could bring them
to a successful conclusion. I hoped for a quick advance, a truce, a
conference and a peace before any blood had been shed; but I

could already see the possibility of having to fight, as in the end I did have to fight, battles in every part of our empire, and I could not foresee the outcome of these battles. So, in crossing the Rubicon, though I could not afford to hesitate, it was not unnatural that I should feel some misgivings and some despondency. There had been other occasions when I had risked life, fortune, career and all my achievements; but on these occasions I had usually been willing to take the risk. Now it was, or so it seemed, under some compulsion that I had to make up my own mind to throw the die. However that may be, the die was thrown.

Soon after dawn we were in Rimini. There was of course no kind of opposition, since the cohorts were already drawn up in their military formations along the streets and in the forum before many people in the town realized that anything unusual was happening. I had two immediate anxieties. One was with regard to my own troops; would they follow me in a war waged against the consuls and the whole authority of the state? The other was concerned with the civilian population of Italy; would the towns on my route open their gates to me and help me with supplies, or would they force me to take those violent measures which, above all things, I wanted to avoid? I soon found that in both cases I had no reason for anxiety at all. I addressed the men of the Thirteenth in the forum and had at my side the tribunes Antony and Quintus Cassius and Curio too, all dressed as slaves, just as they had arrived in their flight from Rome. First I gave the men a clear account of the vindictiveness and illegality of the proceedings in the senate which had led to the expulsion from Rome of the duly elected representatives of the Roman people. Then, speaking with greater emotion, I turned to my own grievances and the grievances of the army. For nine years, I pointed out, we had fought victoriously in Gaul, Britain and Germany. Did we deserve now to have the whole of our own country mobilized against us as though we were robbers or incendiaries? I asked them to try to remember if I had ever failed to do my duty to them as a commander. Certainly I had demanded from them harder work and a higher standard of efficiency than could be exampled in any other

Roman army. But had I not always rewarded them for their exertions in a way that was beyond their expectations?

Before I had finished my speech some centurions started to shout out that further words were unnecessary. They would continue to guard my honor and they would see to it that the tribunes were restored to their places in the senate. All the army took up these cries and their enthusiasm infected even those of the townspeople who were not on my side already. From this time onwards recruits kept offering themselves for service and were constantly being trained for use in the future.

Next I sent out detachments under Antony, Curio and others to occupy towns of strategic importance on the roads leading south. Our men were welcomed everywhere. In some places garrisons of Pompeian troops were expelled by the local town councils. In others these enemy troops came over to us and were incorporated in our army. In these operations Antony and Curio were remarkably effective. They were both natural leaders of men; they had the advantages of youth, good looks and good birth; they were popular with all classes of people, energetic and absolutely devoted to me personally. I had other good officers, but not many with all these assets. And it was not long before I received the news that the ablest of all my officers, Labienus, had deserted to the enemy. It is true that he had always been attached to Pompey and had some reason to be loyal to him. But I too had always been a friend to Pompey, and Labienus owed his reputation and his fortune to me and to me alone. Moreover he must have known perfectly well how untrue were the rumors about me which my enemies were circulating in Rome — that I aimed at destroying the Constitution, that I would cancel all debts, free the slaves, and so on. Yet he must have possessed considerable powers of deceiving himself. Certainly he told Pompey that many of my troops were disaffected and that it would be most unlikely that I could persuade any of them to march on Rome. It is difficult to believe that he would have said this if he had not thought that he was speaking the truth.

In all probability no one had dared speak the truth to him. Labienus resented any opposition and even a veteran centurion would think twice before expressing to him an opinion which he would not like to hear. For a short time the party of Pompey and the senate were greatly elated at receiving the active support of Labienus. Later they were surprised to find that no other officer of mine took the same course as he had done. Yet Labienus, by his desertion, did me much harm, not least from the military point of view. I respected the generalship of Pompey, which I knew by study and hearsay, but I was well aware by experience that the generalship of Labienus was of the first order. After his desertion, I saw to it that all his personal luggage and property was sent after him to Rome.

I should have to wait, I knew, for more than ten days before I could be joined by even the first of the legions which I had summoned from Gaul. And though I had invaded Italy with only one legion I should need more than that to achieve any of my objects. In assessing the general situation I had to think of many different possibilities at once. Pompey, I was told, had claimed that he had ten legions ready for the defense of Italy. This statement had been made when some senator, rather belatedly, had inquired precisely how Italy was to be defended if, as had been rumored, I was planning to invade it from the north. At the outbreak of the civil war this claim of Pompey's was simply untrue. In Spain he had seven legions under good officers and mostly of good quality. In Italy he had the two legions which I had sent him for the Parthian war and which had subsequently been detained for use against me. Recent measures of mobilization may have raised enough men to form one or at the most two more legions. Many of the recalled veterans from Pompey's old armies would be excellent material, but there would also be numbers of untrained men who might or might not turn out to be good soldiers with some heart for the business. Thus, unless Pompey was to bring a large part of his Spanish army into Italy, he could not possibly put into the field the ten legions of which he boasted. And unless I were to remain inactive in the north for at least a month, he would not be able to make the necessary arrangements for moving the Spanish troops.

I, when I crossed the Rubicon, had only one legion with me together with a considerable force of Gallic and German cavalry. I should, in about a fortnight, be joined by the two legions which I had summoned from Gaul. I had a reserve in Gaul of seven other legions, some of which would be needed to secure the Province and others to keep a watch on Pompey's Spanish army. So far as immediate operations in Italy were concerned, I considered that I was at an advantage. Pompey might have some slight numerical superiority, but my troops were more experienced than his, better trained and, I believed, more loyal. I doubted, for instance, whether he could fully count upon those two legions which had so recently been under my own command. I believed therefore that, in a very short time, I should have at my disposal the physical force to make myself master of Italy. Yet I was most reluctant to use this force. What I wanted was a political rather than a military settlement; for, if I drove Pompey out of Italy, I could see no ending to the war. What I hoped was that Pompey, who was perfectly capable of appreciating the realities of the military situation, would come to his senses and would agree to negotiate with me before things had gone too far.

It was a reasonable hope, yet now, as I look back on this time, it seems to me as though some force more powerful than reason and patriotism was controlling events and making them move, with the inevitability of a Greek tragedy, in the direction of disaster. There was a fatal incompatibility between the demands of my safety and of Pompey's pride. Pompey had to appear, in his own eyes and those of others, as though he had won the war; I, in order to survive, had to act as though I was prepared to win it. Every success I won, while it increased my own safety, decreased the chances of a negotiated peace, since Pompey had determined to impose peace rather than have it imposed upon him. Yet if I had suffered setbacks, or even remained idle, I should have been seen to be at a disadvantage and my enemies, with

Pompey as a willing or half-willing accomplice, would have made certain of my destruction.

As it was the news of my occupation of Rimini and of the welcome accorded to my troops by the towns in the north produced a state of panic in Rome. In a day or two rumors were spreading to the effect that my cavalry had already been seen at the outskirts of the city. Those who, a short time before, had convinced themselves and others that I neither could nor would do anything to defend myself, were now crediting me with a quite supernatural speed of action. They began to turn on Pompey, whom they had dragged into the war, and to ask him to produce from nothing his promised legions.

As for Pompey himself, this must have been a bitter moment. I am inclined to think that he must have believed that I would submit tamely to his demands and that there would be no war. It was twelve or thirteen years since he had commanded an army, but he still enjoyed the greatest military reputation in the world and, at this moment, he showed that his reputation was deserved. At the time, of course, I could only conjecture what his intentions were; but now it seems to me probable that he had almost at once decided that he would refuse to negotiate with me and would adopt a strategy which was certain to result in a long war — a war in which he expected, not without some reason, to be finally and crushingly victorious. He very soon startled all those senators who had believed in the easy enforcement of their own wills by confronting them with the realities of the struggle upon which they had entered. They were to evacuate Rome and then to evacuate Italy. Troops were to be withdrawn southward and concentrated at Brundisium. The senate, the army, all naval vessels and transports were to leave Brundisium for northern Greece. I should be left in an Italy that had been stripped of men and supplies, in a Rome from which most of the legally constituted government had fled. I should be threatened from the west by Pompey's Spanish armies which could either be landed at the right time in Italy, since Pompey had complete command of the sea, or else could invade by way of Gaul. Pompeian armies in Africa would have the powerful support of King Juba of Numidia, an insolent barbarian whose beard I had once pulled in the senate. These armies could either be used in conjunction with the Spanish forces or else could invade Italy by way of Sicily. And in the East, where Pompey's personal influence and prestige were still enormous, a huge army would meanwhile be mobilized and trained. It was from here that Sulla had successfully invaded Italy. Pompey had far greater military and political assets than Sulla had possessed at that time. It must have appeared to him that what Sulla had done, he could do still more effectively.

This plan of Pompey's was a good one and, like most of his military operations in the past, had been conceived on a grand scale. Yet its success in practice depended to some extent on the assumption that I should be either inactive or irresolute. While in one sense it could be truly maintained that I was encircled, being threatened from the east, the south and the west, in another sense it would be equally true to say that Pompey's considerable forces were divided so that I should, if I could act quickly enough, be able to deal first with one division and then with another, without ever having to meet the full weight of his power at any one moment. Nevertheless, as events were to show, Pompey, with the whole East at his command, was likely to be powerful enough even without the help of his forces elsewhere. Moreover for once he was showing some political acumen. I should certainly gain prestige by driving him from Italy, but, so long as he was accompanied by a sufficient number of the senate, I could never achieve the properly and legally constituted position in Italy which I required. I did not want war and I did not want to gain the reputation of a revolutionary and an adventurer. Yet he was forcing me to fight and to behave as though in fact I was setting myself up against and above the state.

I did not immediately realize what Pompey's plans were or what would be their full import, though I could see well enough that if the war were to spread outside Italy it was likely to be long and bitter and that, whatever its final result, it would cause wounds in the structure of our society that would take at least a

generation to heal. I therefore continued to use every means possible to persuade Pompey to agree to meet me, assuring him of my
certainty (which was genuine) that if we could discuss our differences together we could find a peaceful solution to them. I knew
that that minority of the senate which had now got its own way
would oppose any suggestion that Pompey should meet me face to
face. Though they appeared to think little either of my patriotism
or of my generalship, they feared me as a politician and as a nego-
tiator and believed, quite rightly, that if I were allowed to discuss
matters with Pompey in a calm atmosphere, it was probable that
Pompey would come to an arrangement with me. Such an arrangement would prevent war and would safeguard the rights and interests of Pompey and myself; but it would also, as Cato, Scipio,
Lentulus and the rest were perfectly well aware, make the extremists in the senate impotent for the time being. They were
therefore bound to object to any meeting between Pompey and
me. I still hoped, however, that Pompey, both as a patriot and as a
military expert, would shrink from the difficulties and dangers of a
long war in which he personally had everything to lose and not
much to gain. I see now that both my hopes and my calculations
were misguided. The war was inevitable. Yet how apparently
small and trivial are the weights and impulses which finally set in
motion a tremendous process! It is certainly true that, as in the
days of Marius and Sulla, the contradictions and inadequacies in
our economy and general system of government demanded some
solution and it is possible that the divergencies of interest and
feeling were so great that such a solution could only be reached
by means of war. Yet still this war would never have taken place
had it not been for a defect in the character of one man — I mean
that vanity of Pompey's which made it impossible for him to tolerate the idea of an equal.

The nearest he came to showing any willingness to negotiate
was at a time towards the end of January, when he had already
evacuated Rome and I had not yet moved from Rimini, though I
had sent some advanced detachments a little way south. His message, which was in reply to my own offer to disband my army so

long as he did the same and so long as all mobilization orders in Italy were canceled, was evasive and unsatisfactory. He would, he said, withdraw to his province of Spain if I retired to Gaul and then disbanded my army; but until I had completed my part of this bargain, mobilization in Italy would continue. No mention at all was made of a conference between him and me. If I had accepted these conditions, I should have been left entirely at the mercy of my enemies. No date was given for Pompey's eventual withdrawal to Spain and the consuls would no doubt request him to remain in Italy long enough to achieve their object of destroying me.

There was now nothing for me to do except to advance and to hope that by gaining some success or other, whether military or political, I could induce Pompey and the senate to negotiate on more reasonable terms. My small force of barely ten cohorts was welcomed at all the towns we occupied as we moved southwards, and by the middle of February I had been joined by two veteran legions from Gaul, two more legions of recruits and further contingents of cavalry. By this time we had marched nearly half the length of Italy and were in front of the fortified town of Corfinium where my old enemy, Domitius Ahenobarbus, gave me just the opportunity which I desired for winning a striking and a bloodless victory. This hot-tempered and incompetent commander had been appointed by the senate to succeed me in the command of Gaul and the Gallic legions. He had marched northward with an army of his own, enrolling new troops on the way, and had occupied Corfinium with a force of rather more than two legions. He had heard how small my own invading army was and, without bothering to inquire how soon it would be reinforced, had decided that he was capable of destroying it. Pompey had sent to him, urging him to fall back towards Brundisium where the rest of the army was concentrating; but instead of doing so Domitius, as though he were the commander in chief, had written to Pompey requesting him to march northwards. In this difficult mountainous country it would be quite easy, said Domitius, for his and Pompey's combined forces to exterminate me and my army.

Pompey, who had no intention of losing the whole war in order to gratify Domitius, simply wrote to say that he would have nothing to do with a plan which he had never authorized and told Domitius to retreat while there was still time. But the time had run out. My veteran legions, the men who had built the lines at Alesia, were already engaged on the much simpler task of blockading Corfinium. The situation of Domitius was hopeless. Nevertheless he could still have come to some sort of honorable arrangement with me; however it appears that he and many of the other senators who were with him had so deceived themselves with their own propaganda that they genuinely believed that they would be killed or, for all I know, even tortured if they fell into my hands. So, frightened for his own safety, Domitius prepared to abandon his troops and to escape by himself before our lines of investment were complete. His plan became known and his troops, not unnaturally, resented it. They put Domitius under arrest and sent delegates to me, promising to surrender the town and obey my further instructions. It was arranged that the surrender would take place on the following day, and all that night I had the town surrounded by a continuous chain of men. I was particularly anxious that no senator or leading personality should escape, since I wished to make it clear to everyone that my intentions were to avoid bloodshed and to show mercy.

The most important person in the town with Domitius was Lentulus Spinther, an ex-consul who in the past had been a friend of mine and who owed much to me for the help which I had given him in his career. Just before dawn he made contact with our outposts and begged to be brought to me. When he appeared, he fell upon his knees and implored me to spare his life. Indeed he made an extraordinary exhibition of himself, but I soon cut him short and told him that he had nothing to fear, even though he had proved most ungrateful to me. I had not, I said, marched into Italy in order to harm anyone, but only to safeguard my own rights and those of the tribunes. Spinther appeared as surprised as he was pleased. He asked permission to return to the town and to tell others of what I had said. Some of them, he

told me, were already contemplating suicide. Nor was this an exaggeration. The example had been set by Domitius Ahenobarbus
himself who had asked his Greek physician to give him poison and
had taken the dose prescribed. It appears that when Spinther returned to the town with the news that I had no intention of injur-
ing anyone, Domitius much regretted his hasty decision. He
was relieved to find that his Greek attendant had been more intelligent than himself and had merely given him, instead of poison, a
sleeping draught.

Next day, at dawn, I arranged a formal ceremony of surrender.
It was an impressive occasion and I intended that it should be
widely publicized. First some fifty people of importance in Rome
— members of the senate, well-known financiers and high-ranking officers — were brought to me in a group. They did not succeed in disguising the terror which they felt. Their own soldiers
had turned against them and my Gallic veterans were in an ugly
mood, feeling embittered both on my account and on their own,
since they had expected their achievements to be honored in
Italy and found it intolerable that their own fellow countrymen
should have been led against them. Now they laughed and jeered
at the members of the Roman nobility who passed between their
ranks and, being in the habit of receiving some reward after a
successful siege operation, half-jestingly demanded that these
prisoners should go into the slave market. However I soon put a
stop to this not unreasonable but rather insulting behavior of
theirs. I made a short address to the prisoners. I pointed out that
many of them were personally indebted to me and that all of
them were indebted to me and my army for our work in Gaul and
Germany. I asked them to reflect on their own ingratitude, but
told them that they had nothing else to worry about. They were
free to go where they liked, free even to rejoin my enemies; none
of their property would be touched. I even restored to Domitius a
considerable sum of money which he claimed to be his own, but
which was in fact public money intended for the payment of his
troops. I incorporated the troops themselves in my own army and
sent them off immediately under Curio to occupy Sicily. If the war

were to continue and to spread I should need Sicily both as a
source of food supply for Rome and as a base to be used against
the enemy forces in Africa. As for the released prisoners at Corfinium, they declared themselves to be grateful; and indeed in a
civil war I do not think that such forbearance has ever been
shown before. Afterwards several of them, including Domitius, re-
joined Pompey and my enemies who they believed would be the
eventual winners.

By this time Pompey had concentrated his army and shipping
at Brundisium. We hurried after him by the coast road, over-
running on the way a number of contingents of his troops, most of
whom were glad to join my army. In command of one of these detachments was a personal friend of Pompey's, whom I released and
sent ahead with a message to the effect that I was on my way to
Brundisium and that once again, before it was too late, I begged
to be given the chance of an interview in order to discuss honorable terms of peace. This offer also was rejected. By the time my
message arrived Pompey had sent the two consuls and the greater
part of his army across to Greece. His pedantic and legalistic
reply to me was that in the absence of the consuls it was impossible for him to negotiate. It therefore seemed to me that my only
hope of ending the war quickly and satisfactorily was to prevent
him from leaving Italy and to capture or destroy both his army
and himself. I had six legions, four of them veteran, at Brundisium and we began at once to do what we could to block the harbor. But we were handicapped by lack of shipping and Pompey's
countermeasures were energetic, thorough and intelligent. In the
middle of March (it seems strange that this was only five years ago)
he evacuated Brundisium and, practically without any losses at
all, sailed with the rest of his army to Dyrrhachium on the opposite
coast.

In sixty days and without any bloodshed I had made myself
master of Italy. But I had at best a most dubious legal position in
Rome; I was almost entirely without shipping, and in every
province of the empire except for Gaul armies were gathering
which were devoted to my destruction.

Chapter 3

Rome: A Short Visit

As I watched the last of Pompey's transports sail from Brundisium (he had organized the evacuation perfectly), I was filled with a bitter sense of frustration and, for the first time, with a feeling of hatred for my enemies. If I had had the ships, I could have followed and would, in all probability, have ended the war rapidly and decisively. But it would take many months to build a fleet large enough for my purpose, and in the meantime these few irreconcilable enemies of mine had condemned me to the fighting of a war whose issue was doubtful and which I would have done almost anything to avoid.

I saw that, as so often before, my safety depended on taking very rapid action. My two immediate dangers were from Pompey's sea power and from his well-led and well-organized armies in Spain. He was capable of using his sea power to cut off Italy (and particularly Rome) from the necessary imports of food. My position in the country, which was, in any case, not an easy one, would become quite untenable if it were shown that I was unable to avert famine and all the consequent dislocation of normal life. It was therefore necessary to gain control at once of the food-producing areas — Sicily, Sardinia and, eventually, Africa. So far as Sicily and Sardinia were concerned, everything went well. My troops occupied Sardinia without the slightest difficulty. I sent

Curio to Sicily with an army large enough not only to secure that island but to go on from there to deal with the Pompeians in Africa. I knew that I could depend on Curio's loyalty, energy and enthusiasm. He had already shown that he had military abilities of a high order; but he was apt to be impetuous and I therefore attached to him a thoroughly experienced general of mine, Caninius Rebilus.

In Sicily the local population once again welcomed us and the speed of Curio's arrival there precluded any possibility of resistance. No doubt, if there had been time, some resistance would have been made, since Pompey had entrusted Sicily to the most consistent and bitter of all my enemies, Cato himself. As it was, Cato had no course open to him except to evacuate the island and sail off to Greece to join Pompey. But Cato would never let slip an opportunity of attempting to prove everyone to be in the wrong except himself. On this occasion before leaving Sicily, he made a speech in which he blamed everything on Pompey who, he said, had entered upon an unnecessary war with inadequate resources. Such criticism of a commander in chief hardly befits a subordinate officer; and in any case Cato's strategical opinions can be discounted as worthless. But he was right when he declared that the war was unnecessary. It is therefore all the more remarkable that he had so consistently opposed every proposal that could lead to peace — a course which he continued to pursue until his dying day. He was a Stoic and no doubt was prepared to see the whole world, let alone Italy and the provinces, in ruin, so long as what he conceived to be "justice" was done. Certainly he contributed greatly to the ruin that is inevitable in civil war, and what he conceived to be "justice" (namely my defeat in battle) was not done. But it is for his arrogance and his persistent animosity that I still hate his memory rather than for his principles.

My great-uncle Rutilius also was a Stoic and held the principles which Cato held. He showed that he was willing to sacrifice his life and his fortune rather than compromise with or submit to injustice; but he would not have been willing, as Cato was, to sacrifice everyone else as well as himself. The Stoic moralists regard both Rutilius and Cato as martyrs. Personally I see a great difference between them and, while I am prepared to agree that there was a kind of integrity in Cato's character, I observe there too much that was immodest, uncivilized, pretentious and unfeeling. I myself at a very early age (indeed at the time when I saw my great-uncle victimized by his unworthy enemies in the Roman law courts) had decided that I would not be, if I could help it, a martyr. Not that I should have enjoyed even this doubtful honor of martyrdom, if I had obeyed the illegal decision of a terrorized senate and returned to Rome without the defense of my army or of my command. I could have expressed no abstract principle of justice before the courts which would have been organized to condemn me. I could argue only from expediency, from humanity, from grounds of efficiency and from instances of mercy. And I would have known that no argument — not even the fact of my achievements in Gaul — could have saved me.

Now I was fighting for my life and my honor; but I was also fighting for something which, while it does not deserve the Stoic name of "justice," is perhaps equally valuable in human affairs. I was fighting for what was necessary and efficient and could be generous; opposed to me were dead, desiccated, envious and vindictive hands which, in spite of their apparent hold of a tradition and of institutions which I revered, were restrictive in their use of power and could offer nothing for the future except a meaningless and oppressive parody of the past.

If I had to fight, I should do my best to win; though even now I had some hopes that a settlement between Pompey and myself might be reached which might lead to peace before our full forces were engaged. As it was, once I had taken appropriate measures to secure Italy's food supply, it was evidently necessary to deal with Pompey's armies in Spain. For the operations which I planned I should need money, and it would greatly help me if I could receive from what was left of the senate in Rome some sort of official authorization for the measures which I should have to take. I did not despair of receiving the kind of authorization which I required and I did what I could to make various pub-

lic figures, and in particular Cicero, realize the dilemma in which
I was placed so that they might help me, if it were still possible,
to bring about a situation favorable to peace.

I hoped most from Cicero and in Cicero I was chiefly disappointed. I knew him to be an intelligent man, who hated the idea
of civil war and who had in the past attempted unsuccessfully to
persuade Pompey to accept my earlier proposal that I should remain in the North with only the small province of Illyricum and
only a force of one or two legions. Also, though I had not seen
him for ten years, I could remember times in our early youth when
we had been friends; even now he was bound to me by ties of
some interest and some affection. We were in the habit of corre-
sponding on literary matters; his brother had served with me in
Gaul; and I had been able to help Cicero himself not only by
lending him money, but also by doing favors to various protégés
of his whom he had recommended to me. He had always been,
of course, an admirer and to some extent a friend of Pompey's;
but he was too intelligent to think much of Pompey as a politician
and he might, I thought, remember how, at the time of his
exile, both Pompey and most of the members of the great families
had shown him no gratitude whatever for the services which he
had done to them in the past. I was all the more hopeful that he
might prove helpful because he had not so far followed Pompey
to the East and, having heard from his friend Lentulus Spinther
of how I had treated the prisoners at Corfinium, he had written
to me in the most cordial terms, congratulating me on my action.
I fancied that he knew well enough that if either Pompey or
Domitius had held the same advantage over me, neither of them
would have shown any mercy at all. So I had replied at once to
his letter and I had instructed my friends in Rome, Balbus and Oppius, to make further approaches to him and to keep me informed of his whereabouts.

The country house to which he had retired was not far off
my route from Brundisium to Rome. I called on him here and had
a most unsatisfactory interview. Cicero is only four years older
than I am, but he looks older still and on this occasion he was

evidently (though quite unreasonably) frightened of the armed men in my retinue. As our conversations developed I began to see that, though he was genuinely horrified at the idea of civil war, what chiefly upset him was the thought that he might himself, at some time, be forced to commit himself definitely to one side or the other. I told him that I wanted peace and he concurred enthusiastically; but when I asked him whether he would speak in the senate for peace and would sponsor my plan of sending another deputation, this time from the senators remaining in Rome, to Pompey, he began immediately to raise objections and to make excuses. He was, of course, afraid that Pompey and the rest of them would regard him as a mere agent of mine if he took this sensible and patriotic action. He had too high an opinion of himself (or, with equal truth, one may say that his opinion of himself was not high enough) to put himself into a position where he might have to face criticism from some members of the aristocracy. Besides he did not know which side would win the war and Pompey had already declared that he would treat as an enemy anyone who came to any sort of an understanding with me. I then pointed out, as clearly as I could, that, unless there was a genuine prospect of peace, it would be necessary for me to defend myself and that, in particular, I should have to guard against the threat of Pompey's armies in Spain. One would have thought that any child would have seen the force of this argument, but it was apparently beyond the comprehension of Cicero, who merely reiterated his laments and kept urging me on all accounts not to extend the war.

As I continued to treat him with courtesy and to explain patiently the necessities of the situation, I could see that he began to regain a certain oratorical courage, though he was not troubling to understand the argument which I was developing. Finally, raising his normally thin voice to the very impressive tone which he was able to command when speaking in public, he said: "And if I come to Rome, as you ask, and speak in the senate, how would you like it if I were to urge my fellow senators to do all they could to prevent you from carrying the war to Spain or from even

planning a campaign in the East?" I told him that I would not at all
like to hear such a speech, which was, in any case, absolutely out
of touch with military necessity. "Then," said Cicero, "I shall
not come to Rome." He spoke as though he were making some
noble or tragic gesture. In fact he had merely found for himself
a poor excuse for the inactivity which, at the moment, he preferred and which he has always preferred at moments of crisis
except when he personally could be regarded as the leader of one
of the opposing factions. Since then I have never trusted him,
though I still enjoy hearing him speak and I admire his wry sort
of wit. After this early moment of the civil war I did not see him
again until, when the main battle had been decided, he approached
me, begging for his own safety and for that of others who had
fought against me. Of course I gave him back everything which
he had lost. He has appeared sometimes to be grateful and recently in the senate he has loaded me with rather fulsome praises.
But I do not trust him. I suspect that, if I were murdered tomorrow, he would be one of the first to congratulate the murderers.

I left his house in an indignant state of mind and went straight
on to Rome. It was nearly ten years since I had seen the city
in which nearly all of my youth had been spent. I had hoped to
re-enter it as a legally elected consul and to celebrate in it the
triumph which my army had earned in Gaul, Germany and Britain. Now I found myself approaching it as an unwilling conqueror. I was careful to respect, as far as possible, the proprieties.
Since I still held an official command, I invited members of the
senate to meet me outside the city boundary. Quite a number attended the meeting and all listened with apparent respect to the
speech I made justifying the measures I had taken already. There
was applause when I declared myself still ready to seek peace by
negotiation. But when it came to the discussion of any practical
steps which might be taken to make peace, I encountered exactly
the same timidity and lack of realism which I had observed in
Cicero. The senate were in favor of sending a deputation to Pompey; but no one was found courageous enough to serve on such a
deputation. Only one of the two ex-consuls present had any other

definite proposals to make, and he, like Cicero, merely implored me
not to extend the war to Spain. I found myself in much the same
position as that in which I had been during my first consulship.
Then too the senate had had an opportunity to join me in wise,
generous and constructive government, but had preferred an attitude of angry or indifferent inertia. So, once again, I was forced to
act without the senate. I informed them that it was my wish that
they should share with me the ardors and the responsibilities of
government; if, however, they were reluctant to play their part, I
would take up the burden alone.

So, after wasting as much as three days in these inconclusive
discussions, I took the measures which seemed to me most appropriate. I intended to leave immediately for Spain. During my
absence from Italy it was necessary that both civil government and defense should be in capable and trustworthy hands; it
was also desirable that the officers whom I appointed should enjoy some sort of prestige. I was already accused of being a revolutionary; many of my best friends and most efficient officers came
from unknown families and were therefore suspect both to the
senate and to the financiers whom I did not wish to antagonize.
Thus, though I knew that my friend Balbus or even some junior
officer could have governed Italy with efficiency and moderation, I had to find, if possible, people whose names were already
well known and my choice was circumscribed by the fact that
most of the aristocracy had already joined Pompey. Fortunately
I could count on one of the praetors, Lepidus. He came of an
excellent family, being the son of that Lepidus who, in my very
early youth, had attempted a revolution which had been supported
by various friends and relatives of mine, but which I had refused to have anything to do with, since I could see that it had no
prospect of success.

One of the leaders of that revolution had been Brutus, the
husband of my old mistress Servilia and the father of that
young Brutus whom I have known since childhood and of whom
I am still exceptionally fond. The revolution had been suppressed by one of the consuls of the time with the aid of Pompey,

who was then at the very beginning of his brilliant career. In
the course of operations Pompey had captured and then treacherously murdered Servilia's husband. Since then the young Brutus
had always refused to greet or to speak to his father's murderer.
It had much distressed me to find that now, no doubt under the
influence of his uncle Cato, this young man had become reconciled
with Pompey and had turned against me. Young Lepidus, however,
either remembered his own father more clearly or else had more
accurately assessed the probabilities of the future. He too was associated with Servilia, having married one of her daughters. I had
no very high opinion of his abilities, but Servilia assured me that
he was reliable. Though somewhat pompous, he was undoubtedly
a gentleman and would, I thought, command a certain respect.
I therefore left the civil administration of Italy in his hands and
have never regretted my choice. Lepidus is indeed admirable in
any position where he does not have to make a decision or to deal
with military affairs. I have rewarded him in various ways which
have gratified both him and his mother-in-law, Servilia. He has
had the distinction of being consul for a longer period than any
other Roman, since I saw that he received this honor in that
year which, owing to my reform of the calendar, lasted for fifteen
months. He has twice been Master of the Horse to me during my
dictatorships and, when I set out in the next day or two to the
East, I am again leaving Italy in his charge. He will do exactly
as he is asked to do by Balbus and Oppius, both of whom know
my mind. I dined with him last night and feel quite sure of him.

Even on this first occasion when I left Lepidus in a position of
considerable responsibility, he acted with tact and good sense.
The same cannot quite be said of young Mark Antony whom I
put in charge of the armed forces and the general defense of the
country. During my absence he made an unnecessary display
of his personal power and wealth. He was too frequently seen
drunk in public and he caused much scandal by carrying about
with him not only his very attractive Greek mistress, the actress
Cytheris, but also a kind of harem of young people of both sexes.
On the other hand I had no one better qualified for the posi-

tion which he held. Antony was elected tribune before the civil war began; he comes from an old and distinguished family; he has always been popular with the troops and has never allowed his tendency to drunkenness and debauchery to interfere with the discharge of his military duties; he was at that time, and I believe still is, utterly loyal to me; I could count on him, if by any chance Pompey were to attempt any move against Italy in my absence, to act quickly and intelligently.

I gave other important tasks to those other members of the aristocracy (there were not many of them) who had already committed themselves to my side. Young Dolabella, Cicero's son-in-law, and young Hortensius, the son of that Hortensius who had been, before Cicero appeared on the scene, the greatest orator of the time, were entrusted with the urgent duty of building the fleets which I should soon need. And I sent Marcus Crassus, the eldest son of my old friend and one who had already served under me with distinction, to command the province of Cisalpine Gaul.

Before leaving Rome I appropriated for use in the war the large sum of public money which the consuls, in their quite unreasonable panic, had neglected to remove when they fled from the city in January. When I was on the point of taking this treasure one tribune attempted to lodge an official objection. By this time my patience was almost at an end. I had done what I could by legal methods and I was being forced to reshape legality by the use of arms. It was sufficient, however, merely to threaten this tribune in order to make him withdraw his opposition. I was glad not to have to use violence, since so far, in this strange war, I had shed no blood. Yet I was exasperated enough to have used violence had it been necessary.

So, after staying in the city for a bare week, I left Rome again for the North and the West. There were, of course, crowds who escorted me for part of the way; there were shouts and acclamations from my supporters among the people and there were demonstrations also from those who, under the influence of hostile propaganda, had believed that I was capable of organizing some kind of massacre of my enemies or that, at least, I should have al-

lowed my veterans and my Gallic cavalry to have looted Rome
and the countryside. These people were undoubtedly relieved to
find that their apprehensions had been unjustified. Now they, with
the rest, invoked blessings on my name. Yet still those were not
the blessings which I wanted to receive or which they wanted to
give. Among the various cries raised by the crowd was often to
be distinguished the cry of "Peace! Peace! Give us peace!" and
indeed there can be no real joy in watching a general march out
against his fellow countrymen. I knew that those who were cheering me would be glad when I was gone, simply because the war
would have been transferred from the vicinity of Rome to the
provinces and they would not, at least for some time, have to give
it very serious consideration. They had friends and relations in
my armies and they had friends and relations too in the armies of
Pompey and in the armies of Afranius in Spain. Naturally they
wished for peace, but what they wished for most was to be allowed
to continue their ordinary lives of eating, drinking, making money,
marrying, fornicating, going to the theater or the games. This too
was natural enough. But how few of them could see that these
ordinary lives depended on all sorts of factors to which they had
never given thought!

The state of the roads, the price of grain, the efficiency of mer-
chant fleets, the dangers of barbarian invasions — all these had
from time to time been discussed in public meetings. And ordinary gossip had no doubt dwelt on an antagonism of ambition
between Pompey and myself. We were widely regarded as con-
testants in some sort of boxing match. Yet none of this had anything to do with this war. The war, I felt (though I had never
wanted the war), was for the clean and effective use of organization and of power; it was against obscurantism, corruption and de-
cay. And all these people who raised their feeble, though heart-
felt, cries for a peace which I had always sought, were incapable
of seeing that, though they themselves would welcome any kind
of peace at all, a peace made on the terms of my enemies would
not in fact guarantee them even the safe or long enjoyment of their
ordinary pleasures. It was in one sense a simple matter. The old

regime had shown itself unfit to govern and unable to administrate. I am deficient in neither capacity.

Nevertheless, as I left Rome the cries for peace were still aimless and uncomprehending. How could I blame the common people when I had found among the great intellectuals and the noble senators precisely the same aimlessness and lack of understanding?

Chapter 4

Spain, Marseilles, Africa

IN MY BOOK ON "THE CIVIL WAR" I HAVE WRITTEN OF THIS SPANISH campaign at some length, partly for reasons of historical accuracy and partly because it is a campaign of which I am proud. I was faced with considerable difficulties and I overcame them dexterously and with a minimum of bloodshed.

In Spain, Pompey had seven legions, all of good quality, and could count on raising large numbers of auxiliary troops from the native population. These legions were well situated both for an offensive and for a defensive war. They might, for instance, have advanced into Gaul and occupied the Province. I myself was certainly doing my best to engage in my own service great numbers of Gallic cavalry and to retain friendly relations with the Gallic tribes which I hoped that I had conciliated. But I could not be quite sure that Gaul would remain loyal to me. A clever propagandist might still, in the interests of Pompey, play upon those feelings of nationalism which, logically, should have disappeared after the failure of Vercingetorix. Therefore one of my first steps was to order three of my own Gallic legions, under the command of their general Fabius, to occupy the passes over the Pyrenees. Fabius accomplished this task speedily and efficiently. He met with very little resistance and it began to become clear that Pompey had instructed his commanders in Spain to fight a delaying action, avoiding battle except when the odds were heavily on their side, and meanwhile recruiting and training forces which would no doubt be used when the time came for a general offensive against me from both east and west. Six of his regular legions, under his very competent commanders Afranius and Petreius, were in northern Spain between the Ebro and the Pyrenees. The other legion, under Varro, who, though a very poor general, has proved himself to be an admirable scholar, was in the south, and Varro's main task was to organize supplies of men, money and materials.

I planned to reinforce Fabius's three legions with three more legions and a considerable body of cavalry under my own command. Fabius, with his comparatively small force, would of course avoid contact with the enemy until I arrived. But he had established himself not far from Afranius and Petreius, who occupied a strong position at Lerida, and he was doing good work by sending messages and agents to all the neighboring Spanish tribes in an attempt to win them over to my side.

My first setback in the campaign occurred when I was on the way to Spain. The government of the Greek city of Marseilles, having first informed me that they wished to remain neutral, very soon went over definitely to the enemy. They welcomed into the city Domitius Ahenobarbus, the discredited commander at Corfinium, whose life had been spared once by his Greek physician and once by me. Domitius brought with him to Marseilles a fleet manned by his own retainers. As at Corfinium he held out hopes that Pompey himself might intervene, if the defenders stood firm. He was received enthusiastically and the city was in fact defended with great skill and resolution. The Massiliots were in complete command of the sea approaches and I soon found that their fortifications on the land side would be impregnable until very extensive siegeworks had been constructed. I immediately ordered ships to be built at Arles and meanwhile supervised the seige operations which I still hoped might be carried out successfully even before the ships were ready for service. But I encountered an unexpectedly vigorous resistance. Indeed there was one occasion when the enemy actually succeeded in surprising our men and in destroying most of the siege instruments which we had made.

I realized that the news of my failure in front of Marseilles might have serious effects both in Italy and in Spain; and above all it was necessary for me to eliminate Pompey's Spanish armies before the winter. I therefore left Trebonius with three legions to continue the siege of Marseilles and I put Decimus Brutus in charge of the naval operations which would certainly be necessary. I summoned three more legions from Italy, so that I should have altogether six legions with me in Spain. Then I crossed the Pyrenees, leaving behind me an Italy insufficiently garrisoned and a hostile Marseilles across my lines of communication. It was a risk, but one which had to be taken. I assumed, correctly as it turned out, that Pompey's forces were still not sufficiently organized for him to be able, in spite of his control of the sea, to take the offensive either in Italy or at Marseilles.

In Spain I found myself opposed by resolute leadership and by troops who had traditions of their own and were not afraid of facing my veterans in battle. In one skirmish, which was, in fact, the first fighting between Romans in the civil war, I lost at least seventy good men killed and had six hundred wounded. Then, as had happened in Britain, luck and the forces of nature seemed to turn against me. As the result of a sudden storm my army was isolated in a narrow space between two swollen and impassable rivers. Both our bridges had been swept away; none of our convoys could reach us, and we became seriously short of food. I was concerned myself by our predicament, but not so concerned as were my friends in Rome, where it was generally assumed that the war was virtually over. It was reported, and believed, that my armies had been defeated at Marseilles, that I myself was on the point of surrendering and that Pompey, in full force, was marching along the coast of Africa on his way to Spain.

The effect of these rumors was considerable. There was a great exodus of senators and others from Rome, all hurrying to join Pompey and what seemed to them to be inevitably the winning side. Among these was Cicero. And in Spain, many of the tribes

began to turn away from me and to send embassies to Afranius
and Petreius, while in the south Varro, who up to this time had
behaved moderately and had even been heard to speak well of me
in private, now began to act with unusual energy, imprisoning or
fining anyone who raised his voice in favor of peace. He too
evidently wished to establish the fact of his loyalty to the winning
side. His public utterances were violent and, whatever their merits
from a literary point of view, inaccurate and unfair.

We overcame our bad fortune by hard work and ingenuity. I
remembered how in Britain I had seen the natives building light,
almost circular, boats, which, though very difficult to steer, were
navigable even in quite rough water. With the materials to hand
we constructed a regular fleet of these coracles. First a detachment
of picked troops was ferried across the river and fortified a strong
position before the enemy had any idea of what we were doing.
Then a whole legion followed and bridge building began from
both banks. In two days the bridge was finished. I was now able to
use my cavalry, in which I was greatly superior to the enemy, not
only to guard my only convoys but to cut off his foragers and interrupt his supplies. At about this time I received news that Decimus Brutus had won a great naval victory at Marseilles. It was not
decisive, but it was important. Both at Marseilles and in Spain we
were regaining the initiative. I found now that in Spain the de-
sertions of tribes and cities were rather from Afranius to me than
in the opposite direction; and from Rome I received news that
many of those who had already packed up their belongings and
were prepared to join Pompey had decided to postpone their
departure until the issue of the Spanish campaign was settled.

In the end this campaign was won by hard marching and digging. I am glad to reflect that no full-scale engagement took place
and that the loss of Roman life was very small indeed. Soon after
we had escaped from our entrapped position between the two
rivers, Afranius and Petreius wisely decided to fall back beyond
the Ebro to an area more friendly to them, well supplied and
admirably suited to the kind of delaying action which they intended to fight. But by really remarkable exertions my men, who

had a much longer and more difficult route, managed to race the enemy to the passes over which his road lay. Here we had an opportunity to destroy the enemy in battle and my troops, who were elated by their successes and wanted to see the war finished quickly, clamored to go into action. But I refused to give the order. I could see the possibility of winning this war without a battle and I had every reason for wishing to do so. However much my men might want to fight I did not want to sacrifice their lives unnecessarily; nor did I wish that the slaughter of Romans on the other side should add to the sum of bitterness that must always exist in civil war; I hoped too that if I could once again, as at Corfinium, treat a virtually defeated enemy with a generosity beyond anything that he could expect, I might make it clear to Pompey, to Cato and to all the world that I was no Sulla, no ambitious savage — that, in reality, I wanted peace. I was also influenced, as I often am, by an aesthetic consideration: it is cleaner and more glorious for a general to win a campaign without bloodshed, if this can possibly be done. So, when I had the enemy at my mercy, I refused to attack. My own men were furious. Many of them shouted out that, if I were to throw away victory in this way, they themselves were not going to fight next time I asked them to do so. But I knew how quickly their tempers would subside. Indeed next day there took place an incident which convinced them, at least for the time, that I had been right and they wrong.

The camps of the two armies were close together. At a time when Afranius and Petreius had ridden off some distance away to supervise the digging of new fortifications, the soldiers from both sides began to fraternize. Parties of men went freely from one camp into the other and were entertained by their friends. Very soon it became evident that the enemy had no great heart for the war; but they were good soldiers and did not want to prove false to the oath of loyalty which they had sworn to their commander. However when my men told them in detail of how I had behaved at Corfinium and assured them that, if peace were made, Afranius and Petreius would have nothing to fear at my hands, they became eager to make peace as soon as possible. Deputations of

leading centurions and officers came from their camp to mine
and asked me for the kind of guarantees which I was perfectly
willing to give. Meanwhile in the two camps there was a general
air of festivity, as though the war were over. Drinking parties
were organized. The enemy soldiers thanked our men for having
spared them on the previous day, when they were so much at a
disadvantage, and our men were so impressed by these declara-
tions of gratitude that they almost came to believe that it was they,
not I, who had deserved them.

These scenes of relief and jollity were abruptly cut short.
Afranius and Petreius, with some squadrons of Spanish cavalry,
returned to their camp. They had to decide immediately what
attitude they would take with regard to the situation which they
found. Probably Afranius who, though he lacked all social and
intellectual graces, was an experienced commander of troops,
would have bowed to the inevitable. But Petreius, a resolute man
who disliked me personally and no doubt, in spite of everything,
feared for his own life, was determined upon war. Certainly he
acted with energy. He went from cohort to cohort, begging and
imploring his men to remain faithful to their oaths and not to betray their absent commander, Pompey. Meanwhile with his
Spanish cavalry and some armed retainers of his own he rounded
up all those soldiers of mine whom he could find in the camp.
Many of these, in spite of the truce which, though undeclared,
had been evidently accepted by both sides, were killed on the
spot. The rest wrapped their cloaks around their left arms to serve
as shields and fought their way with their swords back to our
camp, which fortunately was not far away. I, on my side, arranged
for all the soldiers of Afranius and Petreius who were in my camp
to be sent back to their own camp unharmed. Quite a few of
them, including some senior centurions and junior officers, decided to remain with me and enlist in my army.

So this promising initiative of the men came to an end. The incident seems to me significant of the general desire for peace,
which I shared, and to indicate also the insensate hostility which
I have aroused among that small circle of people who, for no very

adequate reason, have been, and perhaps still are, determined to destroy me. Now, in the camp of Afranius and Petreius, everyone had to go through the solemn procedure of taking a new oath of loyalty. Everyone was pledged to fight when it had been shown that fighting was unnecessary and when, in fact, this army of theirs would very soon be compelled ignominiously to surrender.

For Afranius and Petreius were now in a position of great difficulty. I was able to use my cavalry both to prevent them from getting supplies and to slow them down on any march they attempted to make. Wherever they turned, we were ahead of them. In the end we cut them off from their water supply and forced them to capitulate. I insisted that the surrender should take place, not at a private interview (as Afranius suggested), but publicly in front of both armies; and, after Afranius, in an abject speech, had begged for mercy for himself and his men, I spoke at some length, since I wished it to be as widely known as possible who, in this war, was prepared to be merciful and who was not. Their own behavior to those of my men whom they had found peacefully trying to arrange the truce for which they were now begging had already deprived them of all ordinary claims to mercy. And as for their six legions — a fine fighting force, as I was ready to admit — why had they ever been raised and why supported except on the assumption that at some time or other they would be used by my personal enemies against me personally? The force was too big for efficient use in Spain. It had been from the beginning designed to crush me, although I at no time had threatened or even thought of employing my own legions against Italy until my enemies had subverted the Constitution and made me defend myself. I was now careful to explain that I was able still to endure almost any provocation. I asked for nothing except that these legions who had been induced to fight against me and who were now in no state to fight at all should lay down their arms and be decently demobilized. As for their commanders, Afranius and Petreius, who had butchered my soldiers and had prolonged the war and the sufferings both of my own men and of theirs, they were free to go wherever they liked. All I demanded was that they should leave Spain.

Even after this I had some trouble with Afranius and Petreius who were reluctant to pay their troops. I settled this matter and I saw to it that, before the enemy army was disbanded, all property which had been taken from any of them by my men was restored. I think that the majority of my men approved of the liberality with which I had treated the defeated enemy who were, after all, their fellow countrymen. But I was aware that some of them were angry and disappointed. In Gaul they had been used to making a good deal of personal profit out of each successful campaign. Now they resented the fact that they were forbidden to loot Spanish cities or to rob other Roman soldiers. Others too, who had already long years of service behind them, were inclined to envy the enemy army which was now returning to civilian life. These feelings were natural enough, but I did not believe them to be strong enough to be dangerous. Nor indeed were they, though later they did cause me some unexpected anxiety. But I knew that in the last resort my men would fight to the death for my honor and their own. They knew that, though victory might be far distant, I would reward them when victory was attained. They were also perfectly well aware that, though I would share all their dangers and hardships with them, I would not be in the least influenced by their complaints or by their notions of what might be just or unjust. It has always seemed to me that it is for the soldier to win the favor of his commander in chief, not for the commander in chief to go at all out of his way to win the favor of the troops whom he commands.

Afranius and Petreius showed no gratitude to me for having spared their lives. Both went to join Pompey and fought against me to the end. I heard later that Afranius was accused by some of those amateur strategists who surrounded Pompey of having sold his armies and his provinces to me for a sum of money. This kind of criticism was typical of those enemies of mine whose hatred of me was so intense that they still, against much evidence, found it impossible to believe that I could win a campaign on my merits as a commander. Pompey, of course, knew better. In fact Afranius had done as well as he was able to do.

In the southern province of Spain I had no difficulties at all. Varro, to do him justice, attempted to make, with his small force, what would have been a very gallent resistance, if he had received any support at all. As it was, Corduba, Gades and other towns whose people remembered me when, as my first official appointment, I had served as their governor, all declared for me, and Varro had no other course than to surrender. He too, after the things which he had said about me, seemed frightened for his life and appeared surprised when I told him that he had nothing whatever to fear. I found that, though his government had been oppressive, all accounts and details of administration had been recorded in an admirably meticulous manner. Indeed he is not only a great scholar but a great organizer. Two years later I was most glad to be able to put him in charge of the planning and organization of the great public library which I wish to exist in Rome and to be as complete and as valuable a collection of books as that which was so unfortunately damaged at Alexandria.

The Spanish war was over and the news which I received from Decimus Brutus and Trebonius made it clear that the long resistance of Marseilles was almost at an end. I had hoped that now, with the whole of the West secure, I should only have before me the still formidable task of dealing with Pompey's army in Greece. But before I left Spain I received news of the disaster which had overtaken my friend Curio in Africa. It was a severe setback and it meant that the Pompeians could now count on a secure base in Africa as well as that which they already occupied in northern Greece and the East.

Curio had begun his campaign in Africa with only two legions and a small force of cavalry. He had, as I expected, shown inspiring leadership and had evidently also paid intelligent attention to the advice given him by the more experienced Rebilus who was with him. Very soon he had won some considerable successes against the Roman defenders of the province and, when he heard that they were being reinforced by an army under my old enemy King Juba of Numidia, he had wisely fallen back on a strong and well-chosen position and had sent Rebilus back to Sicily to bring the other two legions which he had at his disposal. After this he was ruined by his natural impetuosity. He believed some false news which reached him with regard to the enemy's strength, felt confident that, with his two legions, he could win a glorious and decisive victory and fell into a trap. His crushing defeat was not unlike that suffered in Parthia by Crassus. Like Crassus he made his men march into battle too far and too fast and then, on unfavorable ground, was surrounded by great numbers of cavalry. Most of his men (they were the soldiers who had surrendered at Corfinium) were killed or captured. Only a few escaped among whom was, I am glad to say, my young literary friend Pollio. Curio himself died as boldly as he had lived. He had only served under me for a very short time, but he showed the spirit that I was accustomed to find among the best centurions and officers of the Gallic wars. He was offered a horse and could have ridden away to safety, but he preferred to die with his men. "Caesar gave me an army," he said, "and I have lost it. I should never be able to look him in the face again."

So, though in Spain I had effectively disposed of an enemy force of more than seven legions, I had to reflect that so far in this war it was my troops and my friends who had suffered in battle and after the battle was over. Afranius and Petreius had been left free and their troops had returned unharmed to their homes, but prisoners from Curio's army had been butchered by King Juba, the barbarian ally of the Romans who now held Africa. I had also suffered some losses in the Adriatic where Pompey's admirals had destroyed most of the fleet which Dolabella had been able to collect and had then isolated and forced to surrender nearly two legions of my troops in Illyricum. These successes were both important in themselves and would certainly minimize the effect of my conquest of Spain and of the forbearance which I had shown there.

On my way back from Spain in the early autumn I accepted the

surrender of Marseilles. The inhabitants of this place had behaved treacherously from the beginning and, in the course of the
siege, had violated an agreed truce. I had some reason to act
severely and would certainly have gratified my tired legionaries
if I had allowed them to pillage the city and enslave its people.
But I respected the antiquity and traditions of this Greek colony
and I still wished to make it clear beyond all possible misunder-
standing that in this way my character and my policy would always
incline me to mercy. Domitius Ahenobarbus had managed to escape by sea just before the capitulation, so I was deprived of the
opportunity of pardoning him for the second time. I merely saw to
it that the city was disarmed and I confiscated the fleet and the
public treasure for my own use.

   Meanwhile I had arranged through Lepidus that in Rome I
should be nominated Dictator for the last few months of the year.
There was much for me to do in Rome and I was eager also to begin the campaign against Pompey with the least possible delay.
So I stayed at Marseilles only long enough to be sure that the place
was properly garrisoned. I then set out for Italy and on the way
there received reports that legions of my Spanish army, which
had preceded me, were in a state of mutiny and were devastating
the country around Piacenza. I had encountered nothing like this
since I first marched against Ariovistus. I can still remember the
very great anger which I felt.

Chapter 5

Beginning of the War in Greece

I HAVE A PECULIAR HORROR OF MUTINY IN AN ARMY JUST AS I HAVE a horror of treachery in a friend. Perhaps the two events in the history of my times which have most shocked me (in a moral and in an aesthetic sense) are the mutiny of Lucullus's victorious army in the East and the assassination of Sertorius by those who were supposed to be his friends. There is something tragic about such happenings, for both Lucullus and Sertorius were great soldiers who had earned success, and both were, at critical moments, deserted and betrayed by weak ignoble subordinates whom they trusted. As for me I suppose there is always a chance that I may be assassinated; but I do not think that I shall ever prove incapable of dealing with incipient mutiny among my troops. I know them too well and, in the end, they know me.

Nevertheless the outbreak of lawlessness among the legions at Piacenza caused me, at the time, much anxiety. I found that the trouble was centered in the Ninth Legion where a small group of agitators had succeeded in influencing most of their comrades, including a few centurions. Emotional disturbance spreads quickly in an army and, by the time I reached Piacenza, other legions also were implicated in what amounted to a revolt. In a sense the apparent success of the agitators made matters easier for me, since they had become as organized as mutineers can be and had either chosen or had thrust upon them a committee of twelve men who claimed to represent the rest. Their supposed grievances were suggested to them by greed and self-pity. By various tortuous arguments they had persuaded themselves that they deserved greater rewards than those which they had received, and there were loud complaints (never heard except when they were idle) about their state of health, the hardships they had endured in the past and the constant pressure which I put upon them to undertake still more campaigns and still greater hardships. One of their favorite orators was fond of such sentences as this: "Even the metal of swords and shields gets worn out in the end, yet this general of ours goes on and on using us relentlessly for his purpose, though we are not metal, but flesh and blood." I considered this rather effective oratory, though, of course, utterly unfair. And I was infuriated to discover that my soldiers were being encouraged to believe that I was dragging out the war deliberately, when every action of mine since the beginning had indicated my desire for peace.

It was evidently necessary for me to appear in person before this disorderly mob which only recently had been a disciplined body of men. I came to them surrounded by an unusually large and powerful bodyguard of picked men, known for their achievements throughout the army. Not that I was afraid of the fate which long ago had overtaken my father-in-law Cinna, who, because he had taken inadequate precautions, had been killed by his own mutinous troops. I wished merely to show my men that they were unworthy of my trust, and I could see immediately that my gesture was effective. These soldiers were disturbed at seeing me so unexpectedly remote from them. No doubt their so-called leaders had persuaded them that all they had to do was to threaten to join Pompey and they would find me anxious to comply with any demands they might make. They now began to remember what, in fact, they knew perfectly well — that I am not to be intimidated and that I would rather die than accept orders from my own troops. There were a few angry shouts from the outskirts of the crowd when I began to speak; but after my first few sentences I was listened to in complete silence.

I began quietly, by reminding them of what they and I had done together in Gaul and I mentioned a fact which, I said, was, I thought, obvious — namely that I loved my soldiers and wished to be loved by them. I was not, however, as they knew, one of those generals who tried to win popularity by sharing in or condoning the soldiers' faults. I then pointed out that in all their campaigns they had not only won a great name but had been better and more regularly paid than had any Roman army in history. They knew how I personally had attended to all problems connected with supply and with their comfort; they knew how I had rewarded them after every successful action. No doubt they remembered the great exertions which I had demanded of them. Did they also remember the joy and exultation which they had shown in the midst of hardship? Did they remember the victories that had made them famous throughout the world?

I said that it was difficult for me now to recognize in them the men whom I had known and trusted. I found them in their own country, ravaging the goods of their own countrymen — behaving, in fact, worse than the Celts and Belgae whom they had defeated. They had disgraced themselves and they had disgraced me.

It was not, I pointed out, possible for me to believe that all of them were equally involved in the cowardly and irresponsible actions that had taken place. Certainly I preferred to think that the majority of them had been misled by a handful of ambitious and disgruntled characters, probably in the pay of the enemy, who were neither good soldiers nor good men. But even this was bad enough. These few scoundrels had evidently succeeded in corrupting the mass. They had been persuaded to act against honor and against nature. For it was a law of nature that some must command and others obey. If this law were broken, every organization of human beings would fall into chaos and confusion.

As for me, they themselves knew whether or not I was fitted to command. I was descended from the original founders of Rome, indeed from the immortal gods themselves. And I had been entrusted by the state with the powers of praetor, of consul and of proconsul in command of provinces. What good to me was my an-

cestry or the powers with which I had been invested by the Roman
people, if I were to take orders from a few nobodies in my own
army? Did these miserable agitators imagine that they could
frighten me? In what way? Was it death that I was supposed to
fear? But even supposing that the whole army had decided to do
away with me, I would far rather die than abdicate from my
rights and duties as a commander. Did they think that they could
influence me by threatening to desert and to join Pompey? If this
was their notion of loyalty and if this was really their spirit, Pompey was welcome to them. I would rather have such soldiers
against me than on my side. But they must not imagine that I was
going to provide them with free transport to Greece or to permit
them to march through Italy, plundering their own country. They
might think only of themselves, but I had to think of the interests
of the Republic and of my own. I did not want mutinous unwilling
men in my army, but I was not prepared to tolerate robbers and
brigands in Italy any more than I had tolerated them in Gaul.

At the end of this speech most of the centurions and officers
came forward, fell at my feet and implored me to forgive the men
under their command. I could see that they did indeed represent
the feeling of the army. Yet it still seemed to me that some disciplinary action should be taken. On the basis of the information
which I had received I had had a list made of one hundred and
twenty names which included all the ringleaders and most of their
more ardent supporters. This list was read aloud and I could see
from the reaction of the men that my information had been generally correct. Out of this number twelve were chosen by lot to be
executed and I saw that matters were so arranged that the twelve
should be those who so far as my information went were the real
leaders of the revolt. Once again, when these names were read out,
the army appeared to express a kind of satisfaction and a respect
for what was assumed to be the efficacy of the luck of the draw.
One of the men however protested loudly and I could see that his
protests were regarded sympathetically by the rest. I had his case
investigated and found that he was a good soldier, who had been
absent on leave when the mutiny began and had not been im-

plicated in it in any way. He had been denounced to me by a centurion with whom he had had a personal quarrel. It seemed to me fitting that this centurion should take the place on the condemned list of the soldier whom he had falsely accused. This was done; the twelve men were executed; discipline was entirely restored. I was now free to go on to Rome and could feel confident that there would be no further trouble in the army.

I entered Rome as Dictator. I had several reasons for arranging, by means of Marcus Lepidus, that I should hold this post. I was able to preside over the elections, to carry out quickly some necessary legislation and to restore confidence, so far as possible, in the stability of the present regime. I found that quite a number of those who had hurriedly set off to join Pompey, at the time when I was in difficulties in Spain, had failed to get an immediate passage across the sea and had returned to Rome on receiving the news of my victories. Many of these, however, had only failed to join the enemy because they feared the discomforts of sea travel or of camp life. And, though I had shown clearly enough that I was capable of forgiving my enemies, the rich financiers were still often under the impression that I might behave towards them as Catiline had threatened to behave and introduce a law for the cancellation of all debts. It was observed that I had attracted to my party many able young men, such as Antony and Curio, who had been as heavily in debt, almost, as I myself had been at their age. People seemed to forget that I had paid not only their debts but my own and were too ready to assume that, simply because many penniless adventurers followed me, I should act in the interests of the penniless at the expense of equity, order and stability. So, in the general uncertainty, the rich were unwilling to lend and the debtors were unwilling to pay even the interest on their debts.

The financial measures which I took to deal with this situation proved very successful. I was able both to relieve debtors of a certain proportion of their debts and to convince creditors that it was still profitable to lend and that there would be, so long as I remained in power, no revolutionary change in the existing social order. I also, as Dictator, carried out an act of justice that was

long overdue by reinstating in their rights all those descendants of
the people murdered in the bloody massacres of Sulla which,
though they had happened some thirty years ago, were and still
are fresh in my memory. Sulla had not only killed the fathers, but
deprived the children and grandchildren of property and status.
Among them were many who had been friends or partisans of my
Uncle Marius, of my father-in-law Cinna, of my mother and of
those liberal statesmen whom I remembered in my boyhood. And
I myself, of course, had been closer to death at the hands of Sulla
than I had ever been in all the Gallic wars.

I also arranged for the recall of men who, by judicial means,
had been exiled by Pompey and had afterwards offered their
services to me. This seemed to me an act of ordinary gratitude,
though I was careful to see that these exiles were recalled in accordance with the proper constitutional forms, since I did not wish
to appear to be depriving the Roman people of any of its rights —
and particularly not of the right to exercise mercy.

Then, after holding the elections, I laid down my office as Dictator, an office which I had only held for eleven days. I was
elected consul for the following year, thus attaining, at the moment
which I had intended, the position which I had wished to hold
peaceably and with no civil disturbance. Now my enemies were
forcing me to devote my energies to war rather than to the
peaceful organization which I had planned. For my colleague in
the consulship I had Servilius Isauricus, the son of that general and
elder statesman who had been one of my chief rivals when I stood
for election as Chief Pontiff. Isauricus came of an excellent family,
and could be relied upon to do exactly as I wished.

I had every reason for wanting to bring the war to an end as
soon as possible and so, about the middle of December, without
waiting until I could officially be installed in my consular office, I
left Rome and joined the legions at Brundisium. I knew that during the past year, when I had been actively engaged in Spain and
at Marseilles, Pompey had had no army in the field against him
and so had been able to use his good military sense and his excellent administrative abilities to the fullest advantage. The nine

legions under his command were well trained and equipped and each of them was, numerically, above the strength of my veteran legions, which had suffered considerably from the long marches and from the changes of climate. They had been healthy enough in Gaul and Spain, but the time spent in southern Italy had done much harm and I soon realized that many were too sick for immediate use. Then, in addition to his legions, Pompey had organized a very fine force of cavalry — Greeks, Germans, Gauls, Cappadocians — all under competent commanders. He had collected archers and slingers from Crete, Sparta, Syria and elsewhere. And he had great stores of provisions and of military equipment. Many of these advantages came to him as a result of his control of the sea. By this time he had raised an enormous fleet from Asia, Egypt, Syria and all those many Greek cities and islands with long seafaring traditions. In supreme command of this fleet was my bitter enemy and one-time colleague in the consulship, Marcus Bibulus. That Bibulus was a very intelligent commander may be doubted; but there was no doubt at all of his almost maniacal hostility towards me personally. At whatever sacrifice of health or pleasure (and indeed in the end the poor man did die of overwork and exposure) he would do his best to destroy me.

At Brundisium I had twelve legions, all considerably below strength, and a number of Gallic and German cavalry which, though much inferior to Pompey's great cavalry force, would be enough for my purpose. If I could have brought my whole army across the sea at that time and could then have forced Pompey to fight, I should have felt confident about the result. But in warfare one seldom has the opportunity for such simple decisions, and on this occasion I was certainly confronted with a great many difficulties. First, I had not enough shipping to bring the whole army together across the sea. Then I lacked the warships necessary to guard even those transports which I had. If we were intercepted by Bibulus's squadrons, it was possible to imagine a complete and irretrievable disaster. The only way of avoiding this risk would be to march overland through Illyricum into northern Greece; and, though I considered this project, I soon saw that it would be impossible because of the difficulties of supply and of the kind of country through which we would have to go. Moreover, while we were tied up in the northern mountains, there would be nothing to prevent Pompey from transporting his whole army to Italy and then blockading us from the sea. It seemed necessary, therefore, to take the very great risk of attempting the sea crossing with an inadequate number both of ships and troops and at a bad time of the year.

Before embarking, I told the troops at Brundisium that, though I hoped that we were entering upon our last campaign, it was going to be a campaign where difficulties and hardships had to be expected. We were short of shipping and therefore the men would have to leave behind them all heavy luggage and all slaves which they had acquired in earlier campaigns. They must go abroad only with what was strictly necessary for fighting. They could rely on me, however, to see that they would be none the worse off in the end, when victory was won.

There was now a very fine spirit among the troops. Those who, for lack of transport, had to be left behind were indignant that others seemed to have been preferred to them. No one appeared in the least alarmed at the great risk which we were going to run. So, with only seven legions I put to sea on the fourth of January. Every harbor on the opposite coast was in enemy hands and Bibulus with a hundred and ten ships was at Corfu, not far to the south of us. We had only twelve warships to protect our convoy and, when near the coast of Greece, were spotted by an enemy patrol of eighteen. This patrol, presumably out of cowardice, failed to attack, though they could have done us much damage. So, sailing on northwards, we found beaches where we could land not far south of Apollonia. As soon as the disembarkation was over, I ordered the fleet back to Brundisium to bring over the rest of the army which I had left under the command of Antony. Our luck so far had been good and it seemed to me that once more, as so often in the past, I might be able to profit from acting more quickly than the enemy would anticipate. If I could only get the rest of the army across to me now, I should be in a position to threaten Pom-

pey's control of the seaports and should, I hoped, force him to
fight a battle almost immediately and on my own terms.

As it happened, there was still a long way to go. Bibulus reacted
more energetically than I would have imagined. He had put to
sea as soon as he received the news of our voyage and, though he
was too late to prevent us from disembarking, he was in time to
intercept some of our transports on their way back to Brundisium.
Altogether he captured about thirty of our ships. These he set on
fire and, in his savage rage, burned the captains and the crews
alive with their ships. Meanwhile the rest of our transports had
reached Brundisium and, in accordance with my urgent orders,
were taking aboard the legions and the cavalry under Antony's
command. They had actually left harbor when they received a
message from me informing them of the enemy naval preparations. So they returned to Brundisium. Had the message not
reached them at this moment, they would almost certainly have
been destroyed. As it was this large part of my army was saved,
but it was of no use to me, since now there was no slackness in the
enemy's naval blockade. I had indeed surprised the enemy by
landing an army in Greece, but the army was not big enough for
my purpose.

I could not go back and I could not wait where I was in the
hope that some negligence on the part of Bibulus would enable my
transports to sail. I could import no supplies by sea and had therefore to find what I could on the spot. I began immediately to occupy towns on the coast that were garrisoned by detachments of
Pompey's troops, in this way acquiring some of the supplies we
needed and also cutting the enemy fleet off from easy access to
fresh water. For, if they could patrol the sea, I could patrol the
land and thus force them to make long voyages to Corfu for the
drinking water which they required. We seized Oricus and Apollonia within a matter of days and then marched rapidly north
towards Pompey's main base at Dyrrhachium. At the same time I
had sent a personal message to Pompey through a trusted officer
of his, Vibullius Rufus, who had twice fallen into my hands as a
prisoner — once at Corfinium and once in Spain. I stated in my

letter that I was still prepared to make peace. I would disband my army in three days, if Pompey would publicly swear an oath to do the same thing. And I pointed out that each of us had good reason to avoid pushing matters to extremities. So far in the war both Pompey and I had enjoyed some successes and suffered some reverses. We should both know well enough what a part is played by accident in warfare when both sides are strong. Now there could be no certainty as to which of us would survive; the only certainty was, that if things went further, one of us would be irretrievably ruined. Could we not then do good both to our country and to ourselves by making peace?

I meant this letter sincerely, though I had no great hope that Pompey would accept the offer that I made. At the moment, with half my army cut off from me in Italy, I should seem to him, not unreasonably, to be at a disadvantage. And I was probably flattering his intelligence when I suggested that he should be aware of the part played by accident in war. He had not studied Thucydides and he regarded himself as invincible.

I think that Vibullius too felt certain that his chief would refuse to negotiate. He rode by day and by night until he reached him, and his haste was due not so much to any hopes of making peace as because he was anxious that Pompey should be informed as quickly as possible of my position, my strength and my probable intentions. I only heard how my letter was received when the war was over. Vibullius met Pompey as he was marching along the northern road from Salonica to Dyrrhachium, where he intended to spend the winter. Before he had read more than a few sentences of my letter, Pompey interrupted him. "I would rather die," he said, "and I would rather see my country ruined than to have people say that I owe anything to Caesar." This vain and disorderly sentiment was no doubt shared by Cato, Labienus and the other so-called patriots in Pompey's camp.

Nevertheless Pompey's vanity and self-importance did not result in any negligence or indolence in his conduct of operations. Throughout this campaign, almost up till the final moment, he showed all those qualities of generalship by which he had deserved his title of "the Great." Now, on the basis of the information supplied to him by Vibullius, he immediately guessed what my intentions were and reacted most energetically. His route to Dyrrhachium was a better one than that by which my troops had to go, but Pompey did not make the mistake of underrating the ability of my legions to undertake long marches. He drove his own troops so hard that many of them perished on the way and some, not used to this sort of warfare, deserted. It was a critical race, for, if I could have occupied this harbor and base I should have secured an advantage that would have made up for the legions still left behind in Italy. Had Pompey acted with even a trifle less energy, we should have again surprised him. As it was he won the race by a matter of hours. There was nothing for me to do except to fall back on a position from which I could protect Apollonia and the few other towns which had come over to us. We camped on the river Apsus and Pompey made a camp opposite to us on the other bank of the river. I could not, for lack of numbers, risk challenging him to battle on unfavorable ground; and Pompey was not going to attack me on ground of my own choosing. Indeed he had every reason to avoid an engagement. He was plentifully supplied and was growing stronger every day; he could imagine the difficulties which I should have in supplying my army and no doubt hoped that it would either disintegrate of its own accord or become his easy victim in the spring.

During these winter months, with the two armies so close together, one more effort was made to bring about the peace which the soldiers on both sides desired. The men from both armies would often go down to the riverbanks and, with a mutual agreement to refrain from shooting at each other, would shout out items of news or make inquiries about friends and relations in the opposite camp. On one occasion I instructed Vatinius who, in spite of his extreme ugliness, is an excellent speaker to go down to the river and make a political speech dealing with the causes of the war and my own many attempts to arrange matters without fighting. I was still ready, Vatinius said, to send a deputation to Pompey to discuss terms for an armistice; but I should of course

require a guarantee that my envoys would be sent back to me unharmed. Pompey's men were impressed by the speech and by this
offer. They promised that on the following day a senior officer
would come down to the river to discuss the proposals that had
been made. So on the next day troops from both sides were present
in great numbers along the riverbanks. Vatinius stepped forward
and began to speak; but instead of the officer whom he had expected to meet, he found himself confronted by Labienus, whose
figure and aggressive bearing were as well known to my men as to
Pompey's. After a few words of insult to my troops whom he, of
all men, described as traitors and after some personal abuse of
Vatinius, Labienus must have suddenly ordered some of his soldiers to fire. Vatinius had a narrow escape. His own men managed
to cover him in time with their shields. Quite a few of our people
were wounded. Labienus then shouted out: "So much for your
peace conferences! The only way you can make peace with us is
by bringing us Caesar's head."

Chapter 6

Difficulties and Defeat

So THE WEEKS AND MONTHS OF WINTER WENT BY AND MY ANXIETY increased. I could assume that, according to my directions, ships were being built for me in Italy, Sicily, Spain and Gaul; but, however successfully the shipbuilding program might be carried out, it would be very long before I could challenge Pompey's control of the sea. And on land I was faced by some of the same difficulties as those I had found in the war with Vercingetorix. I could not bring the enemy to battle on ground of my own choosing, and I was so much weaker than the enemy in cavalry that I could not send detachments of troops far in any direction to secure supplies. Meanwhile Pompey's father-in-law, Scipio, was bringing from Asia another army and another considerable cavalry force. It was in every way essential for me to have with me the four legions and the cavalry that had been left behind at Brundisium. To bring them through Pompey's naval blockade was indeed to take a tremendous risk; but this risk had to be taken and it seemed to me that the sooner it was taken the better. Our transports had less to fear from winter storms than from an enemy fleet that could operate easily and efficiently in the good weather that would follow the winter.

As it was, in the time after my own crossing, Bibulus had kept so strict a watch on Brundisium and on every harbor available to us that my officers in Italy had been prevented from sailing. Bibulus himself had set an example to the rest of his naval commanders by keeping at sea, on short rations of water, for exceptionally long periods and by showing himself willing to undergo any kind of hardship. In spite of his poor health he persisted in carrying out personally all his responsibilities. I was told afterwards that he seemed to be kept almost miraculously alive simply by the extreme hatred which he felt towards me, by his rage at the fact that I had myself slipped through his blockade, and by his determination that now, at all events, I should be caught and destroyed like a rat in a trap. Before the end of the winter he died as a result of exposure and of forcing himself to work too hard for his capacity. After his death no other supreme naval commander was appointed, but the Pompeian fleets remained alert and well organized. The squadron under the command of Pompey's cruel but very able son, Gnaeus, showed itself particularly efficient.

I was handicapped by lack of information with regard to almost everything except the area in which I was operating myself. From a military point of view Italy was under my control; but Pompey, with his command of the sea, knew more of what was happening in Italy than I did. I sent message after message to Antony with detailed instructions as to where he might attempt a landing; but many of my messages and many of his replies were intercepted by the enemy. I knew that in active warfare I could rely absolutely both on Antony and the other officers whom I had left behind; but this was a question demanding continuous and unremitting attention to the weather and all other sailing conditions. How could I be certain that critical hours might not pass unobserved simply because Antony happened to be engaged in some love affair or some drinking bout? So great was my distress of mind that on one occasion in this winter I attempted to go back to Italy myself so as to see with my own eyes what, if anything, was holding up my reinforcements.

In view of Pompey's naval patrols I chose a dark stormy night for my purpose and I went aboard a very small craft which, though it was carrying me and the whole fortune of the war, would appear, I hoped, inconsiderable. I slipped away from camp with only one or two attendants and went aboard the boat without anyone's knowledge. The captain had been offered good pay and, since I kept my face covered, did not know who I was. No doubt he assumed that I was a messenger, perhaps a slave. At the mouth of the river we ran into a storm so violent that the captain declared that it was impossible to go farther. I then revealed myself and told him that I was entrusting not only myself but everything to him and his men. After they had got over their astonishment, they behaved well. They exerted themselves to the utmost and fought their way into the teeth of the gale. But the elements were too much for them and the necessary hours of darkness began to pass. In the end we were forced to turn back and next day the story of this unsuccessful adventure became known to the troops. They reacted in a most emphatic manner. Large numbers of them in a state of great agitation gathered outside my tent and insisted on seeing with their own eyes that I was alive and well. Then, using their centurions and junior officers as deputies, they loaded me with reproaches. Why should I risk my life, when the whole safety of the army depended on me? Was it that I did not trust them? I would find that, even if their comrades in Italy were too cowardly to make the voyage, they by themselves and without any reinforcements were perfectly ready to engage any force that the enemy could bring against them. Only they begged me to promise that I would never again leave them in this way; and some actually declared that, if I failed to give this promise, they would put a guard on me and preserve me for my own good and for theirs.

I saw indeed that they were right and that my momentary impulse had been wrong. Their demonstrations of loyalty and affection were touching and I was grateful to them. Yet it remained true that by the spring Pompey would be overwhelmingly strong. If he then engaged us in battle, nearly all my centurions and many of my men would fight till they were annihilated. The rest would run away. For Pompey would not make the kind of elementary mistake which enables a weak army to defeat a very strong one.

So my anxiety continued and I sent instructions to Antony and the others, telling them that they must run any risk that was not entirely desperate in order to reach me.

I discovered afterwards that Antony had acted correctly and well. He had been delayed partly by the enemy's naval operations and partly by a dangerous situation in Italy where one of my supporters, young Caelius, had entirely lost his head and had attempted a kind of revolution. I had known Caelius for some time as a brilliant and ambitious youth and had hoped that he might develop the qualities of a Curio or an Antony. He had a witty, engaging personality. For a short time he had succeeded Catullus, whose friend he was, in the affections of Clodia. Indeed, so curiously vulnerable was this great poet of ours, that it seems quite possible that one reason for his collapse in health and early death was the fact that Clodia, whom, for some extraordinary reason, he believed to be virtuous and sincere, had preferred Caelius to himself. This was a most sad affair, though Caelius cannot be blamed for it since if Clodia had not chosen him, she would soon have chosen someone else. Though she must have been greatly charmed by Caelius. It appears that she was furious when he, soon and wisely, left her; indeed she stupidly took legal action, accusing him, among other things, of attempted poisoning. Caelius got Cicero to defend him and Cicero, whose speech I read with great pleasure, obviously enjoyed saying in brilliant Latin what everyone had always thought about Clodia.

All this had happened while I was engaged in the conquest of western Gaul and I now remembered these old scandals sadly. For Caelius since then had shown himself exceptionally brilliant and I had hoped much of him. I had left him in Rome holding the office of praetor and, since he owed much to me, I naturally expected that he would follow the general line of policy which I had laid down and which could quickly be explained to him by Balbus or by Oppius, both of whom knew that I was most anxious to avoid, at least for the time being, any kind of social disturbance in Italy. Personally I was aware that, if one were to think in terms of abstract justice or abstract efficiency, one might well say that my measures for the relief of debtors had not gone far enough. But justice and efficiency cannot, in political life, be regarded as abstractions. It was politically necessary for me, at least until the war was over, not to appear to be acting in the interests of any particular class, however just its claims might be. Caelius had either not grasped this obvious fact, or else was prepared seriously to weaken my cause in the interests of his own theories and ambitions. Perhaps he aimed at becoming another Clodius. Certainly he won considerable popularity with the city mob by pronouncing edicts canceling all debts and, for the time being, all rents on houses and apartments. This was just the policy which my enemies had always said that I would pursue and (though I was aware that there was something to be said for such a policy) I had taken great pains to show that, in this civil war, my opponents had no reason to fear for their money or for their lives. Caelius, of course, pretended that I, if I had been in Rome, would have supported him and many people believed this assertion. However my fellow-consul, Servilius, and other members of my party who held magistracies acted unanimously and firmly. Caelius was deprived of his office and of his seat in the senate. The same thing, I remember, happened to me when I was praetor; but I weathered that storm easily.

Caelius, however, acted in a most exaggerated and irresponsible way. He left Rome still claiming that he was a loyal member of my party — though Servilius, Trebonius, Antony and others had all shown their disapproval of him. Next he attempted to join forces in a common revolutionary front with the aristocratic gang leader Milo, the murderer of Clodius, who, ever since his condemnation, had been living abroad in exile. Milo, in spite of the fact that he had been condemned owing to Pompey's influence, now claimed that he, with his gladiators and ex-slaves, was invading Italy in accordance with Pompey's instructions. In fact this movement, directed by two wholly irresponsible characters whom neither Pompey nor I would own, could have done me much harm and Pompey much good. For a short time there was a possibility of serious disorder in Italy, and Antony, with the legions I so badly needed in Greece, had to stand by ready to intervene.

Fortunately the whole affair came to nothing. Milo was killed by a slingstone when attacking a position occupied by a legion under the command of my nephew Pedius. Caelius was put to death by a detachment of my Gallic cavalry whom he, without having made the necessary inquiries as to their loyalty, had attempted to bribe. So, in a most inglorious way, disappeared two characters who might both have left great names. Neither had any great political sense or understanding; but both had outstanding qualities which should have led to distinction. I often think about their fates, and it seems to me that they held the mistaken attitude which we notice in spoiled children. They thought it certain that things would go their own way and thus they lacked a necessary kind of modesty. I myself have often taken great risks, but I have taken them, as it were, respectfully. I know that sometimes I am able to dominate fortune and in some respects even to alter necessity. It is because of this that today I am worshiped as a god, and there is some sense in this worship. But I know too that forethought is a part of action and that, when we have to take risks, this is an indication of our debility before fortune.

That winter, when I was waiting with such anxiety for my legions from Italy, was one of the occasions when I began to think that I had perhaps risked too much. In fact fortune was on my side. One day, when a stiff southerly wind was blowing, I was informed that a great fleet had been sighted out at sea, sailing northwards. It was soon clear that at last Antony had been able to follow my instructions. Here were the transports and the legions and the very few warships which were available to protect them. The whole fleet, well out at sea, was carried past our lines, past Pompey's lines and then out of sight to the north past Dyrrhachium where, as we knew, an enemy naval squadron was stationed. For two days there was no news. Then a messenger arrived from Antony. His whole force of four legions and eight hundred cavalry had been landed almost without loss at the harbor of Nymphaeum.

He had very nearly been overtaken by Pompey's squadron of excellent Rhodian warships from Dyrrhachium, but a lucky change in wind had saved him and destroyed the Rhodians. He was now marching southwards and proceeding with great caution since he rightly imagined that Pompey would attempt to intercept him before he could join forces with me.

This news of Antony's arrival was one of the best pieces of news I have ever received. Three of his four legions were veterans and, if I could unite his army with mine, I should have a force large and good enough to meet any force on land that Pompey could produce. I did not imagine victory to be certain, but it was evident that defeat had been averted. Pompey, of course, saw the situation as clearly as I did and acted with his usual energy. He had received the news of Antony's landing first and he marched northwards ahead of me, hoping to trap Antony into fighting an engagement before I could reach him. Again there were some anxious days. A less skillful commander than Antony might well have walked into an ambush and had his whole force annihilated. But Antony anticipated Pompey's moves and, at the critical moment, kept his men in camp until I was able to join him. The first stage of this campaign was over. Each side now faced the other in full strength.

Yet it remained true that, while Pompey's strength was growing daily, mine, in this theater of war, must tend to diminish. My men had the advantage of experience and the confidence that comes from many victories, but they were still outnumbered and — more important — some of them were growing old. Moreover it was still early in the year and I could foresee that we should be faced with increasing difficulties with regard to supply, while Pompey could import everything that he needed by sea. Logically Pompey's best chance of winning the war lay in avoiding battle, unless he could fight with a clear advantage, and in continuing to build up his own strength while he watched mine disintegrate. Only two considerations, I thought, would make him deliberately go against this plan: one was the fact that an army which is always on the defensive will tend to suffer in morale; the other (less important from a military point of view, but very much to be reckoned with where Pompey was concerned) proceeded from Pompey's very high opinion of himself. He would find it insufferable for it to be said that he, with superior forces, was afraid to meet me in battle.

As for me I had only one object, which was to bring him to battle as soon as possible. For a long time he frustrated every move I made and before the end he brought me within sight of disaster.

I have several times adopted rather unusual expedients in warfare. The lines of Alesia are an example. They could equally well be described as the work of a besieger or of one besieged. The lines we built at Dyrrhachium were, from a military point of view, even more unorthodox; but the fact that we had to abandon them after a defeat does not prove that the original conception was mistaken. Just south of the town of Dyrrhachium, which was fortified and garrisoned, Pompey had taken up a very strong position by the sea. Before him was a long line of heights; behind him he had a fairly good harbor into which he could import whatever he needed. My attempted blockade of him could never, therefore, be more than a partial success, since he would always have access to the sea. Nevertheless I began to occupy height after height with forts and garrisons and to link these positions together by lines of circumvallation. It was indeed an odd form of siege warfare since, owing to Pompey's command of the sea, the besieged were much better supplied than the besiegers. Yet there were sound military reasons for undertaking this operation. In the first place I aimed at neutralizing Pompey's very powerful cavalry force. If they were free to range all over the country they would make my own difficulties of supply, which were great enough already, still greater. Moreover while it would be possible to keep this cavalry force in existence even behind the lines, it would impose a severe strain on Pompey's naval transport if he had to import both food for the men and fodder for the horses. Then too I aimed at undermining Pompey's reputation as a commander. It would not look well for him to appear before the eyes of the world as being anxious, in spite of his superior numbers, to avoid battle and to be boxed up in lines with the sea behind him, as though he had already been defeated.

Indeed I could well imagine how Pompey would feel if such suggestions were made to him and I hoped that he might be led to fight a pitched battle before he was quite ready for it. But Pompey, however vain he might be, was not going to sacrifice the clear military advantage which he had. He stuck to his original plan. My forces were to wear themselves out while his grew stronger. Instead of offering battle he proceeded in his turn to occupy and fortify heights on the periphery of his position with the objects of keeping as much ground as possible under his control and of forcing me to extend my lines to such a length that the whole circuit could not easily be garrisoned in sufficient strength. Every day the building operations continued on both sides and there were frequent skirmishes in which Pompey's troops received just the sort of battle training which they needed. In the end we completed the circuit but our lines extended for as much as fifteen miles and at the southern end, where they went down to the sea, the fortifications were still incomplete. And during all this time we had, as no doubt Pompey had anticipated, been very short of food. In fact it had become impossible to feed the whole army on the spot. I sent off two veteran legions into Macedonia, ostensibly to intercept Scipio on his way from Asia, but actually because I could not feed them at Dyrrhachium; and I sent another legion with cavalry into Thessaly, and five cohorts to Aetolia. I had thus almost dissipated the reinforcements which Antony had brought and still, in the lines of Dyrrhachium, my men had not enough to eat.

We reminded each other of earlier campaigns — of Avaricum, Alesia and of last year in Spain — when we had suffered badly from hunger, yet still had come out victorious. This was not the first time when we had had to supplement our rations with roots, and in fact in this area we discovered a kind of root (the Greeks call it *chara*) which, when mixed with milk, was not bad to taste and could be made into a sort of bread. Once when some of Pompey's soldiers, from an advanced post, were taunting our men with their shabby clothes and starved appearance, they retaliated by hurling a volley of these *chara* loaves at the enemy and shouted out that, so long as anything grew from the earth, they would go on fighting. I was told later that this incident had quite an effect in Pompey's army, in which a number of widely conflicting views about my own troops seem to have been held. Some people apparently believed that my veterans were utterly worn out with the sufferings and wounds of ten years' fighting in Gaul; others regarded them as some species of wild beast, dangerous to deal with but capable of being trapped; and others still, against all the evidence, thought that my men, enriched with the spoils of Gaul, were an effeminate, pleasure-loving lot who even now, when food was scarce, indulged themselves lavishly in drink and in sexual debauch. Among the members of the senatorial nobility in Pompey's camp strange views were also held with regard both to his and my generalship. Pompey was accused of cowardice and lethargy (in spite of the fact that his engineers and soldiers were working and fighting as well as my own); and I was ridiculed for having undertaken an operation of which no example could be found in the handbooks of military strategy.

However by the beginning of spring my unorthodox methods were beginning to prove effective. Behind our lines the grain was ripening and my men knew that it would not be long before their privations were over. Meanwhile, though Pompey's men were well fed, fodder for the horses was running short. It seemed to me that in the end he would not only be forced to fight, but to fight on ground where his great cavalry strength could not be used to its full advantage.

In fact Pompey made two energetic and extremely well-planned attempts to break out. We frustrated the first of these attempts, but the second succeeded so well that if Pompey had made full use of the situation which developed he might have destroyed my army and won the war. In planning this second attempt at a break-through he was greatly helped by two Gauls, good soldiers of distinguished families, who just at this time deserted me and went over to the enemy. These two, together with Labienus, were, I think, the only soldiers of mine to desert and in all three cases the motives for desertion were, I should say, temperamental rather than rational. The two Gauls had been embezzling money that should have been used for paying the troops under their command. They had been found out, but I had been content with reprimanding them and making them guarantee to repay what they had stolen. They were good officers and I wanted as little trouble as possible. However their pride was wounded and, for the sake of this wounded pride, they forgot all the kindnesses which I had done to them in the past and, with all their personal attendants, went over to the enemy. Pompey made a most intelligent use of them. He rode with them all along his lines, showing them off to his men and encouraging them to expatiate on what they claimed was the misery and starvation of my army. And, more important, he got from them a most exact account of the disposition of our troops and the state of our defenses.

Very quickly and skillfully he planned his attack on the basis of the information which he now had. He aimed at breaking through our lines at the extreme south where they joined the sea. Here the fortifications were still incomplete, though before long they would have been exceptionally strong, since they had been designed in double lines. My own camp was at the very other end of our fortifications, some fifteen miles away from the threatened sector. So it was some time before I received information of the attack and of its initial success. It appeared that Pompey had landed a large division of troops from the sea to the south of our lines and had at the same time launched a frontal attack from the north. He was using no less than six legions and great numbers of light troops in this operation. He had achieved complete surprise, had soon overrun the sector of our lines near the coast, and, though hampered by the complicated system of entrenchments, was moving inland against our first fortifications on the hills.

I started at once for the scene of action, bringing with me all the troops available from the northern defenses. Meanwhile the situation had been partially restored by Mark Antony who commanded one of the hill forts nearest to the sea and had marched out at once against the enemy with a considerable force of fresh troops. By the time I arrived the original panic among our men was over and the enemy were falling back, presumably to consolidate the positions which they had won. But we had undoubtedly suffered a setback and Pompey's men had, for the first time, seen my soldiers in full flight. I was anxious to do what I could to restore the position (the breach in our lines was still not a great one) and also to win some success which would counterbalance the evident success won by the enemy. I saw an opportunity for achieving both these objects when my scouts reported to me that one enemy legion, out of contact with the others and considerably in advance of them, was beginning to occupy a system of fortifications which in the past had been used at various times both by Pompey and myself. I led thirty-three cohorts and some cavalry against this one legion. We went by a circuitous route and attacked before Pompey, who was some distance away with the main body of his troops, had any idea of our intentions.

At first everything went well. Pompey's men put up a good resistance for a short time, but we broke into the fortifications in the east, where I myself was organizing the attack, and they were soon in flight. Indeed we were having everything our own way when there occurred one of those strange chances or mistakes which do occur in warfare and against which, except in very obvious circumstances, it seems impossible to guard. Logically speaking we should, after our initial success, have annihilated Pompey's legion and then either held and occupied the position we had won or else fallen back in good order on our lines to the rear. But this did not happen. Some officer or centurion of mine (no doubt he was killed later) must in all good faith have given a wrong order and led a large part of my force along an old line of fortifications in a direction which turned out to be away from the scene of action. Thus many cohorts were separated from the main body. There was delay in joining up again and a lot of confusion in the narrow exits and entries to the old camp and the system of entrenchments. At this point Pompey brought up his other five legions in battle order to rescue, if he could, the legion of his which was so hard pressed.

Under normal conditions my men would undoubtedly have kept their heads. Indeed they were in a strong position and had nothing to fear. But now, as a result, I suppose, of the fact that half of them had already somehow lost their sense of direction, there was panic. The panic began with the cavalry and spread to almost every man among the infantry. Someone shouted out that we were surrounded — which was untrue — and everyone began to escape as quickly as possible from what was considered to be a trap. Standard-bearers threw away their standards; centurions ran with their men; hundreds, jumping down from the old ramparts, broke their limbs or crushed each other to death. I myself was appalled both at the sight of this disgraceful flight and at the realization of my own impotence to prevent it. For some time I threw myself in the way of those who were running — shouting to them, cursing them, imploring them, calling them by their names, grasping their arms, their shoulders, their garments. They passed me or brushed me aside as if I were someone unknown to them. One man, who, I think, knew nothing except that someone was trying to prevent his escape, actually raised his sword and would have struck me down with it if my own shield-bearer had not intercepted the blow.

It was an utter rout. To this day I do not know why it was that Pompey failed to follow up this great and sudden success; for the majority of our men were so demoralized that we could have put up no effective resistance on that day. But Pompey, of course, could not immediately have known this. I imagine that he must have been perplexed and confused by what he would naturally regard as an unnecessary flight and that he came to the conclusion that some, at least, of the disorder was planned with the object of leading him into a trap. So he advanced cautiously and gave us time to reorganize behind fortified positions. It was a great mistake on his part, but not a mistake for which he can be blamed. In the evening I said to some of my friends, "We should have lost the war today if Pompey had known how to win it." But, though I made this statement with as confident an air as possible, I could not be certain that Pompey had not won the war already. In this battle we had lost a thousand men from the legions and two hundred cavalry. Thirty-two centurions had been killed; thirty-two of our standards had been taken. No one could now hold the beliefs that my armies were invincible and that my soldiers never ran away or surrendered. In fact a number of prisoners were taken. Labienus asked to be allowed to deal with them and Pompey granted his request. They were paraded in front of the victorious army and insulted by Labienus in their misery. These were his own comrades-in-arms with whom he and I had won victories in Gaul or Germany. Now he made use of that savage tongue of his which they knew well, asking them whether it was usual for veteran troops to run away like children at the sight of steel. Then he had every one of them put to death.

I myself was still ready and indeed anxious to spare the lives of those Romans who were my enemies. But now I made one exception. If Labienus had fallen into my hands, I should have treated him as he deserved and as my army would have demanded.

Chapter 7

To Pharsalus

AFTER THAT BATTLE I SPENT A SLEEPLESS AND MISERABLE NIGHT. It was perfectly clear to me that all the labor and hardship of the winter months had been wasted and that by no manner of means could I regain the position I had lost. Pompey had not only broken through our lines but had shattered them entirely. If I were to survive, I must adopt a new plan altogether. And I began to suspect now that the old plan had been, from the beginning, too ambitious. It might have succeeded against a general less skilled and energetic than Pompey. As it was, it had failed, and it seemed to me now that, against appearances, it had been Pompey, not I, who all this time had held the initiative. He had forced me to extend my lines to breaking point and to weaken my army by sending large forces away from the scene of action. And meanwhile he had continued quietly and efficiently to build up his own strength. I might, until that morning, have claimed that I had penned him in with his back to the sea; but since he had complete control of the sea, this position might have been one that he had chosen for himself. Now he not only had the sea close behind him but had complete freedom of movement on land. If I remained where I was, I should either have to fight a battle at once or allow Pompey's cavalry to cut us off from the few sources of supply on which we could still depend.

I thought seriously of offering battle. By the morning, I knew, my men would be bitterly ashamed of themselves and would probably be urging me to give them an opportunity to avenge their defeat. But the risk was too great. A defeated army does not regain its morale quite so quickly and part of the confidence that the men would show tomorrow would be mere bravado. Moreover why should Pompey risk everything on a general engagement, when he could achieve all his objects simply by wearing us out and starving us — just as I had done with his armies in Spain?

It seemed to me that there was only one thing to do, and that was to break off contact with the enemy as soon as possible and then move inland to Macedonia and join up with the two veteran legions under my general Calvinus who had gone eastwards to watch the movements of Pompey's father-in-law Scipio. By adopting this plan I hoped to draw Pompey after me to Thessaly, where he would be far from his naval bases and depots and where it might be possible to fight a battle on more or less even terms.

There was, of course, the chance that, instead of following me, Pompey might transport his whole army to Italy. If he did this, I should be in a very difficult position indeed and I greatly feared that, for one reason or another, Pompey might be persuaded to abandon Scipio, whose army would certainly be destroyed by the combined forces of Calvinus and myself, and to leave me stranded in northern or central Greece while he reoccupied Italy and attempted the reconquest of Gaul and Spain. With no naval transport I should have had to undertake the difficult journey by land through Illyricum once again to invade Italy from the north. Nevertheless I did not expect that Pompey, good general though he was, would take this step which I most feared. He was honorable enough not to be willing to abandon the army which Scipio was leading to him; he was vain enough not to want it said that he had once again retired from me instead of advancing; and, after the victory at Dyrrhachium, he had some reason to believe that he could avoid further campaigns by finishing the war off in Greece, where, so far as he could see, my army was already showing signs of disintegration.

As for me I had in any case no other plan which seemed to offer any hope of final success. I had to move away from Pompey and away from the sea. Next day I paraded the troops and said what I could to encourage them. It was of the utmost importance that they should retain their faith in me as a commander and I very carefully pointed out that, whatever might have been the cause for yesterday's disaster, it could not be attributed to faulty generalship on my part. I had led them to a position where victory was assured and then something had gone wrong. Someone (not I) may have given a mistaken order. Someone (not I) may have shown cowardice. Or the whole thing might be the result of one of those tricks of fortune which have to be accepted in warfare, which, when they occur, look almost like examples of supernatural intervention. I then reminded them of all their triumphs in the past. I mentioned in particular the curious setback which they had suffered before Gergovia, and how this setback had soon been followed by absolute and complete victory.

As I had expected, the troops now clamored to be led against the enemy. I saw on all sides of me old soldiers weeping with shame as they thought of how disgracefully they had behaved on the preceding day. Some of my best officers and centurions were so impressed with the men's determination that they strongly advised me to fight at once. I myself recognized their enthusiasm, but I preferred to give it time to harden into resolution. Once again I demanded hard work and hard marching. The men, in their anxiety to show their spirit, vied with each other in doing every necessary job speedily and efficiently. Indeed their centurions scarcely had to bother to give orders. We had struck camp and were on the move before Pompey could have imagined it possible. However he lost little time in setting out after us. His cavalry was well handled and was presumably under the direction of Labienus. I was told afterwards that this was one of the rather numerous occasions on which Labienus had guaranteed a victory. If indeed he did make this boast he must have forgotten some of our experience in Gaul. There, in dealing with the greatly superior cavalry of Vercingetorix, we had often found that a small mixed force of cavalry and first-class light infantry was remarkably effective in defensive actions. So, on our retreat from Dyrrhachium, when Pompey's cavalry came up with the tail of our column at a difficult river crossing, I made use of about four hundred shock troops together with a few squadrons of my own Gallic and German horse. They completely routed the much greater numbers of enemy cavalry. Some of them reported to me later that the enemy showed a particular distaste for coming anywhere near the upward thrusts of lances. They seemed, as one man put it, to be more careful of their faces than of their horses. I took particular note of this point.

It took us three days' hard marching to shake off Pompey's determined pursuit. My next objective was to join up with Calvinus and his two legions. I had already sent messengers to him instructing him to move southwards in the direction of Thessaly and I had no reason to believe that he was not carrying out my orders. In fact, however, he never received my orders at all. The effect of my defeat at Dyrrhachium had been so great that nearly all those inland towns and districts of Epirus and Macedonia which up to this time had obeyed my authority had suddenly changed sides and declared for Pompey. So my messengers were intercepted and Calvinus, who had had no news at all of the battle, very nearly led his army straight into a trap laid for him by Pompey. He was saved by a lucky accident. One of his patrols happened to fall in with some of the attendants of the two Gallic chieftains who had previously deserted and given Pompey such valuable information about my dispositions. Gauls enjoy boasting and these Gauls could not resist the temptation to tell Calvinus's men of what they described as my total defeat at Dyrrhachium. By the time the news reached Calvinus, Pompey's main army was only four hours' march away; but, by acting promptly and intelligently, Calvinus saved his force intact and, after a difficult march over the mountains, joined me in the northwest of Thessaly. His two veteran legions gave me the extra strength which I required and I was now ready to fight if the opportunity presented itself.

It was not clear, however, whether Pompey would give me this opportunity. There had been, I discovered later, a council of war

after the battle of Dyrrhachium and at this council Afranius had
strongly urged Pompey to invade Italy and leave my army to disintegrate of its own accord in Greece. But the general opinion had
been overwhelmingly against this suggestion. By the amateur
strategists who surrounded Pompey, Afranius was accused of cowardice and the old story of his having sold Spain and his army
there to me was brought up again. It was confidently asserted that
I was now on the run and that it would prove a very simple matter
indeed to dispose of me finally. Indeed many of these noble
Romans, who were politicians rather than generals, were so certain
of a quick and, for them, satisfactory end to the war that they
were already making plans for the next elections in Rome; many
of them sent agents back to Italy in order to rent houses con-
veniently near to the Forum; and there were quite serious quarrels
between Spinther and Domitius Ahenobarbus as to who should
take my place as Chief Pontiff after I had been put to death. Later
Scipio put his own name forward for this supposedly vacant post,
and the quarrel became more embittered still.

Pompey himself was not, of course, the victim of the easy de-
lusions of his supporters. But he wished to win the war in Greece
without giving the impression that he was running away and without abandoning his father-in-law, Scipio. He believed that he
could still do me most harm by interfering with my supplies and
by constantly harassing me until in desperation I should have to
offer battle on unfavorable terms. So he too, by easier routes,
marched to Thessaly and joined forces with Scipio at Larissa.
His army now very greatly outnumbered mine, particularly in
cavalry.

Still the grain was not ripe and our men had had to endure considerable hardships on the march. There was much sickness in the
army, the result, probably, of the state of semi-starvation in which
we had been before Dyrrhachium. But I think that what impressed
us most was the attitude of the people in the towns and villages
through which we passed. In Gaul, Spain and Italy we had been
looked at sometimes with hostility and often with fear; very often
too we had met with the kind of wild enthusiasm with which

people greet victory and success. But now we experienced an entirely unfamiliar sensation. People turned out in numbers to watch us pass or to attempt to sell the few foodstuffs which they might be able to spare; but in the eyes and gestures of these people we observed nothing of what we were accustomed to see. Some looked at us with compassion, others almost with contempt. It took us some time to realize that we were regarded as a defeated army. Indeed Pompey's propaganda agents had been all the more effective because they believed their own propaganda. It was now generally assumed that the war was virtually over and there was some speculation as to whether my men would fight at all. In fact, as the troops became gradually aware of how they were regarded, they were first astonished and then outraged. I noticed in them a slow and savage determination. There was not much boasting, but it was clear enough that the whole army, sick and weary as it was, looked forward to the time when it could show unmistakably its real distinction in courage, experience and training.

It was unfortunate for the inhabitants of the Thessalian town of Gomphi that they chose to defy my army when it was in this mood. Previously the citizens of this place had sent me an embassy offering to help me in every way and asking me for a garrison. Now they had decided that mine was the losing side and they closed their gates against us. The town had high walls and plenty of defenders, but it seemed to me and to the army an insupportable insult that such a place should venture to resist the men who had taken Avaricum, Alesia, and Marseilles. I gave the signal for assault in the late afternoon. The town was in our hands by sunset and until next morning I allowed the soldiers to do what they wished with the inhabitants and with their property. It was a rich town and great stores of food and wine were discovered and consumed. Next day practically every man in the army was drunk; but, curiously enough, it was a form of drunkenness which did not leave them lethargic. Even on the march they were singing, dancing and drinking still more of the local wine which they carried with them. The column looked more like a Bacchanalian procession than a Roman army. No doubt next day they did not feel so well; yet this was a strange case (in my experience the only case) where a prolonged debauch seems to have done actual good to the health. After the sack of Gomphi there was no more sickness in the army. Indeed some medical men with whom I have discussed the matter have suggested to me that, in some circumstances, a sufficiently large quantity of wine can alter for the better the whole balance of the constitution — particularly when the balance has been disturbed by illness and exhaustion. This may be true, though I am inclined to think that the explanation for the army's sudden return to health is to be found rather in psychological causes. They had demonstrated to themselves that they still possessed the ability to overpower resistance. Then, perhaps, the wine helped them to forget that they had ever been defeated.

The knowledge of what had happened to Gomphi induced the other towns in the Thessalian plain to open their gates to us until we approached the large city of Larissa where Pompey and his father-in-law Scipio were established with their united armies.

I moved into the plain of Pharsalus, hoping that here, in country that was ideal for the use of cavalry, Pompey would be willing to fight a decisive battle. But it was soon clear that Pompey would make nothing easy for me. He too led his army into the plain and camped on some rising ground not far from my own position. For some days, he drew up his army in battle order just below his camp. Evidently he hoped that I might be induced, in desperation, to order my men to attack him in this very strong position where he would not only have the slope of the hill in his favor but would also be able, if things went wrong with him, to retreat behind his fortifications. But I was not so desperate as to make elementary tactical mistakes. I drew up my army on the level ground below the heights, challenging him to come down and meet us on equal terms (though on whatever ground we fought he would have great numerical superiority); but he showed no sign of being willing to accept my challenge. Once again he seemed to be imposing his will on mine and I began to think that I should only be able to gain the initiative by once again marching away from him and by attempting in some way or other to intercept his communications

either with Larissa or with his bases on the Adriatic. It was the
height of summer and I fancied that, old as they might be, my
veterans could still march faster and farther than any troops under
Pompey's command — though, since the battle of Dyrrhachium,
I was not disposed to minimize the fighting qualities of his men.

So, having lost hope of fighting the kind of general engagement
which I wished to fight, I gave the order to strike camp. It was a
still dawn, quite hot even at this early hour. The soldiers had begun to pack up their tents and I had already made arrangements for the order of march, so that we should be protected from
any attacks which might be made on us by Pompey's cavalry.
Suddenly the leader of one of my patrols rode up to me (I
was standing in front of my tent) and, evidently excited, told me
that he had observed a quite unusual amount of hurrying to and
fro in Pompey's camp. My first thought was that Pompey had
somehow guessed or been informed of my intentions and was about
to send out all his cavalry to impede us on the march. But now
other reports came in in rapid succession. Pompey's whole army
was on the move and it was soon quite clear that he was leaving
his position on the heights and forming up in order of battle on
the level ground. The moment for which we had waited had suddenly and unexpectedly arrived. I gave the order at once for the
scarlet tunic to be displayed outside my tent and, as the soldiers
saw this signal for battle, a great shout arose and spread from
company to company and legion to legion. The men dropped the
tents and ran to arms. There was something joyful in their alacrity;
for, though many of them no doubt shrank from the dreadful prospect of shedding the blood of their own countrymen, they were
convinced by this time that the peace which I had so often and so
vainly attempted to make could only be gained in this way. Moreover they, who were accustomed to think of themselves as invincible, had a defeat to avenge.

While they began, quickly and precisely, to take up their proper
places in the line, I rode out as far as it was safe to go in order to
see what I could of the enemy's dispositions. It was soon evident to
me that Pompey intended to fight this battle in just the way in

which I had expected that he, with Labienus to advise him, would plan to do. The plain of the Enipeus was excellent ground for cavalry and it was clear that they would make the fullest possible use of this arm in which they had so great a superiority over me. So I was not surprised when I saw that their right wing, with no cavalry support, was resting on the river Enipeus and that all their light troops (they had excellent slingers) and all their cavalry were concentrated on their left, where there was plenty of room to maneuver. The intention, obviously, was to throw my right wing into disorder, encircle it and then attack my infantry from the rear. It was not a bad plan and, if I had not taken the correct action, it might have proved successful. Later, of course, it was said that Pompey had been more or less forced against his will to take the risk of fighting at all. He himself, so the story went, had been most averse from venturing everything on one battle; but he had been stung to action by the taunts of the politicians who surrounded him, who were anxious to get back to Rome and who claimed that it was only Pompey's passion for retaining supreme power that was preventing him from quickly and easily making an end of me.

This story is merely a part of the sentimental propaganda of what are still the remains of Pompey's party. For some reason or other these people like to believe that their great leader found, for no fault of his own, his judgment warped at a critical moment. They would be doing Pompey more honor if they really accepted the fact of his greatness. He was, of course, far too good a commander ever to have allowed his mind to be made up for him by people who had no knowledge of war whatever. It is possible that he may have paid rather too much attention to Labienus who seems to have imagined that my army had suffered an irreparable loss of efficiency simply through his own defection from it; but I believe myself that Pompey, having weighed all proper considerations, had come to the conclusion that he had every reason to expect a complete and a fairly easy victory. Indeed, as I was told later, he had actually suggested at a council of war, which took place just before the battle, that he hardly expected his infantry to be engaged at all. The cavalry thrust would be so effective that my whole army would be on the run before they were within javelin range of his own men. At this council of war Labienus had once again assured his hearers that the flower of my army had already gone — wasted by disease, exhausted by hardship, or killed at Dyrrhachium. He vowed that he would never return to camp unless victorious. Had he, I wonder, forgotten that a rather similar oath was taken by the leaders of Vercingetorix's cavalry before Alesia?

But as I rode out on that early morning to watch the movement of Pompey's legions and squadrons in the plain, I had no time to speculate on why or with what assurance he was offering battle. I knew that I should be outnumbered. Pompey would have some forty-five thousand men in his line of infantry and I, to oppose him, would have twenty-two thousand. But the disproportion between the cavalry forces was much greater. Pompey had seven thousand cavalry with great numbers of slingers and archers in support. To meet this mass of men I had only a few more than a thousand cavalry, mostly Gauls and Germans. Once again, it seemed to me, I was having to improvise: it was Pompey rather than I who was dictating the terms on which the battle would be fought; and if I could not meet and throw back his seven thousand cavalry, I might be defeated. Yet I knew that battles are often won by improvisations and that a successful defense can be turned into an overwhelming attack.

Curiously, though at the time I was thinking of improvisations, this was one of the few battles in which I have taken part when everything went almost exactly as I had foreseen or hoped. It will no doubt rank as a textbook battle, partly because of the rapidity and completeness of the decision, partly because the obvious factors which led to victory or defeat are easy to memorize. It was also, of course, in view of the issues involved and the numbers of men engaged, the greatest battle that had ever been fought between Romans. I should like to be able to claim that, in winning it, I showed some remarkable skill or forethought — something of the quality which marked all the victories of Hannibal or Alexander or, in our own days, that almost forgotten man, Quintus Sertorius. But I can make no such claim. Once again it was Pompey, not I, who had the initiative. I did not lure Pompey into making what turned out to be a mistake. I merely met an obvious threat by methods which I had tried before against the Gauls. Otherwise the battle was fought along absolutely orthodox lines. It was won, like most of my battles, by my soldiers. From the beginning I fancied that it would be won, and my soldiers shared my confidence.

I had just about the right time to make the necessary provision. The legions were, of course, drawn up in three lines and I instructed the third line not to go into action until they received the order. All my cavalry was on the right. I could not expect them to do more than hold up for a few moments the overwhelming attack of Pompey's cavalry, but I had also, behind my right wing, a special force of six cohorts which I had withdrawn from the third line of the infantry. I told the men in this force that the result of the battle would depend entirely on how they conducted themselves. Their task was to charge forward on foot, at the right moment, against the whole weight of Pompey's seven thousand cavalry. They were not to hurl their javelins, but to use them as stabbing spears. I told them to stab upwards at the faces of the riders and I encouraged them to believe that these riders, young men from the best Roman families, were more familiar with dancing schools than with battlefields and would shrink like girls from cold steel directed by strong arms. Some of the Pompeian cavalry would certainly fall under this definition; but I was well aware that he also had some excellent cavalry from Gaul and Cappadocia; and I knew that it was not accurate to suggest that all Roman aristocrats are cowards; I could myself, indeed, serve as an example for the contradiction of such a statement. What I did know, however, and what Pompey and Labienus seemed to have forgotten, was that no cavalry force on earth, unless it is in absolutely overwhelming numbers, can make much of an impression on resolute, well-trained and well-armed infantry. I did not consider that the numbers commanded by Labienus were overwhelming. It seemed to me that, if they could be routed by my six cohorts (cav-

alry, when they are on the run, very soon disappear from a battlefield), then Pompey's left wing would be exposed to just the
same danger of encirclement as that with which he was threatening my right. All along the rest of the line I imagined that my men
would give a good account of themselves.

There was a strange solemnity about these moments that preceded what everyone knew was the decisive encounter. On both
sides the traditional sacrifices of animals were made and in the
formality of these proceedings there seemed to be something almost frightening. We had had no time for such ceremonies when
we engaged the Nervii, but now there was time enough as we
prepared to fight our brother Romans. Some of us experienced the
uncanny feeling that we were looking, not at the enemy, but at
ourselves in a mirror; for in front of us were no painted Britons or
monstrous Gallic or Germanic headdresses; instead we saw the
arms, shields and standards of Roman legionaries. I felt once more
a cold anger in my heart against those relentless enemies of mine
who, by threatening my life and honor, had brought themselves
and me and my men to this dreadful moment of decision. But there
was no time, or need, now to reflect upon the causes of the event
which was certain to take place. My head and indeed it seemed
my whole body became filled with that alacrity, eagerness and re-
strained force which I have often known before and during battle.

I had decided upon the battle cry that would soon ring out from
more than twenty thousand throats. It was *"Venus Victrix,"* for
Venus is, if one is to believe in the gods at all, the guardian of my
family. I was aware that her name had been used in battle orders
both by Sulla and by Pompey himself. Now she and the army of
Gaul would play the parts that I required. I rode forward and
went along the lines of the Tenth legion which, as usual, held the
right wing. At any second now the trumpeters would sound the
charge, for Pompey's cavalry were already moving forward and I
was not going to delay the general engagement until they had
deployed their squadrons to their satisfaction. As I looked at the
men's faces I could see that they shared the eagerness I felt myself. Among them I noticed the veteran Gaius Crastinus. He had

been senior centurion of the Tenth when, last year, he had left the service. He had soon re-enlisted and he was now calling out to his old comrades and to the younger men, all of whom knew of him and of his reputation as one of the best and bravest soldiers in the army. I shouted out to him: "Well, Gaius Crastinus, what do you think of our chances?" and he shouted back: "We shall win, Caesar, and win gloriously. And by the end of the day you will be proud of me, whether I am alive or dead." I loved the man as I heard his words. At that moment the trumpets sounded and Gaius Crastinus went forward, leading the attack of the right wing.

Chapter 8

Victory and Pursuit

IN SOME BATTLES IT IS IMPOSSIBLE, UNTIL THE WHOLE AFFAIR IS almost over, for even the commander in chief to know much about what is happening. But at Pharsalus it was easy for me to observe the shape of the action, though there were certainly anxious periods during which I was doubtful of the result. First, as I watched our line charge forward, I was surprised to see that Pompey's line was standing still and not charging to meet us. I am still not quite certain why Pompey gave this most unusual order. It may be that he had expected his cavalry to be in action and to have won the battle before his legionaries were engaged; or he may have thought that our men, having had to cover double the expected distance in their charge, would be exhausted by the time they had thrown their javelins and begun to fight hand to hand. In any case I consider that here Pompey made a mistake. The moment of entering battle is a dreadful moment and most men, if they had the leisure or the ability to think rationally about it, would hesitate to expose themselves lightly to death, to pain, to ugly wounds and mutilation. Indeed some of the followers of Epicurus have made out a very good case for pacificism. Yet, if one is to enter battle at all, one will be safer and more successful if these rational arguments do not occur to one. What is needed is a particular elation of the spirit which seems to provide a man with unusual physical courage and

abnormal powers of endurance and resolution. And the spirit becomes elated by a number of means which are artificial. Indeed
the whole discipline and splendor of an army is designed to prepare the ground for the right sort of elation at the right moment;
and, when the moment comes, we and all races known to history
employ other artificial stimuli. In our army trumpets sound in all
parts of the field; barbarians use drums and various percussion instruments. Then there is the effect of the battle cry shouted out at
the same moment by every soldier. I could feel the effect of it myself as I listened to the great roar of *"Venus Victrix"* shouted along
the line. And it is important also, if possible, to enter battle at the
double. The very movements of the limbs and the sensation of inevitability help to promote the spirit required in a soldier.

So I consider that Pompey's order to his men to stand firm and
meet our charge without advancing was a mistaken order. If his
idea was that our men would be tired out or have lost order by the
time they had covered the distance between the two armies, he
had not made allowance for my soldiers' training and experience.
I saw from my position the whole line run forward, with Gaius
Crastinus a little in advance of the rest. Then, when they saw that
the enemy were not advancing to meet them, they slowed up and
halted. After a moment or two of rest, they shouted the battle cry
once more and surged forward. I could still just see the figure of
Crastinus. The javelins were thrown and Pompey's soldiers stood
up well to the volley before hurling their own javelins. Then the
two lines merged with each other, sword against sword. I heard
later of how Gaius Crastinus had been the first man in action, how
he had cut his way through Pompey's first line, killing three men
and how he had died still fighting, stopped suddenly by a sword
thrust in the face. If anyone knows anything after death, Crastinus
will know of my pride in him and of my gratitude.

As soon as the main lines had joined in battle I gave all my attention to what was taking place on my right. Pompey's great cavalry corps had taken, I imagine, rather longer than he had wished
to make themselves ready for the attack, but now they were coming
into action. Behind them were great numbers of slingers and archers

— troops of excellent quality, as we had discovered at Dyrrha-chium. It was intended, no doubt, that while the victorious cavalry were attacking us from the rear, these light troops would keep up a steady fire on our unprotected flank. And indeed the cavalry looked as though they were made for victory. The standards, the ban-ners, the rich colors, the gleaming armor, were magnificent. Was it the magnificence of a parade ground or of men ready to fight to the last? I watched the whole force move forward. It was, I as-sumed, under the command of Labienus, who hated me. Every-thing was under control. Labienus would wait until he considered himself to be in an absolutely commanding position before he gave the order for the great charge which was to sweep up and destroy the Tenth Legion, his old comrades, and myself. I gave the order for my own cavalry to charge, rather with the idea of interrupting Labienus's preparations than for any other reason. They had been instructed to fall back when they found the opposition too much for them and then to hold themselves in readiness for fur-ther action. As I had anticipated they soon retired, keeping reason-ably good order, and now the whole mass of enemy cavalry began to take up their position for what was intended to be the de-cisive charge.

I gave my six infantry cohorts the order for which they had been waiting. Up to this time they had been screened behind the main battle line and my own cavalry, so that their sudden charge was unexpected by the enemy. They charged with the greatest im-petuosity and they came into action at what was, for us, exactly the right moment. Pompey's cavalry were waiting for their final orders and had made no provision for the attack which they now had to meet. The predictions which I had made to my men before the battle were fulfilled in a way which far exceeded my expecta-tions. Pompey's enormous cavalry force made virtually no resist-ance at all. In what seemed a matter of moments the whole mass of them had turned about and were galloping off into the dis-stance towards the hills. The whole thing was so sudden that Pompey himself, watching it, might well have believed that he had been the victim of treachery. He must have realized immediately that the battle was lost. Our men, once the cavalry were out of the way, fell upon the slingers and archers, killing nearly all of them. They had now outflanked Pompey's main battle line and began to attack it from the rear. Up to this time the infantry fighting had been stubborn. Indeed Pompey's soldiers had been standing up to us better than I had expected. But I now ordered my third line into action. Pompey's line, attacked by fresh troops from in front and by another force from the rear, broke and the battle was decided. The fugitives streamed back in disorder to the shelter of their camp, pursued on the way by my inconsiderable body of cavalry. Their own cavalry had disappeared from sight.

It was noon. The sun's heat was intense and the men were very tired; but I decided that we must not give the enemy time to reorganize themselves behind their fortifications and, in order to put a final end to the war, I was most anxious to secure the person of Pompey himself. So I at once led an assault on the camp. There was a vigorous resistance for a short time, but in the end we broke through the defenses. However the enemy, though thoroughly defeated, were not utterly routed. They still listened to the orders of their officers and centurions and so the majority of them were able to withdraw in good order to the high ground behind the camp. We followed them up for a little way and in the course of this pursuit my old enemy Domitius Ahenobarbus was killed. He was a cruel and cowardly man. I had spared his life once at Corfinium and should not like to have had to spare it again.

We remained in Pompey's camp for a time long enough to satisfy our hunger and thirst; and there was plenty of opportunity to do so. Everything we saw indicated that the enemy had been perfectly confident of victory and had for long been living in a state of luxury which was most unbecoming in an army that was about to do battle with my veteran legions. The tents of Lentulus and of other nobles were more like summer houses than accommodation for soldiers. They were shaded with ivy and floored with carefully cut green turf. Tables were laid and much silver plate was to be seen. The wine was ready to be served cool and the cooks had almost completed their preparations for what was designed as a banquet to celebrate victory. These, I reflected, were the men who were in the habit of accusing both me and my men of effeminacy.

I was particularly anxious to find out what had happened to Pompey himself and on this subject the information I received at this point from prisoners turned out to be correct. When the battle began Pompey had been with the troops facing me and the Tenth Legion. As soon as he had seen his cavalry routed and his line being attacked from the rear, he had ridden back to his camp and, after having given a few orders for its defense, had sat down in his tent like a man utterly dumfounded and appearing not even to hear the words that were addressed to him. I could imagine his feelings. Probably he would have preferred to die fighting with his men; but how could he be certain that he would die? If he had been taken prisoner, I should of course have spared his life, but he was too proud a man to consent to owe his life to me. This battle, he must have known, was lost and to him the idea of defeat was something almost inconceivable. So, while he was sitting in his tent, he felt, I should imagine, astonishment and horror rather than despair. He was aroused from his state of lethargy by the sounds of our assault. Then he rose to his feet. All he said was: "What! into my camp too?" He left behind him his general's cloak and all other badges of office, took a fast horse and, with a small company of friends, galloped out of camp on the road to Larissa. I did not imagine that he would ever make peace, and so I sent a detachment of cavalry after him and meanwhile prepared to deal with what was left of his army.

By now it was the middle of the afternoon and my men were not unnaturally looking forward to some rest; but I and other commanding officers whom they knew well went about among them and told them that they must leave the plunder for the time being and make one more effort that day so that their victory would be complete. I pointed out that the enemy would be in a very much worse state of exhaustion than they were. They saw that my purpose was the correct one and co-operated magnificently, setting to work to build entrenchments all round the hill where the enemy had taken up position, so that they would be cut off from water.

Soon the enemy realized their danger and began to move along the ridge in the direction of Larissa and the river Enipeus. I took four legions with me and marched after them for six miles, keeping them in view all the time. It was now nearly dark and they halted on a slope above the river. My men were in a state of extreme exhaustion, yet still they did what was required of them. In the failing light they built a line of earthworks covering the descent to the river and so making it impossible for the enemy to reach the water. Before midnight a deputation from the enemy arrived to discuss terms of surrender.

Next day, according to my instructions, the whole of the defeated army (except for some senators who had escaped during the night) came down from the hill and handed in their arms. The men knelt on the ground with their hands outstretched, begging me to spare their lives. I told them to rise to their feet; they were all pardoned; and I ordered my own centurions and officers to see to it that my men did them no harm and allowed them to retain possession of their property.

In this battle of Pharsalus we only lost about two hundred legionaries, but at the beginning the fighting was very fierce and thirty of my centurions, all excellent soldiers, were killed. Fifteen thousand of the enemy were killed in the battle and at the storming of the camp. Twenty-four thousand were taken prisoner. We captured a hundred and eighty standards and nine eagles.

According to my information, most of the important enemy leaders — Labienus, Scipio, Afranius and the others — had fled in the direction of Dyrrhachium, where Cato had been left in command of the naval base. They had plenty of shipping at their disposal and it would be easy for those of them who refused to submit to sail to Africa. I had nothing to gain at the moment by trying to pursue them and in any case I considered that the best way of securing peace was to make sure of the person of Pompey himself, who, so I was told, had passed rapidly through Larissa and gone on eastward by sea to Amphipolis. I imagined that he would continue his voyage to Mytilene, where his wife was; after that I could not be at all sure of his intentions. He might go to Syria, which used to know him as the greatest conqueror since Alexander, or to Egypt, where the royal children had reason to be grateful both to him and to me, or to Africa, where he had an army already in existence and could also depend upon the support of King Juba. Whatever his intentions might be, it seemed to me that I should follow him up as closely as possible. For the time being I had no ships and so I should have to go by land. I planned to hurry ahead with a cavalry escort, traveling as far each day as our horses would carry us. I had to give the legionaries a little rest, but in a day or two one legion was to march after me towards the Hellespont.

There was much to do in Larissa before I left. I had little sleep and only an hour or two of relaxation. These hours came to me by a happy accident. For ever since the battle I had been making inquiries with regard to one of my enemies whom I wished particularly to preserve, and now, at Larissa, I received a visit from the man himself. I was happy to be able to tell him that he had nothing to fear and I was happy in conversing with him privately about his own ideas and his own future. I have always been fond of Marcus Brutus ever since the time I knew him as a small boy, when my long and agreeable love affair with his mother Servilia was just beginning. I remembered well the small boy, who, I think, had loved me when I was an almost unknown young man; and I remembered watching the boy grow up and doing what I could to counterbalance what I regarded as the pernicious influence of his uncle Cato, who was as unlike Servilia as anyone could be. Cato succeeded in making the young man somewhat uncouth in appearance and somewhat priggish in manner, but he could not alter the real sweetness of the boy's character or pervert his excellent intelligence. I had wanted Brutus to marry my daughter Julia, and Servilia had been enthusiastic about making the match. Indeed she was vexed when, just before my first consulship, I told her that for my daughter I had much more splendid prospects. She was going to marry Pompey himself, and on this alliance the whole of my fortune would be based. Servilia saw the force of my arguments, but was still distressed. I bought her the most expensive piece of jewelry that has ever been purchased in Rome. Since that time I had not seen Brutus at all. I offered him a post in Gaul, but he declined it. He was, I heard from Servilia, a studious young man, still too much influenced by his uncle Cato, but full of good qualities and full of ability. From a distance I always took an interest in him and in fact there have been times, both when I was in Gaul and more recently, when I have actually thought of making him my heir.

One wishes somehow (and the wish is not derived from vanity) to leave behind one not only an achievement but also a person, a son or at least a trusted colleague, who can guarantee and perhaps improve upon this achievement. I have thought from time to time of various candidates who might become, as it were, my successors; but I have not been wholly happy in making any choice. So far as my own relatives are concerned, I hoped that my sister Julia's grandson, Quintus Pedius, might show the qualities I required. But, though Pedius is a fairly competent soldier, he has no grasp of politics at all. I have thought too of some of my best generals — of Decimus Brutus and of Antony. But Decimus Brutus lacks imagination and Antony, though absolutely loyal, lacks stability. I have therefore bequeathed my name and most of my property to young Octavius. His father was undistinguished, but my niece Atia brought him up well and in the last few years I have become quite convinced of his abilities. He is extremely intelligent, extremely ambitious, public-spirited and absolutely ruthless. And, if I were to die suddenly or even be assassinated, this last quality would certainly be required.

It is a quality which Brutus does not possess. Brutus was made to function in a period of order. I can imagine him certainly, in the name of some principle or other, taking a violent course of action; but he would shrink from pursuing efficiently a policy of violence, even if it were shown to him that only by such means could he safeguard his precious principle. Not that this problem is an easy one. It is important to preserve a distinction between men and monsters. I myself have at times acted with deliberate savagery in Gaul, but I deplore the necessity for such action and there are indeed some actions which I do not think I could ever bring myself to take. I could not, whatever might be gained from it, betray a friend or be a party to any treacherous act of assassination. Curiously enough I think that it is just possible that Brutus might, of course from the highest motives, be guilty, very occasionally, of acts from which his moral nature would rebel. This is not unusual in people who derive their notions of morality largely from the study of books. As for me, I am merciful and I would refuse to betray a friend for the simple reason that I am Caesar; Brutus and his uncle Cato tend rather to seek precedents or pretexts for their humanity. And young Octavius, I think, would stop at nothing in order to make himself powerful; yet, in seeking power for himself, he would be genuinely and sincerely pursuing my own great aim — the aim of order and efficiency and civilization. He would never dissipate power, as Antony would; nor would he turn his back upon it in a kind of arrogance, as was done by Cato and might be done by Brutus.

These men tend to believe that they are themselves greater than the power they exercise. It is a dangerous and immodest belief. And those egotists, like myself and Octavius, whose thoughts are chiefly occupied by the affairs of others are perhaps more valuable to society than those other egotists, more holy in appearance, who concentrate upon their own natures or upon some abstract conception of right and wrong. Personally I differ from Octavius in being more versatile and less cruel; but I differ still more from the others whose best intentions are thwarted by the fact that they have, through tradition or pedantry, failed to understand the nature of our life and times — who are out of touch with the physical reality of the men and women who form a world which is inevitably in course of change and who, whether one loves, tolerates or despises them, must be everything to us, since there is nothing else in existence except rocks, vegetation, birds and beasts.

These reflections occur to me now. But at the time when I met young Brutus at Larissa after my victory at Pharsalus, I still hoped that, after I had forgiven him for the part he had taken in the war against me, he might prove himself one who would be capable of understanding my intentions and whom I could help to achieve and to exercise power. And indeed since then I have helped him much. He is now one of the leading people in the state and I imagine that he is grateful to me. But I am certain that he does not understand me. If he were not bound to me by such ties of gratitude, he would probably be my enemy.

At Larissa he behaved with dignity and even charm. For at least an hour I walked with him along a path through a grove of olive trees. It was the first time for many months that I had been, even for a short interval, away from the army and the camp. I spoke to him (though I had not seen him for so long) in a friendly manner, with no kind of formality, and he responded gracefully to my attitude. When I asked him why it was that he had pre-ferred Pompey, who had killed his father, to me, who had always been his friend, he endeavored to give me a sincere answer, without falling back upon the political and moral platitudes and hypoc-risies which might have been employed by his uncle Cato. He told me that he had always disliked Pompey and had even from his early years felt curiously attracted by me. Nevertheless it had appeared to him that the fabric of society, on which everything de-pended, was being upheld by Pompey and the senate and was be-ing threatened by my activities. Closer contact with Pompey, Ahen-obarbus, Scipio and the rest had somewhat disillusioned him. He had observed that these men cared for nothing whatever except their personal ambitions, their reputations and what they imagined to be their right to revenge. He was now ready to admire me rather extravagantly only because I had no desire for reprisals and in-deed took the greatest pleasure in sparing my enemies. I found too that he was genuinely impressed with some of the projects I had for the future — colonies, economic reform, just administration, draining of marshes, reconstruction of the city, improvements in communication — all the thousand things which claim my attention every day.

Often, as I spoke to him, he became almost enthusiastic. But often too a cloud would seem to descend upon his face. "There is something," he said, "which I call 'liberty,' and which I admit is difficult to define. Will any amount of efficiency and happiness make up for the loss of it?" At this moment I felt much affection for the young man. He was expressing himself in a doctrinaire manner; for this "liberty" in our days, if understood to mean the unrestricted and irresponsible play of established forces in Roman politics, had led not only to inefficiency and unhappiness but to a state of affairs where, through insecurity, only rich men and soldiers were capable of exercising any kind of liberty of choice in ordinary affairs. His "liberty" in fact could be plausibly described as a kind of slavery. Yet still what he said was true. There is a kind of liberty, dependent in part on political institutions, which is so valuable that, without it, life would not be worth living.

I thought, while we were walking in the olive grove at Larissa, that I might have convinced Brutus that I understood the meaning of this kind of liberty at least as well as he did and that our differences might be made to appear merely verbal. But now I am not so sure. He is offended by the divine honors which have recently been accorded to me, and he is appalled at the thought that I might adopt the title of "King," though he knows perfectly well that I lay no claims to the only attribute of divinity which matters, immortality, and that if I did allow myself to be called "King," it would be for reasons of state rather than because of any wish to behave tyrannically. Neverthelesss I still love him and shall do my best to see that his great qualities are given ample scope. This, indeed, is my idea of freedom.

At Larissa I parted from him on very friendly terms. I knew that he would not take up arms against me again and both he and I hoped that no more battles would be fought between Romans, though we knew that Labienus, Afranius and probably Scipio would attempt to build up new forces if they were given the time and the opportunity to do so. They would naturally rally again under Pompey if that were possible; so that it was essential (and Brutus could understand this point) that I should as soon as possible either secure Pompey's person or reach with him some understanding which would amount to his surrender. So, after the briefest possible delay, I set out with a strong force of cavalry in his pursuit.

Chapter 9

Arrival in Egypt

WE RODE HARD FOR THE DISTANCE OF NEARLY TWO HUNDRED
miles between Larissa and Amphipolis. Pompey, traveling by sea,
had a long start, but he would be forced to halt somewhere in
order to take with him what money and supplies he could still
raise in the East. At Amphipolis I found that he had gone on to
Mytilene where he was detained by bad weather. I also began to
discover how great had been the effects of the victory at Pharsalus. All the Greek mainland and most of Asia had now definitely taken my side. The people of Mytilene, where Pompey's
wife and younger son were staying, had welcomed him in his
fallen state, as was right and proper, but had welcomed him rather
as a defeated friend than as one for whom they were prepared to
exert themselves again. At Rhodes, from which had come some
of Pompey's best ships, the two ex-consuls, Publius and Lucius
Lentulus, both bitter enemies of mine, had been refused permission to enter the harbor, and I soon received from the Rhodian
government offers to supply me with the ships which I so badly
needed. Meanwhile I went on to Asia. One legion was following
me; others were being retained for service in Greece; others were
to return to Italy under the command of Antony. We crossed the
Hellespont at Sestos, making use of whatever boats could be most
quickly collected.

At Troy I stayed long enough to examine the antiquities and to erect an altar near the place where, according to tradition, Hector lies buried. Little indeed is left of the ramparts and towers of which Homer tells us; but still the place seems haunted by famous ghosts. Some of my officers, looking at the site of the city, were inclined to laugh at Homer and at his stories of the ten years' siege and of the enormous battles in which one man — Hector, Patroclus or Achilles — is often represented, in the heroic style, as possessing in himself the striking power of at least one legion. I told them how misplaced, and indeed barbarous, their laughter was. It was perfectly true that for a modern army with superior sea power the investment and capture of Troy presented few difficulties. Our own performances at Avaricum and Alesia were on a far greater scale. It was also true that all the Homeric heroes together could be disposed of quite easily by one Roman cohort. Yet if a time ever comes when men will have ceased to be moved by the truth of Homer, men will have become some different species. Homer sees greatness and weakness together, honor and dishonor, the grandeur and the appalling wastage of warfare. So we weep both for Achilles and for Hector. We exult in the freedom which they, as exceptional, yet human, beings, possess; and we are humbled by the thought that even they, in all their strength and brilliance, can only escape for a short time, perhaps only for some moments, the pressure and manipulation of necessity.

I myself had reasons of a more personal nature to be moved by the sight of Troy, since it was from here, according to tradition, that my own family and the race of Romans sprang. Somewhere in those wooded hills beyond the city the goddess Venus, so the story goes, met in love with Trojan Anchises and bore the hero Aeneas, who, by the will of the gods, escaped from the burning city and took with him to Italy his little son Iulus, from whom our family takes its name. I had already conceived the idea that it would be fitting for me, once peace had been re-established, to build another Troy on the old site and to colonize it with citizens from Rome. This project is very dear to my heart, though in the last few years I have thought of other sites — Alexandria or Byzantium

— which could also be, under certain circumstances, admirably adapted for centers of government and administration. As it was, during this visit after Pharsalus, I wept at the tomb of Achilles and I also had made for me by my secretaries a number of maps, plans and notes which I have found useful recently in discussing arrangements for the future colony.

Soon, with the aid of personal friends and of Greek and Asiatic states who wished to show their loyalty to me, I had nearly all the shipping which I required. I was still not sure of Pompey's movements, but I heard that the citizens of Antioch had given a very cold reception to his envoys and I assumed that he would abandon any plan he may have formed for basing himself on Syria. I had not been in Asia for more than a week when I heard that he had been seen in Cyprus. He had got together a considerable fleet and had with him, in addition to a few regular troops, about two thousand armed slaves. It seemed to me likely that he was making for Egypt and, whether Egypt or Africa was his destination, I decided to go to Egypt first. By this time I had withdrawn another legion from Greece and so had two legions with me. Both were very much below strength, so that altogether I had only just over three thousand men; but I had eight hundred cavalry, ten Rhodian warships and a few others from Asia. It was a small enough force, but, considering the prestige won by my victory at Pharsalus, I thought it would be sufficient. With this force I sailed for Alexandria.

I was, of course, reasonably well informed about the situation in Egypt where the existing regime was indebted both to Pompey and to myself. I have always been interested in Egypt, and most of the somewhat revolutionary plots which in my early youth I made with Crassus were designed in order to give us control of that country. Pompey too had clearly seen the importance of the place and in the year after my first consulship had done what he could to support the claims of the exiled King Ptolemy, who had come to Rome in order to try to get help against his rebellious subjects. At this time the senate were afraid both of Pompey and of any further foreign entanglements. Ptolemy, though he spent much money on bribery and, it would seem, succeeded in having great numbers of his Egyptian enemies who came to Italy to oppose him, assassinated, achieved no solid success until three years had passed and, as a result of our meetings at Luca, Pompey and Crassus became, with my support, consuls. In this year Ptolemy was restored to his throne by a Roman army from Syria under the command of Gabinius, who at that time was a friend both of Pompey and of myself. I used also to be, I remember, very devoted to his wife.

Before sailing for Alexandria I had just heard, with deep sorrow, that Gabinius, who had taken my side in the civil war, had died of illness, after having made an unsuccessful attempt to bring troops into Greece by the land route. He used to be a great drunkard, as Antony is now, but he was a good soldier and a loyal friend. I had heard both from him and from Antony, who was on his staff during the Egyptian adventure before he joined me in Gaul, enthusiastic accounts of the wealth and splendor of Alexandria. Gabinius had enriched himself enormously as a result of his expedition from Syria, but had suffered for it later in the Roman courts and, not receiving the support from Pompey which he had expected, had been in exile until I, after driving Pompey from Italy, recalled him. Even Antony, as a junior officer, had made enough money to pay off a few of his debts. I myself was owed a very large sum for the part I had played in securing Ptolemy on his throne but when he died I had voluntarily given up my claim to nearly half of this debt. I wished to perform an act of bounty to the new sovereigns of Egypt who were, in accordance with the late King's will, his eldest son, Ptolemy, who was still a boy, and his eldest daughter, Cleopatra, who was a young woman of about seventeen.

In accordance with ancient Egyptian tradition, the brother and sister were married. This is one of many examples of the way in which the Greek rulers of Egypt have, apparently without difficulty, adapted themselves to the customs of the natives. Normally a Greek or a Roman views incest with a peculiar horror. Among the upper classes it is practiced only by rather eccentric libertines, like Clodius, and even then is not openly admitted. Yet in Egypt the authority of religion and the pressure of public opinion seem sufficient to counterbalance what is, among us, a very real, if possibly an irrational, prejudice. These unions between brother and sister, however, appear to be at least as precarious emotionally as are most ordinary marriages. So, in this instance, within three years of the late King's death a civil war had broken out between young Ptolemy and Cleopatra. Most of the influential courtiers had seen that they could best keep power in their own hands by supporting the boy King against his sister who, by all accounts, had a strong will of her own. She had raised an army and was prepared to fight for the throne; but Alexandria was in the hands of Ptolemy and his advisers.

This was all I knew when I set out from Asia to Egypt in pursuit of Pompey. If, as I expected, Pompey had taken refuge in that country, I hoped that, with my small but superior forces and with the aid of the prestige of my victory, I should be able to induce the Egyptians to surrender him. I did not expect what I found, nor did I have any intimation of it. I felt, indeed, some elation, as I always do when confronted with something new and unfamiliar, at the prospect of my visit to the city which contained the tomb of great Alexander and also the finest library in the world. My mind was alert and I was ready for almost anything except what happened.

We reached Alexandria on a still bright morning. It was the time of the late summer when the winds blow always from the north, so that our voyage had been easy. Even from the sea one could admire the splendor of the city — the white palaces, the colored flags and awnings, the villas on the shore, the famous lighthouse and the beautiful curves of coast and harbors. As we drew near, a galley put out from the shore to meet us, carrying, as I had hoped, a deputation of prominent court officials to bid me welcome. The deputation was led by a Greek called Theodotus, a professional lecturer who had made something of a name for himself and was now among the inner circle of the King's advisers. As he greeted me, he smiled with what seemed to me a kind of indecent pride;

then one of his attendants brought forward a bundle wrapped in cloth and proceeded to undo it. I still had no notion of what to expect until the last moment, when the wrappings were removed and I saw lying on the deck of my ship the severed and embalmed head of Pompey. Theodotus was still talking to me. I think that he was attempting to claim some credit for himself in the organization of the assassination of my enemy; but I scarcely listened to his words, though I mechanically stretched out my hand to receive Pompey's signet ring which he was offering me as additional, if unnecessary, evidence for the success of his treachery.

For some moments I could only gaze with horror at the bodiless head and at the face which I had known so well — the face of my friend, my son-in-law, my enemy, my fellow citizen. It seemed that I had to tear my eyes away from this face. Then I looked at the well-known signet ring on which was engraved a lion holding a sword between his paws. Then I burst into tears and for some time was unable to speak. I have been asked since to explain these tears, and there are some, I know, who will regard them as hypo-critical. For undoubtedly (as Theodotus with all his rhetorical skill was insisting) it was to my advantage that Pompey should be dead and that I myself should be entirely freed from all guilt in the mat-ter. Yet still my tears were sincere. I wept at the horror, the pathos, the incongruity of the thing. How could Pompey the Great be reduced to a severed head lying on wood? I wept for the misery and disorder of our world in which, so far as the individual is concerned, nothing whatever is certain. And as I heard the full story of the assassination, my alarm and pity increased. It seemed to me almost unbearable to imagine that the fate of Pompey should have been settled by a committee of eunuchs, mercenaries and rhetoricians and that he should have been struck down by a Roman soldier who had once served under him as a centurion. Yet so it had happened. The King's advisers had decided that for them Pompey was safer dead. (Theodotus was proud of his epigram, "Dead men don't bite.") Romans in the service of the Egyptian army had been sent to meet their old commander, and one of them had stabbed him from behind. The day was the day before Pompey's birthday and it was an anniversary of the time, exactly thirteen years previously, when, dressed in the costume of Alexander the Great, he had entered Rome in the triumph granted him for the greatest conquests ever made by a Roman. How he must have wished that he had died then, with his glory unimpaired!

My immediate impulse was to arrest Theodotus and have him put to death together with all the rest of the King's counselors who were in his complicity. I knew how wholly insincere was the Egyptian claim that they had murdered Pompey because they were friendly to me. In fact they were frightened of both of us and, if they could have killed me safely, they would have done so. But I was not strong enough to take the measures which I wished to take. The Egyptians had an army very greatly superior to mine in numbers and by no means negligible in its fighting capacity. In it were many Romans who had originally come to the country with Gabinius and had settled down there. They and the rest — highwaymen, retired pirates, runaway slaves from Syria, Greece or Cilicia — had little idea of Roman discipline; but they were used to power; they could make and unmake Kings; and they had a number of good officers. I could not meet this army in the field; yet it seemed to me important that I should assert the authority of Rome and look after my own interests. The late King had, in his will, begged the Roman government to see to it that his wishes were carried out; and the Egyptians still owed me personally a great deal of money, which I now required for the payment of my troops. I had both legal and personal reasons for attempting to arbitrate, in a peaceful way, in the quarrel between Cleopatra and her brother Ptolemy. I therefore decided to go ashore with my army and to take up my quarters in the royal palace.

At the very moment of landing I was able to see that I had perhaps relied too much on the prestige of my victory and that I was now endangering my army and myself. There was no doubt that we were entering a hostile city. I came ashore with the fasces, the rightful sign of a Roman consul, carried in front of me; and at the sight of this piece of normal ceremony there was an immediate outbreak of violence from the great crowd of Alexandrians on the

quayside, who considered that my appearance in state was a deliberate insult to their King and threat to their independence.
Some lives were lost while we were re-establishing order.

Next I found the utmost difficulty in negotiating with the boy
King's chief minister, the eunuch Pothinus. There was no trust
whatever between the two of us. I knew that he would be glad, if
he could, to have me assassinated, and I suspect that he was quite
aware that I, if I could find any convenient excuse, would not hesitate to get rid of him and the rest of Pompey's murderers. Out-
wardly, of course, the eunuch was friendly. His main wish was for
me to leave Alexandria and to allow him and his friend, the army
leader Achillas, to secure their hold on the country in the name of
the young King. Had I been prepared to do so, I think he might
even have paid the debt that was owed to me. But I was determined to assert the authority of Rome and insisted that both
Ptolemy and Cleopatra should appear before me, so that I might at
least attempt to arrange some settlement of their differences in accordance with the terms of their father's will. Pothinus illegally and
insolently protested. According to him my offer of arbitration was
an insult to the royal family and a threat to the independence of
Egypt. He strongly advised me to attend to the more important
business I had waiting for me in Italy and in Africa, and he promised that, if I would only do this and return to Egypt later, he
would see to it that the money owed to me would be collected
and the quarrel between the royal children decently settled. I told
him that in making my plans I did not need the advice of an
Egyptian; also that I wanted the money at once. Pothinus arranged
matters so that it should appear that the state treasury was empty,
but he did send for young Ptolemy, who was with his army in
Pelusium. He professed that he could do nothing about Cleopatra.
She had raised an army in Syria and was, according to him, making war against her own country. He could not guarantee her
safety if she came to Alexandria.

Meanwhile events every day showed me that I was in a difficult and possibly dangerous situation. If my soldiers went about

in the city in small numbers they were almost invariably attacked by bands of Alexandrians who would shout out patriotic slogans and usually turned out to be in the pay of Pothinus. I at once sent a message to my general in Asia, Domitius Calvinus, ordering him to bring two legions to Alexandria without delay; but I knew that it would take some time for these reinforcements to arrive. I determined to do nothing in the meantime that could precipitate a crisis. I behaved with the greatest courtesy to the young King when he arrived at his palace; I attended lectures on philosophy in the Alexandrian schools; I visited the sights and showed myself frequently in public. However my task as arbitrator between the two monarchs was rendered impossible by the absence of Cleopatra; there was not a single Egyptian whom I could trust; and from the information I received it appeared that Achillas, the commander of the King's army, was moving detachments of his troops from Pelusium in the direction of Alexandria. I had already seen that the great structure of the royal palace together with some of the adjoining buildings could be made into an excellent position for defense, should the occasion arise; and I was ready to act at a moment's notice.

So long as I insisted on seeing to it that justice was done, fighting, I think, was inevitable. Pothinus, Achillas, Theodotus and the rest of Ptolemy's party would not give up their power without a struggle, and it seemed to them that, in military force, they had the advantage over me. And no doubt the unexpected appearance of Cleopatra made them more eager than ever to destroy both me and her while they still had the force to do it. I found myself engaged at the same time both in a delightful and absorbing love affair and in some very arduous military operations. And I must own that, looked at in a certain light, the whole of this Egyptian war is somewhat ludicrous. Ever since the death of Pompey I have been, I suppose, indisputably the greatest man in the known world; yet here was I, a few weeks after my victory at Pharsalus, fighting for my life in the streets and on the jetties of Alexandria. Also, though past the age of fifty and with a great experience of women, I must have appeared so infatuated with a girl of twenty that I was risking my honor and my safety for her sake.

This picture of the situation is not entirely a true one. I had recognized from the first that it was dangerous for me, with my small force, to attempt, against the will of the population, the occupation of Alexandria. But I am used to taking risks and I regarded it as my duty to take a risk in this instance in order to make it clear that Rome had a legitimate interest in Egypt and that we were prepared to stand up here for our rights. What I underestimated was the extreme fanaticism of the Alexandrians and the considerable military skill of their army commanders. As for Cleopatra, my own honor and safety became, through force of circumstances, involved with hers. Certainly I was and am greatly charmed by her. She is a woman of immense energy and ambition, extremely intelligent, daring and ruthless. In these respects she rather reminds me of Fulvia, who used to be married to Clodius and is now Antony's wife. But Cleopatra has a kind of serpentine and feminine grace and charm in which Fulvia is lacking. Of the two women even Antony would undoubtedly prefer the Queen of Egypt. Indeed, after meeting her recently in Rome (she will still be here, I think, for a few more days), he spoke to me of her with a rather extraordinary enthusiasm, expressing his envy of me for the ascendancy which I still have over her.

Personally I know that this ascendancy comes mainly from the fact of my position of power. Cleopatra owes everything to me and only I can guarantee her tenure of what she has. If Antony were in my position, she would very soon transfer her affections to him and (this is a rather charming quality of hers) she would persuade herself that the transference was sincere and disinterested. Probably this would be a bad thing for Antony who is too easily moved by passion and could be induced by her to act against his own better judgment. Not that I think that she is without affection for me. It is possible indeed that she loves me as much as she is capable of loving anyone. I give her pleasure in many ways and not least by the fact that I understand her. She can be honest with me, since I am neither shocked nor surprised by most of her thoughts and schemes; and it is a relief for her to be able, sometimes, to be honest. She is also proud of having borne a son to me and I have permitted her to call the child Caesarion. But on these subjects women cannot be expected to be wholly honest, and only time, I think, will indicate whether this child is mine or not. Probably he is, but he might possibly be the child of Apollodorus the Sicilian, who was a faithful friend to Cleopatra and, I imagine, her lover.

Certainly I was surprised and very much attracted by the manner of her first appearance in Alexandria. With her brother's army still hostile to her, I had imagined that it would be impossible for her to reach me at all, unless she were escorted to the city by Calvinus and the two legions which I had summoned from Asia. But she executed a most daring and provocatively impudent plan of her own. With only this Sicilian friend of hers to help her, she made her way into the harbor of Alexandria in a small boat. She had wrapped a loose cloak round her and she kept her face well covered, while Apollodorus steered the boat up and down in front of the palace. Beneath her cloak she was dressed like a queen and she even had with her earrings in the shape of serpents and other pieces of royal jewelry which she was prepared to put on at the proper moment. At dusk the boat was brought up to the quays below the palace. Cleopatra slipped into a long sleeping bag and lay there at full length, holding the jewelry in her hands. Apollodorus put her over his shoulder and carried her ashore.

There were Egyptians as well as Romans in front of the palace, so that it was necessary to be cautious. Pothinus, had he been able, would certainly have got rid of her at once and the King, her brother and husband, would have supported his minister. But Apollodorus told some reasonable and convincing story to the Egyptian guards, and to the Roman sentries claimed that he had a special and urgent message for me personally. Probably he made his way easier by distributing money and jewels as he went; and in the end he and his bundle were escorted into my presence. Apollodorus smiled as he undid the mouth of the sleeping bag. To the immense astonishment of myself and the friends who were with me, a female form emerged from the bag on hands and knees. The girl was somewhat red in the face; I noticed at once the lithe grace of her body. She smiled at me, as though she had been caught out in some childish trick, and while she was smiling she was setting her hair in order and putting the earrings in her ears. She retained that impudent and roguish expression as she pronounced the words, "I am the Queen of Egypt," and then her face took on another aspect — as of something strenuous and sublime. I saw that she was a Macedonian and indeed a queen. It was easy to realize that she wished not only to secure my help, but to charm me with her beauty, her youth, her wit and her exuberant vitality. I saw to it that she achieved both her objects. This was the first of many nights when we have dined and slept together.

Chapter 10

The Alexandrian War

THE FACT THAT CLEOPATRA HAD BECOME MY MISTRESS WAS, OF
course, soon known by the young King, his ministers and the whole
population of Alexandria. I do not think that Ptolemy was jealous of me in the sense that an injured husband may be jealous. He
was one of the few males who was not fascinated by his sister; indeed he both hated and feared her. But he and his advisers were
infuriated that she was now under my protection and they assumed,
quite unreasonably, that in arbitrating between her and her brother
I should support her claims at his expense. They should have known
that, when it is possible to do so, I always act strictly in accordance
with right and justice. In this instance I proposed simply to see that
the terms of the late King's will were carried out and that Cleopatra
and young Ptolemy should share the throne together. In such an arrangement it was obvious that Cleopatra would become the dominant partner, if she were not subjected to superior military force.
Her sympathies were pro-Roman, and I would see to it that in the
end she could count on being able, if necessary, to meet force with
force. Meanwhile I would stress to young Ptolemy the advantages
that would come to him if he remained on good terms with his
sister.

No one, however, believed in the honesty of my intentions. As
soon as the young King discovered the presence of Cleopatra in

the palace and the nature of my relations with her, he flew into a passion of rage, rushed into the streets, threw the royal diadem on the ground and shouted out that he had been betrayed, that he was a prisoner of the Romans and that Egypt was at the mercy of foreigners. He then returned to the palace and, as I was obviously placing no restrictions on his movements, one might have expected that no one would have paid much attention to his childish outburst. But this was not so at all. A huge crowd collected and began to move towards the palace with the idea of rescuing their King and putting to death every Roman who could be found. I had to use troops to restore some sort of order. Then, later in the day and in a rather calmer atmosphere, I arranged for a public meeting of as large a number of Alexandrians as possible and addressed them in a most conciliatory manner. It was some time since I had made a long speech in Greek, but I was told that my performance was greatly admired by these people who regard themselves as expert judges of oratory. I began by reading and explaining the relevant clauses in the late King's will, thus making it perfectly clear that I not only had a right, but a duty, to be acting as I was acting. I then produced Ptolemy and Cleopatra and asked them to say a few words to indicate that, on my advice, they had made up their quarrel and were prepared to share the throne together as their father had wished. I had had some difficulty in persuading Ptolemy to come forward and speak, and, when he did so, he spoke clumsily. Cleopatra spoke like a queen. I could see that even those in the crowd who had been previously opposed to her were impressed, and before this meeting was over I made a gesture which won for myself, at least temporarily, the good will of the Alexandrians.

Some years previously Rome had annexed from the Alexandrian monarchy the Greek island of Cyprus. This action had offended Egyptian national feeling, and it seemed to me now that by making a generous offer I might win back Egyptian good will, save myself and my army from a rather threatening situation, and at the same time do good rather than harm to Roman interests in the eastern Mediterranean. So, after making a few conventional,

but I hope well expressed, references to my own respect and admiration for the ancient civilization of Egypt and for the more modern and brilliant civilization of Alexandria, I declared that, as
chief officer of the Roman Republic, I proposed to give back Cyprus to the Alexandrian royal family. In the palace was Cleopatra's younger sister, Arsinoe, a girl who was almost as ambitious
as Cleopatra herself, and another Ptolemy, still a young boy.
These two, I said, should be rulers of Cyprus. It was a concession
which, considering the danger, I thought it advisable to make,
though Cleopatra herself, who disliked her sister intensely, was
angry about it. My offer was certainly very well received by the
crowd. Its effect, and that of my oratory, was such that for a day or
two we Romans appeared to be really popular in Alexandria, and
I began to think that matters could be settled peacefully. I had no
illusions however about the hostility felt towards me by the
eunuch Pothinus and the rest of Pompey's murderers. If my policy were to succeed, it was quite certain that their power would
either disappear or be severely curtailed, and I fancied that they
would fight to retain their power if they thought that they could
fight with any hope of success.

I had Pothinus closely watched, but, since he was the King's
confidential adviser, I could not place him under arrest and I was
not able to intercept his correspondence with the army leader
Achillas, on whose attitude depended the question of peace or war.
At this time I took elaborate precautions to see that neither Cleopatra nor I was poisoned or struck down by a dagger; in fact
this is the only period of my life when I have taken precautions
against assassination. It is not a thing that I like doing, and the
nights which I spent in this great palace were, even in the company
of Cleopatra, often uneasy. I got into the habit of sitting up and
feasting until dawn and resting, when I did rest, at unexpected
times. My nerves were bad, for, though I am used to the apprehension of danger, I am not used to the dangers of disloyalty. In
a way I was relieved when the situation became clarified and I
received news that Achillas with his whole army was moving
against Alexandria, ostensibly to rescue the King and the city from

the Romans, really in order to make sure that the King's advisers should rule without any impediment from Cleopatra or myself.

I at once arranged that the King should send envoys to Achillas, ordering him to retire from Alexandria and accept the settlement which I had made. Two distinguished men were sent on this mission and Achillas had them both struck down before they could deliver their message. There was no doubt that we should have to fight to the end, and, until reinforcements could arrive, I was in no position to take the initiative against the twenty thousand troops, including two thousand cavalry, which Achillas had at his disposal. Fortunately I had written not only to Calvinus, who, in Asia, was having difficulties of his own, but also to an old friend of mine, Mithridates of Pergamum, asking him to raise an army and to march to my relief without delay. Mithridates acted speedily and efficiently. He was especially fortunate in securing the help of Antipater, the military leader of the Jews, who brought some first-rate troops with him and led them brilliantly.

However I could not expect any reinforcements at all for some time. Meanwhile we were very heavily handicapped by our lack of numbers. We could put up no opposition while Achillas and his army occupied nearly the whole of Alexandria. Then we had to meet at the same time a determined assault on our defensive position inside the palace and another attack on the area of the naval dockyards, where more than seventy Egyptian ships, most of them in excellent condition, lay at anchor. Achillas hoped that by capturing this fleet he could secure command of the sea and cut me off from both supplies and reinforcements. He rightly estimated that I had not enough men to guard both the palace and the docks. As it was we fought in both areas throughout the day, but I knew that we could not hold them both indefinitely, so we set fire to the whole Egyptian fleet. It was a great conflagration and caused much damage. A number of valuable books which were waiting on the quaysides to be taken to the library were destroyed. The library itself, however, suffered no damage. I am glad to say that there are now excellent relations between the Alexandrian librarians and my old enemy Varro, whom I have appointed to direct the new library in Rome.

Not many days after the failure of this first attack, I intercepted a message from Pothinus to Achillas, which showed quite clearly that the eunuch and the army leader were acting together against me and against their own legitimate King and Queen. This time I had no hesitation in having Pothinus put to death. It gave me some satisfaction to know that one at least of Pompey's treacherous murderers had suffered what he deserved. Another of them met his fate soon afterwards. Achillas, who had actually struck one of the blows which killed Pompey, was himself assassinated. This assassination was the work of another eunuch, Ganymedes, the tutor and friend of Cleopatra's sister Arsinoe. I had known for some time that Arsinoe hated her sister, her brother and myself; so I had placed no difficulties in her way if she wished to escape from the palace. With the character she had, she could not fail, I thought, to be an embarrassment to Achillas, and indeed she at once began to challenge his authority over his troops. Before long she and Ganymedes had him treacherously killed. Ganymedes, of whom I knew very little, took the place of Achillas as commander, but the change was not one that made matters any easier for us. Indeed Ganymedes showed really outstanding energy and ability. Almost at once he caused us the greatest alarm by ingeniously flooding our water supply with seawater. For a day the troops were almost in a state of panic, but in the end we dug new wells which gave us sufficient water for our needs.

Next day a fleet of transports appeared. It was the Thirty-seventh Legion, from Syria. We had some difficulty in getting the transports into harbor. I had gone out myself with a few Rhodian ships to superintend this operation and Ganymedes, with a comparatively small squadron, made a most daring and determined attempt to capture or kill me. When, in the evening, we got back safely to harbor, Cleopatra was, I remember, in an almost dangerously emotional condition. She told me that she had realized for the first time how much she loved me. Probably also she had

not previously realized that I am accustomed to take risks, and
she knew well enough that, without me, she had no chance of rul-
ing and living as she wished. I am glad to think that now the
situation has changed. If I were to die or be killed tomorrow, Cleopatra would still be safe. No one would dare to stop her returning from Rome to Egypt and governing her own kingdom.
Nevertheless during that autumn and winter in Alexandria it often
seemed unlikely that either she or I would survive. After every
setback Ganymedes seemed to gain fresh energy. He could control
an enormous labor force and built fleet after fleet of ships in order
to achieve his aim of occupying the harbor. In one of these actions we nearly suffered a very serious defeat. As it was no less
than four hundred legionaries were killed; a panic broke out in
which all sense of discipline was lost; and I myself had to swim
for my life across the harbor, leaving behind me, as a trophy for
the enemy, my scarlet Imperator's cloak, which hampered me in
swimming and, in any case, attracted too many missiles.

This was a war in which rest and relaxation were seldom or
never possible. Every day the enemy tried some new expedient.
My own soldiers, faced with a quite unfamiliar type of warfare,
and anxious, most of them, to return to their homes, were only
kept under control by the knowledge that they were in danger and
by the trust which they still retained in my military ability. Both
they and I knew that the war could never end until we were so
far reinforced that we could meet the enemy in the open field.
Meanwhile we might at any moment be trapped or outwitted by
our very skillful opponents.

During this period of siege I used to receive frequent deputations from Ganymedes, Arsinoe or Alexandrian notables. The demand was always that I should release their King Ptolemy, and
the purpose of the deputations was to arouse anti-Roman feeling
among the people of Alexandria and to encourage the view that
Ganymedes and Arsinoe were engaged in a patriotic struggle for
their national rights. In fact, if they had been victorious, they
would probably have put Ptolemy as well as Cleopatra to death.
Arsinoe had no more intention of sharing power than her sister

had. It occurred to me that by falling in with the expressed, though
not real, wishes of these deputations I should do my enemies more
harm than good. Ptolemy himself was anxious to be with his subjects. Some of his old advisers were still powerful and he rightly
thought that, if he remained a passive spectator of the war, he
would find at the end of it that his own party would have to give
way to that of Arsinoe and Ganymedes. So I decided to let him
go, having first organized a rather impressive piece of play-acting
to mark the scene of his departure, at which a number of prominent Alexandrians and army officers were present. I gravely
told young Ptolemy that I was entrusting him with an important
duty — to make his rebellious subjects see reason and to lay the
basis of a lasting friendship between his country and Rome. And I
went on to speak at some length on the theme of kingship, order
and good administration. It was not at all a bad speech. I nearly
always converse with Cleopatra in Greek, so that by this time I
had regained a perfect fluency in the language. Indeed for the
moment Ptolemy himself was genuinely affected. He burst into
tears, expressed his entire agreement with everything that I had
said and swore that, so great was his affection for me, he was
leaving me with the utmost reluctance. Strangely enough, I think
that there was a part of him that meant what he said. After that
first outburst of rage, he had realized that it was a great relief to
him to have Cleopatra taken off his hands; he knew that I would
protect his life; and, being an intelligent boy, he was moved by my
oratory.

Naturally when he reached his army all these feelings very
rapidly disappeared. He was ambitious and his one concern was
to supplant his sister Arsinoe and the eunuch Ganymedes at the
head of the national movement of liberation. I had hoped, of
course, that this attitude of his would result in some kind of dis-
organization in the enemy command; but this was not so. Once
again Arsinoe and Ganymedes showed good sense. For the moment at least they were prepared to subordinate themselves to the
young King. Ptolemy himself, wearing a golden breastplate, was
always with his troops among whom he became increasingly popu-

lar. Certainly he showed sufficient military ability to listen to the advice of his very competent officers. Thus, after his departure, the enemy were led at least as well as previously. There was, however, a distinct improvement in the morale of my own men. They were furious at what they regarded as the perfidy of young Ptolemy; and, such is the strange vanity of human nature, they preferred to think that they were fighting against a King rather than against a eunuch and a princess.

Ptolemy, however, had little time in which to exercise the authority which he had won. The relieving army under my friend Mithridates of Pergamum was on the move. After a hard struggle, in which the Jewish troops particularly distinguished themselves, it defeated the advanced forces of the Egyptians and, as soon as I heard the news of the battle, I hastened to join up with Mithridates before he was confronted by the main Egyptian army. I left in Alexandria a very small garrison, just sufficient to protect Cleopatra and to man our defenses for a short time. Even at this stage of the war I could feel by no means sure of what the result of the action would be. I thought of all those Gallic legions of mine which, after Pharsalus, had been brought back to Italy by Antony and were now, according to my information, in a somewhat mutinous mood. I fancied that I could still deal with them and I would have given much to have some of them at my side in the coming battle; for Ptolemy's army had been well led and was still more numerous than my troops and those of Mithridates put together. And when battle was joined, the enemy held out well, so that for some time we were able to make no impression on their defenses. I fancy that they must have erred either through overconfidence or enthusiasm. For at the height of the battle I observed that they were moving up fresh troops to the main front, perhaps as a preliminary to a general assault, and, by doing so, were leaving a sector of their line practically undefended. A quick and vigorous attack by three cohorts on this unprotected sector altered immediately the whole aspect of the battle. The enemy, who had fought so well before, broke and ran. I had seen the same thing happen to my own troops at Dyrrhachium; but I made a more thorough use of my opportunity here than Pompey did there. Practically the whole Egyptian army was killed or forced to surrender. Young Ptolemy, still wearing his golden breastplate, was among the dead.

So, completely victorious, we returned to Alexandria and were met at the outskirts of the city not only by the expected deputation of notables, begging for mercy, but also by a strange and numerous procession of the effigies of Egyptian religion, divinities in human, half-human or animal forms. This religion is, of course, venerable from its mere antiquity; moreover, as I discovered later in many interesting conversations with the priests, it is far from being (as might appear at first sight) simply a loose organization of tribal superstitions. Their ideas of cosmogony make no more sense than do our own or those of the Greeks and, though they are, up to a point, admirable mathematicians, the Egyptians cannot be regarded as deep or original thinkers. All the more precise and important discoveries in mathematics come from the Greeks, and of course metaphysics, in a rational sense, is a Greek invention. Yet still the Egyptians seem to deserve the distinction of being, as Herodotus called them, "the most religious people in the world." To them not only the great, but also the humble, is, in some sense or other, divine. Their rulers are, of course, regarded as children of the sun. Thus Cleopatra was a goddess some time before I became a god. And so emphatic and apparently sincere are their priests on this subject of the peculiar divinity of certain people that I can well understand how Alexander, after his visit to the oracle of Ammon, became in many ways a changed personality.

Yet this divinity which is attributed to kings and to some lawgivers or inventors of the remote past is also attributed to cats, crocodiles, dogs and jackals. The strictest orders had to be issued to our soldiers to prevent them from occasionally killing a cat or a dog, since if anything of the kind happened, a riot broke out immediately. The people will even go to the trouble and expense of mummifying the dead bodies of these animals and of burying them in great cemeteries on land which could easily be put to some useful purpose. For to them these creatures are, to a greater

or less degree, incarnations of divinity. Some are regarded with
greater reverence than others. The sacred bull at Memphis, for
instance, called the Apis, is believed somehow to represent on
earth the spirit of one of the greatest of their gods, Osiris — a
deity for whom we have no equivalent in our religion. After the
Alexandrian war was over I spent some interesting and amusing
hours at Memphis with Cleopatra, feeding the sacred bull and
observing its antics, which were watched closely by the priests for
the purpose of prophesying the future. This is, after all, no more
absurd a method of divination than are our own complicated pro-
cedures of inspecting the entrails of sacrificed beasts or of watching the flight of birds. As head of the state religion I myself have,
of course, to devote some time to these practices which, from
many points of view, must appear to all intelligent men as ridiculous. And one may well imagine that, as more and more people
become capable of rational thought, these particular practices will
disappear altogether. Yet, if this were so, I should not be surprised if they were replaced by others.

Few indeed are the men who do not crave for an assurance that
is not to be found in themselves. Few will accept this life, good or
bad, as it is. Nearly everyone longs to believe, against reason, that
events are not subject to the laws of cause and effect, but can be in
some way manipulated magically. Also in times such as our own,
when war has followed war and when the normal conventions of
society seem to be crumbling, the sense of insecurity is stronger
and more pervasive than ever. People find more often than usual
that their virtues are either unrewarded or a positive handicap.
They come to distrust initiative and to despair of justice. And,
with no impulse in their own lives towards hope, they tend to imagine, as a solace to their injured spirits, some other world after
death in which the obvious mistakes, cruelties and perversities of
this world are somehow rectified and even, in some mystical sense,
justified. We find this feeling not only in the mystery cults of the
Greeks but even in thoroughly rational thinkers such as Plato. In
my own lifetime I have noticed how this demand for assurance in
another world has spread quite remarkably among our own peo-

ple, principally among women, slaves and legionaries who have served in the East.

In a sense, I suppose, I may be said to be opposed to such manifestations of disquiet. My aim has been to create and to maintain order, to organize society in such a way that initiative will find its scope and justice appear to be done. Yet even if such a state of affairs could be brought into existence there would still, I think, be room for misgiving. The injustices of illness, malice and sudden death can be removed by no sort of dictatorial action. And still in each man's character will always linger the germs of perplexity and of self-distrust. Only fanatical atheists like Lucretius or rather exceptional men of action like myself will be able to do without an idea, not perhaps precisely of the gods but of some kind of supernatural reality. Here, though in a very broad sense, it is possible that the long experience and tradition of the Egyptians may be found useful. For the Egyptians are not only "the most religious" of men but also among the most practical. Their genuine preoccupation with a life after death and with such extraordinary beliefs as the divinity of cats and crocodiles has not prevented them from being excellent architects, craftsmen, mathematicians and agriculturalists. Nor are they narrow and bigoted like the Jews (whose religion also I find most impressive). They can both import and export belief. For example I greatly admired the policy of the Greek rulers of Egypt in encouraging the comparatively modern cult of Serapis. Here the mysterious elements of the worship of Osiris are combined with some of the most healthy aspects of Hellenistic religion. The god is partly a spirit, partly an animal and partly a wise, beneficent and powerful man — as it might be Zeus or Aesculapius.

I gave much thought to these matters during my last two months in Egypt. It is a time upon which I often look back with pleasure and even some regret, since it was the only time in the last sixteen years when I have not been under the immediate pressure of extremely urgent military and political events. With the Egyptian war finished and with enough troops at my disposal to feel quite secure in my present position, I was able to rest myself as well as my soldiers. Not that my position in general was at all secure. My friends and agents in Rome wrote to me constantly to say that my presence was urgently needed in the capital, where Dolabella was starting to revive the revolutionary program of Caelius, where Antony was disgracing himself by a too flamboyant debauchery and where there was much anxiety about the food supply, since large hostile fleets were still at sea and a large enemy force was growing stronger every day in Africa. Indeed the situation both in Africa and in Italy appeared to me so dangerous that I should certainly, in spite of the entreaties of Cleopatra, have left Egypt earlier, if it had not been for the fact that still another dangerous situation was developing in Asia. Here Pharnaces, the son of the great Mithridates, who, to gratify Pompey and gain some sort of kingdom for himself, had long ago murdered his father, was now attempting to take advantage of our civil war, just as his father had done in the days of Marius and Sulla. He had defeated Calvinus whom I had left behind in Asia and had celebrated his victory by the murder of Roman businessmen and the castration of Roman youths.

It seemed to me important to deal with Pharnaces before I attended to the dangers in Italy and in Africa. Before I could act effectually in Asia I should have to wait for the spring or early summer. I therefore accepted Cleopatra's invitation to a prolonged pleasure cruise on the Nile. It was a leisurely, interesting and enjoyable progress. Four hundred boats accompanied us, as well as the cavalry on land. I was deeply impressed, as any intelligent man must be, by the stupendous monuments of this ancient civilization, but I was impressed too by its modernity and by its possibilities for the future. As much as the sights themselves I enjoyed the conversations I had every day with priests, mathematicians and scholars. It was during this trip that I laid down the lines for the present reformed calendar. And in particular I enjoyed the company and the conversation of Cleopatra. She was in the last months of her pregnancy and I have never known her in better spirits.

Chapter 11

Asia and Italy

I HAD TO LEAVE EGYPT BEFORE THE BIRTH OF THIS CHILD, CAESArion, who may well be my child. Cleopatra, of course, wished me to marry her and to found with her a new kingdom which would embrace both Egypt and Italy, both the East and the West — something even greater and more permanent than the empire of Alexander. These were some of the fantasies with which we had amused ourselves during the warm days and fresh nights of our travel on the Nile. They are fantasies which some day may, in part, come true. This, however, was not the time for fantasy and Cleopatra was as capable of recognizing this as I was. Indeed one of her great charms is in her sense of reality. In the end she cares more for her kingdom and her position than for anything else. This, to me, is not a disagreeable trait. The very violence of her ambition induces in her sometimes a sweet dissembling charm, and at other times imparts a wild and almost desperate fervor to her love. It is now four years since I left Alexandria. She still retains her love for me and her personal ambition has increased. She hopes that when I have conquered Parthia I shall return by way of Egypt and that then, perhaps, both her ambition and her love will be fully satisfied. During her recent visit to Rome she has been as careful and circumspect as I could have desired. She was delighted when I had her statue placed in the new temple to my divine ancestress, Venus, whose name I still seem to hear shouted along the ranks at Pharsalus; but she has done nothing in Rome that has been unwise. She has been polite to my wife and if Cicero, as was evident, disliked her, that was only because he has never liked a woman who was wittier than himself. Yet behind her excellent behavior and her admirable intelligence, I can always detect the fierce glow of her ambition. She wishes to be a queen to be remembered and would like to use me for her purpose. She shows great good sense in recognizing the fact that I am not likely, without good reason, to subordinate my plans to hers; and she even does me the honor of believing, apparently, that I am at least as capable as she is of planning intelligently.

So, when I left Alexandria on that spring day four years ago, she saw clearly enough that the short interim of fantasy and imagination was over and that I was once again involved in the necessity of action. Even then she appreciated the strength of opinion in Rome and Italy. She herself, though a Greek, was fully aware that, as Queen of Egypt, she had to conform up to a certain point with Egyptian prejudice and custom; and she could see that I, as a Roman patrician, was even more deeply involved in the legalities and conventions of my country. Even now I have offended against these more than I should have chosen to do if I had not had to fight so continuously for my life and honor. As it was, though some people in Rome may have been shocked by my love affair with Cleopatra, no one could have taken exception to my settlement of the affairs of Egypt. I left behind me an army large enough to insure the stability of a regime which was now most friendly to us. I persuaded Cleopatra to take as her consort and husband her surviving brother, a very small boy indeed. In this way Egyptian sentiment was satisfied and the terms of her father's will, to enforce which I had fought the Alexandrian war, were strictly carried out.

I myself sailed from Alexandria with only one legion and even this legion was very much below strength. In my days Sulla, Lucullus and Pompey have all at various times set out to reconquer Asia. None of these began his enterprise, as I did, with a bare thousand men. I could, of course, count on reinforcements. Calvinus, in his defeated army, had one legion of first-class troops. Kings and princes of the East who had previously sided with Pompey were anxious now to follow the victor and supplied me with more legions of not very reliable material. Nevertheless, in spite of my long career of victory, I found myself, as has so often been the case, heavily outnumbered. For this reason, and also because of the comparisons which must naturally be drawn between my own Asiatic campaign and those of Lucullus and Pompey, I am still vain enough to feel a particular exultation with regard to this short war against Pharnaces, the result of which I announced in the words: "Came, saw, conquered."

The words were not ill chosen, though perhaps they disguise the initial difficulties of the campaign which were concerned simply with raising troops and quickly organizing out of a number of elements of widely differing quality a fighting force upon which I could rely. Once this had been done, the rest was easy. And, after the conditions of Alexandria, where movement was blocked and confined by streets, buildings, jetties, islands and canals, it was a delight to find oneself again in open country with liberty to turn in a number of directions. We marched into Asia by the road which had been used by Cyrus and by Alexander. As I went I remembered the plans which, in my extreme youth, I had carefully worked out for dealing with the great Mithridates, father of my present antagonist, and how the governor of the province at that time had dismissed these plans as the work of a young dandy, an amateur strategist who would be better occupied in writing Greek epigrams than in leading troops. There may have been a little truth in the strictures of this governor, who lost his province almost without striking a blow. Not that I was incompetent, or that my plans were bad. But in those days I was inexperienced and probably too much attached to theory. I know now that military, and other, events follow a course that can very seldom be precisely determined. Once a few basic conditions are satisfied — courage, training, supplies — victory may depend more on the ability to alter one's plans quickly than on any excellence in the plans them-

selves. Still I fancy that even in my youth I should have made a
better job of defending the province than did the governor who rejected my advice.

We came into contact with Pharnaces below the hill of Zela on
which his father had erected a trophy to commemorate the defeat
of a Roman army. Whether from audacity or as a result of some
kind of calculation Pharnaces launched an attack on us while we
were entrenching ourselves in a good position on rising ground.
At first I was amazed at his effrontery. Then I remembered that I
had once before been attacked in this unorthodox way. The Nervii
had been the attackers and we had very nearly been defeated.
So on this occasion too the enemy secured an initial advantage by
the surprise move. His scythed chariots were among us before our
line was formed and the infantry which came after fought with
greater resolution than I had expected of them. It was a hard
struggle, though, to my mind, the result was never in doubt. There
was no question of encirclement and I could not imagine troops
under my command running away uphill. In the end we bent back
the enemy's left and then his line broke and all was over. Our
victory was complete. Pharnaces was murdered by one of his own
subordinates. I gave his kingdom to that other Mithridates, my
friend from Pergamum, who, together with the fine contingent of
Jewish troops, had played such a large part in winning the Alex-
andrine war. Unfortunately Mithridates was killed in a minor engagement before he could take possession of his kingdom.

It remained for me to settle as quickly as I could the affairs of
the East and to raise from this area as large a sum of money as was
possible. Reports from both Rome and Africa made it clear that
my presence in Italy was urgently required. It appeared that some
of my veteran legions, including, to my great anger, the Tenth,
were in a state of near mutiny. Meanwhile in Africa the remaining
Pompeian leaders had organized an army of at least ten legions.
In addition they had a cavalry force greatly superior to anything I
could bring against them. And their ally, King Juba of Numidia,
whose beard I had pulled so long ago in the senate, could himself
put a very considerable army into the field. In addition to his

Numidians he had some excellent Spanish and Gallic mercenaries and at least sixty elephants. Scipio, Labienus and the others were already talking of their proposed invasion of Italy. Their hatred of me and their resolution to destroy me at whatever cost to their own countrymen were as strong as ever. I should have to pacify Italy and then, once more with inferior forces, invade Africa.

Meanwhile, both before and after the victory at Zela, I was spending my time in strengthening our position in the East and in diminishing, so far as I could, the number of my Roman enemies. In this latter task I was helped by young Brutus who had joined me at Tarsus, while I was on my way north, and who remained with me for the rest of the campaign. Brutus knew that I was very willing to pardon any enemy of mine who could give me any reason to believe that he would not take up arms against me again, and in the East there were many refugees from the Pompeian party who had not yet made up their minds whether to join their friends in Africa or to trust to my generosity. Brutus persuaded a number of these to take the latter course. Among them was his brother-in-law, Cassius, a very able young man whom, apart altogether from his connection with Servilia, I was most anxious to have on my side. I was told later that Cassius had planned to assassinate me while I was at Tarsus but had been persuaded by Brutus to take the more reasonable course of securing my favor. Whether there was any truth or not in this story I do not know and have never bothered to discover.

Since that time I have helped Cassius in his career and given him many positions of responsibility. He is efficient, strong-nerved and very ambitious. But he is not a person whom I should choose as a friend. I imagine that he resents the fact that he ought to feel grateful to me. Men like that are not to be relied upon in a crisis. Otherwise I should have given him an important command in my forthcoming expedition against Parthia, since he knows the country and is a good soldier. But he is not quite what I should call a good man. His friends commend him for having used his own initiative and, by acting independently, for having saved at least a small number of the great army of Crassus which the Parthians destroyed. The praise is, in a sense, deserved. A Curio or an Antony would have died with his commander in chief and would have achieved by that gesture no valuable military result. Nevertheless I prefer the attitude of a Curio or an Antony.

Brutus brought over to my side many other old enemies besides Cassius. How far they are reliable even now I do not know. But I was glad to have their submission even though I often suspected that it was halfhearted. Above all things I wished to avoid the bloody excesses of previous civil wars — the frenetic slaughter that had marred the last days of my uncle Marius and the cold-blooded and more extensive butchery of Sulla. I wished the name of Caesar to be remembered not only for practical achievement but for mercy. Consequently I was the more embittered against those of my enemies who, after Pharsalus, which should have marked the end of an unnecessary war, were now forcing me to divert my energies from the important tasks of administration and become instrumental in the deaths of still more Roman citizens. Afranius and Petreius, whom I had pardoned in Spain, were now fighting again against me in Africa. So was Labienus, who owed everything to me. So were Scipio and Cato, men who prided themselves on their patriotism and who, to secure the alliance of the barbarian Juba, had promised to give up to him all Roman possessions in Africa. I was at times profoundly dispirited when I realized that what had seemed to be the clear-cut decision of Pharsalus was in fact no decision at all. There had been, indeed, more hope for a negotiated peace when I crossed the Rubicon than there was now. The triumph for which I and my armies had waited for so long still eluded us. I could now be Dictator or consul as I pleased; but the work which I had planned to do in a peaceful year of ordinary legal office still remained to be done. Events were forcing me in the direction of a kind of excess which I have always wished to avoid. Yet I am not the man to be left behind by events.

So, when I set out from the East for Rome, I was in an impatient mood. Since Pharsalus, since Egypt, since Zela, I and the world had changed. I was irritated when I found these facts not recog-

nized. I was partly irritated, I remember, and partly amused by
Cicero who, marching at the head of a long column of dejected
friends, came out to meet me and to beg me to spare him soon
after I landed in Italy. The great orator looked himself as dejected
as anyone and I should imagine that his dejection was caused
equally by his fear for his valuable properties (he could not have
thought that I would take his life) and by wounded pride; for it
seemed to him that he would be more likely to retain his property
if he were to adopt the distasteful attitude of a suppliant. I, of
course, did my best to avoid hurting his oversensitive feelings. I
went to meet him on foot, embraced him and then took him with
me in my carriage for a great part of the day's journey. I quickly
put an end to his anxieties about his property and about various
friends and relations of his (including his brother Quintus) whom
he had persuaded to take up arms against me. He was, I think,
genuinely impressed by my wish to avoid reprisals and to forgive
enemies whenever possible; and he was probably sincere when he
offered me his help in my dealings with the senate. Yet still I could
not look upon this great literary figure with more than an aca-
demic sympathy. So far as modern politics are concerned he is, to
me, a remnant of the past. I could not help remembering how at all
moments of real crisis his eloquent voice had been raised for the
wrong people and the wrong policies.

Now indeed he appeared to be disillusioned with the Pompeian
party and to be genuinely anxious for peace; but most of this dis-
illusionment proceeded simply from the fact that several of the
Pompeian leaders had been rude to him personally and that Pompey himself had not regarded him as a very valuable military adviser. And when he spoke of peace, he used glibly enough such
phrases as "reconstituting the Republic" — a thing which I was very
anxious to do; but he meant by these words nothing more than a
return to that condition of inefficiency and oppression which had
preceded the civil war. I was more interested in his gossip than in
his political platitudes and prescriptions, though most of his gossip was concerned only with himself and his family. He spoke
much of Dolabella, who had married his daughter and, as might

have been expected, had treated her extremely badly. But Cicero, in his desire to be connected with the aristocracy, had given insufficient thought to the happiness of a daughter whom he genuinely loved. It appeared that Dolabella was now the lover of Antony's wife, who had previously been married to Cicero's great enemy, Clodius. He had also, as I had already heard, been making things as difficult as possible for Antony politically. As both Dolabella and Antony were members of my party, their open quarrel had done me nothing but harm. Cicero detested Antony and told me long stories illustrating, what I knew, his tendencies to drunkenness and vulgar display. Not that the behavior of Dolabella in these respects had been much better, as Cicero himself admitted. I was indeed displeased with both of them. Dolabella had taken it upon himself to begin an agitation among the poor for the cancellation of debts. Antony, who could at least be relied upon to follow my instructions and those of my intimate friends, had rightly checked this revolutionary movement; but he had acted tactlessly and made use of unnecessary violence. Once again Rome had been the scene of very serious rioting and on this occasion the initiation and the suppression of the riots had both been the work of members of my party. Dolabella had suffered a defeat, but so, in a sense, had I. And I was particularly angry with Antony for his inability to control the veteran troops. Antony is a very good officer indeed and I felt sure that he could have handled these legions satisfactorily if he had devoted his time to this task instead of to the holding of continuous drinking parties in Rome or the buying up of confiscated estates for large sums of money which he had no intention of paying into the treasury if he could avoid doing so. Dolabella, the champion of the poor debtors, had also been engaged in this kind of investment. I saw to it later that both he and Antony paid fully for what they had received.

From this gossip with Cicero on my journey and later from the more informed comments of my friends in Rome it was soon clear to me that my position both in Italy and abroad was even more dangerous than I had imagined. I was at least as well aware as a Dolabella or a Caelius of the need for economic reform; but the ill-timed agitations of these subordinates of mine had merely aroused among the propertied classes just those irrational fears which, by my general policy of moderation, I had been endeavoring to dispel. Many of these people secretly hoped that I and my armies would be destroyed in Africa and that the embittered remnants of Pompey's party would come back to power, though they knew well enough what sort of reign of terror would be established by Scipio, Labienus and Pompey's two sons. It was evident to me that my first task must be to destroy the enemy army in Africa. And here I found myself handicapped by mutiny in those very legions upon whose loyalty I had counted most. High-ranking officers of mine, whom I had sent with a personal message, had already been chased away from the camp. Cicero had seen them as they returned dejected and frightened from a mission which had almost cost them their lives. Now that I had returned to Italy the men, it seemed, were threatening to march on Rome so that they could put their supposed grievances before me. I was anxious to avoid all further disturbances and sent a very competent officer of mine, young Sallust (who is also a very promising writer), down to Campania, where the legions were encamped, with substantial offers of extra pay. Sallust is a good speaker, but he had no opportunity of speaking at all. He was met by volleys of stones and such demonstrations of anger that he was glad to run for his life. After this the legions carried out their threat and began to move in the direction of Rome. On their way they destroyed property and murdered various property owners including two men of praetorian rank.

No doubt they expected me to come out of Rome to meet them; but I proposed to do nothing which would justify in them a belief that they were not under my orders. I had the city gates guarded by troops upon whom I could rely and sent word to the mutineers that they could enter the city and camp in the Field of Mars, so long as they first laid down their arms. These orders were obeyed to the extent that they only carried their swords with them. Their appearance in the city not unnaturally provoked not only excitement but terror among the richer citizens; for these were the veterans of the Gallic wars, soldiers who were believed to be the finest and most ruthless troops in the world. Indeed they had, among my enemies, the reputation of being scarcely human.

I myself understood these men well and so I was able to deal with them easily. But I was immensely angry with them. I understood them because they and I had become, as it were, parts of a single body. Together we had accomplished impossibilities and had shared in every kind of distress and triumph. They and I were indispensable to each other and this was a fact which they knew well. Yet they were now presuming to trade upon this fact of our interdependence. Clever agitators (and here I seemed to detect the hand of Labienus) had succeeded in persuading them that I needed their services so badly that they were in a position to dictate to me. Could they not see that, if I were to obey and they were to command, the whole nature of the enduring bond between us would be broken and transgressed? I was amazed at their stupidity, their effrontery, their greed and their lack of patience. I was angry with them all, but particularly angry with the men of the Tenth, the legion which I had known best and trusted most, the legion with which eleven years previously I had proposed to advance alone against Ariovistus and which had been delighted at this mark of confidence. What would Gaius Crastinus have thought, if he had lived to see this sorry display of insubordination?

I was indeed so angry that I scarcely noticed how pathetically easy to deal with were these supposedly terrifying veterans whom I knew so well. When I went down to the Field of Mars, rather earlier than they had expected, and took my seat on a platform to listen to their complaints, I did not show my anger by any gesture or tone of voice, but it was probably evident in the attitude of indifference and displeasure which I chose to adopt. As soon as I appeared they came thronging about me. Most of them had not seen me since the day of Pharsalus. Perhaps now they expected me to speak to them and congratulate them on the fighting qualities which they had then shown. If so, they were disappointed. I gave them no sign of recognition. Later I asked to hear their complaints and then listened to speech after speech dealing with the same themes — their wounds, their hardships, their great deeds, the rewards which they expected, their claim to be demobilized. These speeches went on too long. The soldiers themselves became bored and impatient with the repetitious oratory of their representatives. It was evident that it was I, rather than anyone else, whom they wished to hear. When I did speak, I surprised them. I announced, in as indifferent a tone as possible, that they would all be demobilized at once. They could certainly count on me, as they knew well, to give them every penny of the rewards I had promised; but for this they would have to wait until the end of the African campaign which I should fight with other legions who would then, of course, take part in my triumph.

As I spoke I could feel how bitterly the soldiers were wounded by my words. They resented the thought that they would not take part in the final triumph; but what chiefly distressed them was the thought that I could do without them. I began to address them again. They were used, of course, to being addressed by me as "comrades" or "fellow soldiers." Now, with great deliberation, as though to emphasize that I had already discharged them, I used the word "citizens" — a word appropriate to any collection of Romans other than an army. At this there was an immediate outcry. The mutiny was over. Soon the men were begging me to punish the ringleaders and to take them back again into my service. I told them that I would forgive all of them except the Tenth Legion. Later I received deputations from the men of the Tenth begging that the whole legion should be punished by decimation and then again allowed to serve with me. I would not, of course, agree to so cruel and so unjust a punishment; but I did, in the end, forgive the men. Then, with the utmost speed, since it was already late in the year, I began to make preparations for the invasion of Africa.

Chapter 12

Africa and Rome

I HAVE NEVER WRITTEN AN ACCOUNT OF THE AFRICAN WAR AND
doubt whether I ever shall. Nor, for that matter, have I written of
the end of the Alexandrian war, or of the campaign of Zela. But
in the case of Egypt I should find it rather embarrassing to publi-
cize my connection with Cleopatra; and the whole war with
Pharnaces was over so rapidly that it scarcely seems to deserve
literary treatment. The African war, on the other hand, lasted for
nearly five months, was an extremely arduous operation in which I
was twice very nearly routed, and has many aspects which would
interest a student of military affairs. Yet somehow I am averse
from reliving it as I should have to do if I were to describe it accurately. It seems to me that, dangerous and exciting as the operations may have been, I was in reality engaged in killing something
that was already dead. I feel in the same way about that final
bloody battle in Spain at Munda, which took place only a year
ago. Curiously enough, the single suicide of Cato in Africa seems
to me more significant than the appalling slaughter after Thapsus;
and I have indeed taken trouble to write a short pamphlet attacking Cato's memory. This is not because I believe that Cato was
wholly bad. I merely found him boring, pretentious, arrogant, and,
in a rather deep sense, hypocritical. I did not hate him simply because he hated me. I hated him for himself.

As for my little pamphlet, the "Anti-Cato," I wrote that rather with a view to influencing public opinion than in order to gratify my animosity. Cicero had already published his "Cato" — a fine, if sentimental, piece of writing — and it seemed to me that a reply was required to his distorted recollection of this powerful prig. For I can see that Cato may turn out to be more dangerous dead than alive. Already some people are using such phrases as "mourning for the Republic," and they will tend to find in Cato the symbol of a defeated virtue which has gone from political life. His intransigence, his obstructionism, his pedantry, his entire lack of imagination will be colored by the manner of his death and will be made to appear as aspects of that "ancient Roman virtue" of which we have read in our history books and seen very few examples in our lives. Cato, who preferred to commit suicide rather than allow me to spare his life, will be thought of as the great martyr in the cause of liberty. I believe that many intelligent people like Brutus do already so regard him. So quickly have they forgotten that the "liberty" for which Cato died was, at best, an abstraction and, in reality, an excuse used to cover inefficiency and disorderly ambition.

I am sometimes irritated by critics of mine who fail to see that I understand at least as well as they do what was once the dignity, the strength and the simplicity of the Roman Republic. I too have deep feelings for the past, as indeed I must have, being descended from kings and, according to legend, a goddess. But I cannot live in dreams which are out of all relation to reality; I cannot forget how consistently throughout my lifetime the names of virtues have been used to justify all sorts of obscurantism, greed and oppression; I cannot tolerate disorder, and I know that without order there can be no liberty at all. I know, in fact, that, historically and humanly speaking, I am right and Cato was wrong. Yet still I am not wholly satisfied about his ghost, which I feel to be more powerful than would be the case if all that it represented was a lie or a meaningless abstraction or a sentimental hankering for an imagined period of past history. It is true that Cato was in private life absurdly severe and intolerant and in politics absolutely hidebound within certain conventions. In these respects I am his precise opposite and it would therefore seem quite ridiculous to make him, of all people, the symbol of liberty and to regard me as any kind of tyrant. Yet I cannot escape the fact that this absurdity is taking place. Cato is widely believed to have died for liberty. The large caricature which I had made of him and which was exhibited on placards during the procession in my fourth triumph was not well received. I fancy that he can be opposed to me in a manner better described as religious than political.

What people admire in him is his inflexibility, a quality which is quite out of place in politics. And Cato's inflexibility was of a peculiar, unworldly kind. It often seemed that he would have deliberately chosen to be on the losing side. He may really have almost believed in that savage and inhuman slogan of the Stoics — "Let the whole world crash so long as justice is done" — and he was certainly arrogant enough to feel quite sure that he personally knew better than anyone else precisely what justice is. These are qualities which people often admire in a religious leader, and they are qualities which, in the real world, are apt to lead to anarchy rather than to liberty. So, paradoxically, Cato, that great stickler for the forms of law, may be properly regarded as an anarchist, while I, who have, when necessary, altered, evaded or transformed many legal obstructions, must be considered still to possess a much deeper respect than Cato had for the efficient order of social life. Only in the sense that he stood for the anarchy of the individual conscience may Cato be said to have stood for liberty. I myself am more concerned with what needs doing than with my own conscience; and I can immediately recognize that if, owing to some philosophical or religious doctrine, people were, for example, to refuse military service, then ordered life would be impossible. Yet, if it could be possible, I should like there to be room in society for the anarchy which Cato represented. I was sorry that I did not have the opportunity to spare his life.

Nevertheless I have seldom felt less inclined to mercy than I did when, at the end of this campaign, I received the news of Cato's suicide at Utica. For this African war was fought with a peculiar

savagery and desperation on the part of my enemies. When they
took prisoners they nearly always put them to death. This had
been done already by Bibulus, by Labienus and by that arrogant
savage, King Juba, who had massacred the remains of Curio's
army. Now this practice became the order of the day. When
Scipio captured one of my transports he either killed or made
slaves of all the soldiers on board. After this he offered to spare
the life of the officer who was accompanying them, Granius Petro.
I was told later of how Petro had replied: "In Caesar's army," he
said, "we give mercy, we do not receive it." He then fell on his
sword and died. This was the only noble gesture that was made in
the war. True that up to the very end my men behaved with
discipline and restraint; but, so angry had they become by that time,
that when the moment came for them to avenge themselves,
there was no holding them back.

I intended to use ten legions, five of them veteran, for this war.
As it was, because of the mutiny and of inefficient arrangements
for transport, I landed in Africa with only five legions, four of
which consisted of inexperienced and partially trained recruits.
This was in the winter and, though I had certainly arrived before I
was expected, the enemy forces were well organized and well led.
Soon after my arrival my small force was badly defeated by Labienus and Petreius, who showed great intelligence in their use of
cavalry and light troops. We were lucky that night to get back to
camp. And even when the rest of the veteran legions arrived, we
were still in difficulties. We were short of supplies and were so
very greatly inferior in cavalry that we could never be sure of
our communications. I had hoped to force the enemy to fight a
pitched battle in conditions where the superior fighting qualities of
my troops would tell, as at Pharsalus; but the enemy would give me
no such opportunity. Four months went by before the moment
came.

At Thapsus, between the lagoon and the sea, I took up a position where it would be theoretically possible for the enemy to
cut me off entirely from all supplies and to reduce me by siege. In
order to do so, he would have to divide his forces and hold two

lines of entrenchments. It was a tempting prospect and the enemy fell into the temptation. He had apparently overlooked the possibility that my intention was, not to defend myself, but to attack. It was a morning in early spring. As I gave the orders for battle, neither I nor the men had any doubts of the result. Indeed in their enthusiasm the men of the Tenth Legion on our right were again guilty of insubordination. They forced one of their trumpeters to sound the charge before I had given the order to attack and they refused to obey their centurions who attempted to hold them back from running into action. I was angry, but there was nothing to be done but to follow their example. Later I reflected that these men, who had won so many battles for me, had accurately assessed the advantages of the position where I had placed them and were, indeed, expressing an impatience which I felt myself.

This battle was soon over. The first and main action was against the army of Scipio which had been reinforced by a number of elephants. I had troops specially trained for dealing with these beasts and in fact the elephants did more harm to their own side than to us. The enemy infantry soon broke. There was a kind of relentless fury in these veteran troops of mine which would have proved, I think, irresistible against almost any odds. As for the other enemy army, the large force under Juba and Afranius, it began to disintegrate at the mere sight of what was happening to Scipio's legions. We captured and sacked both the camp of Scipio and the camp of Juba. Most of the enemy cavalry got away, but the infantry were left helpless and now suffered for the cruelty and ferocity that had been shown previously by their commanders. For my men were now beyond the control of officers and centurions. On that dreadful day of slaughter no less than fifty thousand of the enemy were killed. We lost about fifty men. As for the enemy commanders, Scipio was intercepted at sea, and killed himself. Afranius and Sulla's son, Faustus, were captured and put to death. King Juba, who had escaped in company with Petreius, had planned to achieve in death the kind of fame which had eluded him during his lifetime. His intention was to retire to his capital at Zama, to build an enormous funeral pyre and there to be burned to death together with his wealth, his family and all the most prominent of his subjects. But these subjects were not in sympathy with the romantic project, and so they barred the gates of the town against him. Then, theatrical to the last, Juba organized a duel between himself and Petreius on the understanding that neither of the two was to survive. Petreius fell in with this rather barbaric arrangement. The only important survivor was Labienus, who managed to get safely to Spain, where Pompey's savage and ruthless son Gnaeus and his more engaging brother Sextus had already established themselves.

I myself, immediately after the battle, set out for the enemy base of Utica, where Cato had been left in command. He had, of course, no hope of making a successful resistance and I feared that he would act just as he did act. I was within a day's march of Utica when I received the news of his suicide. Of all the enemy commanders in Africa he was the only one not to have committed atrocities against my troops. Indeed I was, I think, the only Roman citizen whom he would willingly have killed in cold blood. I was much disappointed at not being able to spare his life.

As the result of this campaign I was able to raise large sums of money from the local communities which had sided with the enemy and, by annexing most of the kingdom of Juba, I added a new and most valuable province to our empire. Before leaving the country I made suitable and detailed arrangements for the organization of the new province and left Sallust in command of it. He is loyal and intelligent. I knew that he would take the opportunity to enrich himself, but I knew too that he would carry out my plans sensibly and efficiently. I had to think also of the triumphs which I would hold when I returned to Rome. I found Sallust very helpful in arranging for the capture and dispatch of great numbers of wild animals. Indeed in the following year he succeeded in producing a giraffe — an animal that had never before been seen.

Altogether I found it necessary to stay in Africa for more than two months after the victory of Thapsus. Some of my enemies have maintained that once again, as in Egypt, I wasted time over a love affair, this time with Eunoe, wife of the Mauretanian King.

Those who know me better know that I do not waste time. The love affair with Eunoe was indeed agreeable, and not only Cleopatra but also Servilia and many other women have informed me that the presents which I gave to this most attractive woman were extravagant. However, much as I enjoyed the company of Eunoe, I left Africa as soon as I could safely do so. Before midsummer I was in Rome.

This was the longest year that has ever been known. For some time I had been planning a reform of the calendar and indeed had often discussed the question in Alexandria with Egyptian and Greek astronomers. Now, with my powers as Dictator officially prolonged for ten years, I was able to carry out the reform. As a result this year lasted for fifteen months and, in spite of my stay in Africa, I spent a long time in Rome. This is the city which has shaped my life. Nearly all my youth was spent here, and here, through every handicap and danger, I learned to become a politician long before I had the opportunity to command an army. I have spent the last part of my life in adding to the power and honor of this city, and in Gaul, Egypt, Asia and Africa I have devoted hours of time to plans for its beautification and better administration. Yet I feel stifled by the place. After that long year of triumphs unexampled in our history, I was almost relieved to find that I had to be present in person at the last desperate and bloody actions of the war in Spain. And now, after another period of less than a year in the city, I am impatient to be again with my legions. I have lived long enough for glory and long enough for my physical frame and constitution. I can understand the weariness which induced Sulla, at the height of power, to abdicate his dictatorship and to retire into private life. But I am neither irresponsible nor cynical, as Sulla was, nor a voluptuary. I have to work, to organize and to create so long as I can breathe. Nevertheless it is healthier and perhaps safer to be securing our interests in Parthia by avenging Crassus than to be surrounded every day in Rome by people clamoring for promotion or forgiveness, to be constantly the recipient of new and unnecessary honors, to be acclaimed as a god and feared as one who might call himself King.

All through that long latter end of the year in which I returned from Africa, I often had the feeling that I was both the victim and the creator of a certain exaggeration. My triumphs and honors were not only greater but very far greater than any which had been known. I wished this to be so and indeed it was necessary for the honor of the army and no more than was warranted by our achievements. Moreover I know well enough that, human nature being what it is, these great honors are bound to lead to jealousy and to extremes of flattery. Yet I am still the same Caesar as I was. I still feel the same affection to my friends and I have never in my life, as tyrants and gods are supposed to do, acted irresponsibly or irrationally. In spite of this many people look upon me as though glory had altered my nature, and a few, no doubt, still hate me with the bitterness of jealous friends or of forgiven enemies.

I had earned a triumph fourteen years previously and, owing to the obstructionist tactics of Cato, had had to renounce the honor so as to be eligible to stand for my first consulship. Now in one year I held four triumphs — for Gaul, for Egypt, for Asia and for Africa. I have always been good at organizing entertainments, and these triumphs, with the games, feasts and spectacles which followed them, were greater and more splendid than anything of the kind that has ever been seen. The people were at first deeply moved and in the end, I think, like myself, almost wearied by the profusion of it all. As for me, I am always affected by the ceremony of tradition, and this triumphal tradition of ours must go back to a very remote antiquity. For the day of the triumph the general becomes the living image or incarnation of the god Jupiter. He wears the god's purple robe embroidered with golden stars; there are gold sandals on his feet; in his hand he holds the ivory scepter with the eagle of Jupiter at its tip; on his head is the laurel wreath and his whole face is painted red so as to resemble the most ancient Etruscan statues. Indeed the whole ceremony is probably of Etruscan origin, as is also indicated by the troupe of clowns, dancing and singing in the Etruscan style, who surround the triumphal chariot.

Far in front of me, as I stood in the chariot, and for most of the route quite out of sight, went the long procession of senators and magistrates, followed by bands of musicians, the noise of whose instruments, deafening as I knew it to be, only reached me as a dim murmur, since behind them came the huge train of wagons and litters bearing the spoils of Gaul, records of our victories, statues of the Rhine, the Rhone and of the Ocean in chains. I was moved indeed when I thought of the names that the crowd would read — Alesia, Avaricum, Marseilles and a hundred others. After the demonstration of our deeds came the animals for sacrifice, white bulls with gilded horns, and then — something which the Roman crowd always enjoys — the famous prisoners in chains. Here — in the Gallic triumph — the great sight was Vercingetorix, who for the last six years had lain in prison waiting for this brief appearance. After the triumph he was to be strangled. He had broken oaths of loyalty and had done too much harm to me and to the Roman people to hope for forgiveness. Behind him and the other prisoners marched my official escort of seventy-two lictors. At their side were musicians playing flutes and zithers and they were accompanied by other attendants with smoking jars of perfume, as in the presence of a god, so that the whole air was aromatic. I followed in the triumphal chariot and behind me came the soldiers of the legions. All wore crowns and all had turned out at the beginning of the day as smartly as possible.

So Rome was able to see, at least for a short time, this army of heroes looking indeed heroic. Soon, however, as there were frequent halts and obstructions of the enormous procession, the men, who were always being offered refreshment by their friends, became almost as drunk as I had ever seen them. They were wild with excitement, exultant at this moment when at long last their hardships and glories were being recognized and applauded. They were proud of me as their leader and they used the traditional license of a triumph to show that they were so closely bound to me that they and they alone were permitted at this moment to be disrespectful. I did not smile as I listened to their jeers and vulgar rhymes. My duty was to retain the bearing and appearances of a god. But I was amused and I was touched, since I knew that even the most shameless verses which they sang about me were, strangely, inspired by that deep love which, whether or not they were mutinous or I were angry, always bound us together. One of their favorites was the old song which they had made up about me years ago:

> *A bald-headed lecher we bring into town.*
> *Look out for your wives, boys, he'll knock*
> *'em all down.*

And of course there was a song about that old scandal, dating from my very early youth, which concerned my supposed homosexual relationship with King Nicomedes of Bithynia:

> *Here comes Caesar, the great*
> *conqueror,*
> *But Nicomedes conquered too.*
> *Nicomedes conquered Caesar.*
> *Nicomedes is not on view.*

So, with such ribald songs ringing in my ears, for four days I assumed the status of a god on earth. I remember most clearly the Gallic triumph, since this was the one to which we had so long looked forward; but the other three triumphs were equally splendid. Possibly the Egyptian triumph was the most splendid of all. Cleopatra herself, accompanied by her boy husband, came to Rome at this time. She helped me design many of the pageants in the procession and she was delighted to watch her sister Arsinoe paraded in chains at the head of the group of prisoners. Both then and in the last few months (I must try to see her tomorrow) Cleopatra has behaved not only like a queen but like an intelligent woman. People in my own party, like Antony and Dolabella, are obviously half in love with her and so are a number of elderly senators whom one would have believed to have outlived such passion. Both in this year of the four triumphs and later she has shown herself particularly anxious to have her child Caesarion in some way legitimized. Now some of the senators whom she has charmed are putting forward a proposal by which I should be

legally entitled to have more than one wife, "for the purpose," as
this suggestion is quaintly expressed, "of having children." But I
am unwilling at this moment to offend public opinion in this respect. Nor is there any point in doing so. Much as she might like it,
I cannot take Cleopatra to Parthia with me. To do so would impair
my own military efficiency and interrupt the necessary reorganization of Egypt which is, both strategically and economically, a
most important area.

In the Egyptian triumph no reference, of course, was made to
Pompey except that large paintings were exhibited depicting the
deaths of his murderers, Pothinus and Achillas. One does not
triumph over Roman citizens, and so the greatest battle, Pharsalus,
was not mentioned. So, in the Asian triumph, what was empha-
sized was that Pharnaces was the son of the great Mithridates,
author of so many massacres of Romans in the East, rather than
the fact that he had been an ally of Pompey. Even in the African
triumph our main enemy was represented as King Juba, though
here it was impossible to pretend that Roman forces had not been
fighting at his side. So there were pictures of the suicides of Scipio,
Cato and the rest. Many, I know, were shocked at these exhibi-
tions. As for me I regarded these Romans who had fought against
me in Africa as having lost all claims to the consideration that
should be given to citizens. They had allied themselves with a
foreign king, to whom they had promised to concede parts of our
own empire, in order to prolong a war which had been already
lost. Even at the time of this triumph the survivors of their party
— Labienus and the sons of Pompey — were strengthening their
position in Spain and had begun to achieve such success that I was
beginning to think that I myself might have to fight yet another
campaign in that peninsula. I had forces operating there under
Fabius, who has often proved himself an excellent commander,
and under my great-nephew Pedius, who is perfectly competent.
Yet these two were not doing well. I knew that Labienus would
continue to do me harm so long as he lived and, by the end of this
year of triumphs, I had decided to finish this matter myself.

As it was, the triumphs were followed by festivities of every kind. Entertainment followed entertainment, so that I myself can scarcely remember in what order they took place. Even Crassus, I think, if he had been alive, would have been amazed at the splendor of the banquet which I gave to the whole population of Rome. Twenty-two thousand dining tables were set out in the streets and squares; the food and wine were of the best. That night, as I returned to my home, I was accompanied by great crowds of cheering and intoxicated citizens, who moved after me in a procession between two rows of elephants. On the backs of the elephants were men in African costumes, holding great torches in their hands. These flaming lights, together with the solid blackness of the great beasts and the star-covered darkness of the night, produced on my mind a powerful impression. I wished that my mother, who had always believed in my destiny, had been alive to see this sight — though she, as she always used to do, would certainly have reproached me for the extravagance of it all.

Then there were the donations to the soldiers, centurions and officers of my army. Each man received more than I had promised and more than he should have expected. Afterwards I also gave a small sum of money to every citizen in Rome. I had already planned to revise the list of these citizens, cutting down by half the number of those entitled to receive free grain. This measure would relieve the state of a crippling burden and would help to encourage emigration to the new colonies which I was planning. But for the moment I wished everyone to receive more entertainment and bounty than he could have imagined. There were plays, wild beast shows and sports to celebrate the dedication of the new Forum, the Basilica and the temple to my ancestress Venus Genetrix. I was in a hurry. Many of the buildings were opened up before they were fully finished. For instance the very fine statue of Cleopatra which I had placed within the Temple of Venus had not yet received its finishing touches; but even then it was a remarkable work of art.

Some of my soldiers began to grumble. This vast expenditure seemed to them beyond reason. Why should not they rather than others receive the fruits of all that we had won? Indeed these old veterans of mine seemed now determined, when they were not actually fighting, to give me trouble. I knew as well as they did that it was time for them to be discharged. However there was still work for some of them. Once more, and for the last time, I should call upon the Tenth to lead the charge on the right of my line of battle. The festivities were scarcely over and I had only begun to plan in detail those very numerous projects for peaceful legislation that had been in my mind for years, when I was forced to the conclusion that I must deal with the Spanish situation myself. In November I set out from Rome to this last campaign of the civil war.

Chapter 13

Munda

BOTH ON THE JOURNEY OUT TO SPAIN AND ON THE WAY BACK I HAD young Octavius with me as a traveling companion. The boy's health is not good and I would gladly have spared him some of the exertion, for which he was scarcely fitted, on the outward journey. For I was anxious, as usual, to reach the front before either my friends or enemies expected. We did the whole journey from Rome to the neighborhood of Corduba in twenty-seven days. In spite of the time of the year, part of the journey was agreeable and indeed I was so impressed by the changes of scenery and temperature that I found myself impelled to write poetry — a thing I had not done for some years. I wrote a piece entitled "The Journey" which describes, I hope with some elegance and point, feelings which I have often had in travel and which, I expect, most travelers will share with me. Certainly there was much in this journey to enjoy, but there was also much hard riding along rough tracks, with icy winds cutting into our faces. Sometimes we got good food and lodging; sometimes we had to be content, in our haste, with filthy dishes of beans and oil, and often had to sleep with no shelter over our heads at all. In these conditions my health and digestion thrive; but young Octavius was unused to such living and I often begged him to wait and to follow me by more easy stages. But he has enormous powers of endurance and

resolution in his frail body. He forced himself to be stronger than
he is and to appear more cheerful than he could possibly have felt.
I admired him for this and (particularly on the way back, when we
had more time) I enjoyed and was greatly impressed by his conversation. He was brought up in the house of my sister Julia and
he has developed several mannerisms which remind me both of
her and of my mother. His intelligence is outstanding and his
political shrewdness, for one of his age, is quite remarkable.

He seems to have made a friend of Cicero and is most amusing
about the way in which he plays up to the old man's vanity. He
evidently hopes that Cicero will be useful to him at a later stage of
his career and he is perfectly well aware of the real power that, in
suitable conditions, can be developed by that great oratory of
which Cicero is a master. According to him, Cicero first singled
him out for attention because of some dream he had. Cicero
dreamed that Jupiter had indicated that, of all the young men in
Rome, Octavius was destined to be the greatest and most powerful. When he told me this, Octavius laughed and suggested that
what really appealed to Cicero about him was the fact that he was
born in Cicero's consulship. But I can see that he is not averse to
taking the dream seriously. Many people in my party
are inclined to dislike him. Antony, for example, thinks of him as a
weakling, probably because he is reluctant to indulge in the kind of
drinking bout which, for Antony, is a normal daily procedure. But
Octavius has, on a very short acquaintance, formed a remarkably
accurate idea of Antony. He sees, and indeed is somewhat priggish about, his failings; but he also realizes that Antony is a most
loyal friend. He has even gone so far as to hint to me that Antony
is almost the only member of the nobility in my party whom I
can trust. This I do not believe. I hope I can be confident in the
loyalty of all who have served under me (though I must own that
I once was entirely confident in Labienus); and now nearly everyone who may disapprove of me is bound to me by strong ties of
gratitude. Some men, I know, become the more embittered the
more kindly and generously they are treated. But this is not true
of men who have any pretensions to honor. Even Cato, I think,

would have been safe if he had allowed me to forgive him. Brutus, however he may misunderstand my intentions, is, I feel sure, quite safe.

However on this journey to Spain I was not thinking of enemies whom I had forgiven. I was thinking of enemies whom, on this occasion, I would not forgive. After my original occupation of Rome, I had hoped for peace, and after Pharsalus and the death of Pompey I had felt sure of it. Then followed the unnecessary and very critical campaign in Africa; and now I was once more faced by enemies who were absolutely irreconcilable. I could imagine what would happen, not only to me and my friends, but to Rome and Italy as a whole, if I were now to be defeated. The massacres of Sulla would seem an intelligent operation if compared to the general and disorganized bloodshed which would mark the entrance of Labienus and of Pompey's brutal son, Gnaeus, into Rome. I was angry too with those cities of Further Spain which had gone over to the enemy in spite of the benefits which they had received from me in the past. My friend Balbus is a native of Gades and I have done much for that town — the place where, in my youth, in front of the statue of Alexander the Great, I nearly fainted away, so acute was my awareness of my own shortcomings, of my wasted days, and, at the same time, of the real and vast expanse of power, action and liberty that is available to an exceptional man. This time I would make even this city pay for its treachery. And as for those troops which had surrendered to me once and had then taken up arms against me again, I should not, as I had done before, preserve them from what now seemed to me the justified anger of my own men — an anger which, at Thapsus, even I had been unable to control.

By the time I reached the front the enemy was able to put into the field a force of thirteen legions, four of which consisted of first-class troops. Both these men and their leaders knew that on this occasion there was no possibility of ending the war by a negotiated surrender, like the one which I had accepted from Afranius and Petreius. This time it must be a fight to the death. And apart from these four legions of picked troops, the remainder of the enemy force was likely to be formidable enough. Much of it consisted of Spaniards who had been trained in Roman methods. I did not underrate either the native courage of the Spaniards or the ability of Labienus to train and to inspire men. I myself had eight legions, four of which were veterans. For once I was superior in cavalry, but I knew (and Pharsalus had confirmed the knowledge) that battles are not won by cavalry.

Gnaeus Pompey, in spite of his unpleasant character, could inspire loyalty and had considerable military ability. But I fancy that in this campaign he must have followed the advice of Labienus who knew my methods and my character and was able to anticipate the kind of action I would take. In particular he knew that, though I had taken risks of many kinds, there was one risk in warfare which I had never taken. I had never asked my men to go into battle with the ground against them. Now, by skillfully avoiding battle for more than two months, he was able in the end to take advantage of my men's impatience and my own, so that, for the first time, I took this risk. It nearly proved fatal.

The battle of Munda was fought almost exactly a year ago. In the two months or so that preceded it I had won a few unimportant successes. After one of these I received from my men the salutation of "Imperator." It was the only time that I had been so saluted after a victory in the civil war and it was an indication of our feeling that we were now fighting against men who had put themselves outside the pale of Roman citizenship and who could expect no different treatment from that which we had given to Gauls or Germans. So, gradually, we were forcing the enemy to fall back southwards from Corduba, but we had never yet been able to make contact with him in full strength. The weather during this first half of March was wonderful. It became a sort of joke in the army to say, day after day, "What a beautiful morning for a battle!" Then, on the plain and slopes of the hills near Munda, the battle took place. Young Pompey and Labienus had drawn up their army in an extremely strong position. Probably they did not expect me to attack and were counting on being able to say, at the end of the day, that they had offered battle to the so-called invincible Caesar and that he had declined the challenge. And indeed I did hesitate to take this challenge up. I knew that, if the fighting was prolonged, the slope of the hill would give the enemy a tremendous advantage. Unless at some point we broke or turned his line, he would be able to fall back, becoming stronger with every step he took. However, I knew the spirit of my troops and believed that no army could stand up against them for long.

So, on this beautiful morning for a battle, we advanced in line, crossed the stream which separated us from the enemy and halted almost at the foot of the hill. Labienus must have known that, if he was going to fight a general engagement at all, he would never have a more favorable opportunity. We soon saw that he was prepared to take it. Cavalry and light troops came forward against us from the wings, and the main body began to move slowly towards us. The preliminaries to the battle were conventional and seemed almost unreal. My cavalry was under the general command of the Moorish King Bogud with whose wife I had been so closely associated in Mauretania. He was a good cavalry commander and his own Moorish troopers were at least as effective as the fine contingents of Gallic and Spanish cavalry which I had brought with me. They had little difficulty in sweeping aside the enemy cavalry and slingers. They were then recalled. My plan was to use them to exploit the real breakthrough, which would have to be an affair of the infantry. By now the two infantry lines were close enough together for the word to be given to charge and to hurl javelins. I had, as usual, the Tenth Legion on my right and had posted other veteran legions on my left. I expected that it would be on one wing or the other that the decisive advance would be made. And as the troops joined battle, the men of the Tenth, fighting furiously and eager as always to be able to claim the honors of victory, did push the enemy back a little. Elsewhere the two lines were locked, with neither side giving way at all.

I watched anxiously, hoping that the moment might come quickly when I could order the cavalry again into action. I was elated, as I always am in battle, but this time I was conscious also of a contradictory feeling, a feeling almost of foreboding. Perhaps this was merely the aftereffect of an epileptic attack which had come over me recently near Corduba; perhaps I was half-consciously aware that I was asking of these old troops of mine almost more than I could expect of them. I saw that our slight initial advance on the right had been held. Nothing now would give us a quick victory and I had committed my army to an engagement where our men's experience and training were counterbalanced, and perhaps more than counterbalanced, by the enemy's superior numbers, greater physical vigor and advantageous position. For more than two hours there was tough continuous fighting at close quarters. We were making no impression at all on the enemy's line and I knew that this fact alone was giving greater confidence to the enemy and weakening our own resolution. I could imagine how Labienus would be feeling. After so many boasts and so many disappointments he seemed on the brink of a triumph which would satisfy his long hatred. And was I, who had shown myself a greater general than Pompey the Great, now to be defeated and disgraced by troops commanded by his sons?

I could not bear to wait upon the result of the action and would certainly rather have died fighting than have seen my men turn and run. I shouted out words which were probably incoherent and in any case could only have been heard by a few. I was desperate and I was indignant. I was losing this battle, and it seemed to me against the order of nature that this should be so. "Are you going to betray me now to these boys?" I shouted. And, snatching a shield and a sword from one of the wounded, I ran forward against the enemy. So I had done, years before, on the hill in northern Gaul, among the thick hedges, when we were surrounded by the Nervii. It seemed almost a lifetime ago. Then also my action had been unpremeditated and its result had surprised me. So now I did not notice the spears and sword thrusts that were aimed at me, but my men noticed me and, whether they heard or understood my words or not, they were not going to allow their general to fight in advance of them. First slowly and then with increasing rapidity I could feel the battle being transformed. Elsewhere the fighting went on with no advantage to either side, but on the right we were winning.

I could see from the faces and hear in the angry voices of the men of the Tenth that they knew that they had won. The enemy left first bent and then crumpled. It was time to let loose my cavalry on the disorganized flank and on the rear. I withdrew from the line to make sure that this was being done and I saw that already King Bogud had seen what the situation was and had massed his horsemen for the charge. I saw too, higher up the hill, a good deal of movement behind the enemy's main line and I realized at once that Labienus was acting most intelligently. He was bringing cohorts of infantry from his right and center to meet the cavalry attack which he expected on his left. It was just such a maneuver that had won me the battle of Pharsalus; yet this time the maneuver, admirable in itself, not only failed in its purpose, but led directly to an utter rout of the whole enemy army. Labienus, to meet the threat, had to move his cohorts quickly; the movement was not expected by the men in the fighting line and its purpose was not understood. By the soldiers actually engaged this sudden rush of standards and cohorts in their rear was assumed to be, not a wise action for their protection, but the beginning of a general flight. A few units became affected with panic and soon the panic spread all along the line. By the time my cavalry came into action there was scarcely any serious resistance.

After Pharsalus I had given the order to my men to spare the lives of their fellow citizens and I have wished that this order of mine should be remembered by future historians of these times. But after Munda I gave no such order, nor would it have been obeyed if I had. Our own losses had been heavier than I had ever sustained in any battle. The men were exhausted. Yet they, with the comparatively fresh cavalry, spent more hours still in killing everyone they could overtake. It was estimated that thirty-three thousand of the enemy died in this battle. Among the dead was Labienus. I saw to it that his body was given honorable burial.

Next we moved on Corduba, where another twenty-two thousand of the enemy had succeeded in taking refuge. Here the towns-people were willing enough to surrender, but the enemy troops had neither the courage to throw themselves on my mercy nor the ability and resolution to resist. Some of them set fire to the town, probably as a means to terrorize the inhabitants, and in the general disorder we experienced no great difficulty in taking the place by storm. Few if any of the twenty-two thousand men in the city who were in arms against us survived. As for the sons of Pompey, young Sextus escaped and is still, with very limited resources, trying to organize a fleet in eastern waters. Gnaeus was hunted down by Spaniards in my service and, when I entered Seville, I found that his head was on show in the main square of the city. I looked at it with indifference; and indeed my feelings had altered since the time when I saw with horror his father's head on the deck of my ship off Alexandria. Then I had still hoped for peace and reconciliation among citizens. Now the civil war, like the war in Gaul, had ended in more bloodshed than I could have imagined.

I spent some months in Spain, reorganizing the province and making arrangements for the payment and the reward of my troops. This time I had no pity on those Spanish towns which, in spite of my many favors, had, from mere perversity, it seemed, or love of the excitement of disorder, gone over to the enemy. I made the rich pay for the luxury of revolt. Nor did I forget the citizens of Gades, and their famous temple of Hercules. After my first campaign I had restored to this temple all the treasure that had been taken from it by Pompey's officers. Now I took this treasure for the use of the army and myself.

Not till nearly midsummer did I leave for Rome. On my way I stopped in the Province at Narbonne. I had many old friends to see there and others came to meet me from Italy and from every part of Gaul. I have always enjoyed visiting this small fertile area, with its beautiful climate and its intelligent people who have been Romanized for so long and who, with the exception of the people of Marseilles, have given me the most loyal support. I reflected that it was only twelve or thirteen years ago that my anxiety for the security of the Province had given me the pretext for intervening

against the Helvetii. From this accident of history had proceeded
the conquest of all Gaul and the invasion of Britain and of Germany. It may be true that if one accident had not fitted in with the
needs of my ambition and my personality, I should have discovered another; yet another might have led me elsewhere —
eastwards, perhaps, towards the Danube where I may still go,
either this year or next, since our frontier requires adjustment in
that direction. As it is I am glad that fortune led me to Gaul and
that afterwards I was able to take advantage of fortune and begin
to create in that land something new and durable. Last year, as I
passed through the Province, I could imagine clearly enough the
wide and different landscapes farther north, from the hills round
Gergovia and Alesia to the forests and marshes where the Belgae
live and those wooded ravines where we had tracked down and
killed so many of the treacherous Eburones. Throughout the civil
war all this great area had been quiet. Yet it was not long ago
when the Province itself had been threatened by the bands of
Vercingetorix and, in order to save my isolated legions, I had had
to march at midwinter across the Cevennes. This was said to be
impossible.

Now, hard as those days were, it was a relief to think of them
after the difficulties and the shedding of Roman blood in Africa
and in Spain. So I was glad to meet in the Province some of my old
officers, notably Antony and Trebonius, and some of those, notably Brutus, who had fought against me and who had accepted my
forgiveness. All these had some reason to expect to find me displeased with them. Indeed there was actually a story (which I
never believed) that Trebonius had planned to assassinate me.
He may well have spoken against me out of some perverted disappointment of his own; for he had been governor of Further Spain
and he had entirely failed to prevent the enemy from making much
dangerous progress in that province. So had my generals Fabius
and Pedius. All were somewhat ashamed of themselves. All are
good officers, but they do not like to admit that they lack the
genius of Labienus. I thought that they deserved honors and I arranged matters so that Trebonius and Fabius should have the con-

sulship for the remaining part of the year and that, after the triumph which I proposed to hold myself in Rome during the autumn, Pedius and Fabius should also hold a triumph. As for Antony, he had been given both honor and responsibility after Pharsalus. I had not expected much political wisdom from him, but had imagined that he would at least have kept the legions in a state of efficiency and content. I still believe that he only failed to do so because he was too lazy to take the necessary trouble and, since the time of the mutiny in Campania, I had made little use of him. Yet I have always been fond of him and now, it seemed, was the time to give him again an opportunity to distinguish himself. I promised him that he should be my colleague in the consulship for this present year. So far he has behaved well, except that nothing will induce him to make up his quarrel with Dolabella.

Brutus, I remember, was in a very subdued mood when he came to meet me in the Province. I had heard excellent accounts of his conduct as governor of Cisalpine Gaul, a post which I had secured for him even though he was not legally qualified to hold it. And, both for his mother Servilia's sake and his own, I was anxious to help him in the future. I had once even thought of making him my chief heir. As it is I have made young Octavius my heir and have (though this is not yet generally known) adopted him as my son. He is of my own blood; he has, unlike Brutus, a most keen and realistic intelligence so far as politics are concerned; he is at least as ambitious as I ever was. He is, I am afraid, somewhat lacking in generosity and he has little of the charm which Brutus, in spite of his grave manner, still retains. Both he and Brutus may be said to be cold characters, but Octavius differs from Brutus in realizing that, in dealing with men, this coldness is a defect. I can see that he envies Antony for the freeness and easiness of his manner and for the obvious appeal he has to women and to soldiers. In fact I have heard that, in his efforts to capture something of this useful quality in Antony, the young man sometimes forces himself, with his usual thoroughness, to indulge in drinking bouts or long spells of sexual debauchery for which he is quite unfitted by nature. This is another example of his resolution and, though of course I cannot applaud such pathetic displays, I am not shocked by them as Brutus would be; nor would I laugh at them, as Antony does. I hope that I shall be remembered not only as the conqueror of Gaul but as the man who put an end in Rome to the long period of civil wars and irreconcilable antagonism between individuals. But in my lifetime I have grown used to estimating the strengths of character and the abilities of men who are or who might become antagonists. Of these three — Antony, Brutus and Octavius — I have no doubt that Octavius, if he could secure for himself any following at all, would be much the most dangerous enemy.

But on my way back from Spain I was thinking not of enemies but of friends. So I was glad to be able to relieve Brutus at once of any anxiety he might have felt about whether or not I should receive him cordially. Certainly he could not expect me to approve of the marriage which he had just made. If I had been consulted, I should have advised him strongly against it. But, though I am Prefect of Morals and Perpetual Dictator, I am not a Sulla, who used to tell people whom to marry and whom to divorce — and who was obeyed by everyone except me. Brutus had married presumably for love, since there did not appear to be much political advantage in allying himself with a woman whose whole life had been spent in the society of my greatest enemies. For Portia was the daughter of Cato and the widow of Bibulus. It would have been difficult to have found another woman in Rome who, in the nature of things, must have heard me reviled so bitterly and so continuously. I think that Brutus was pleased as well as relieved when I told him that it was not my way to bear ill-will to the dead and that I wished him happiness in his marriage. I doubt, however, whether he has found it. Lately he has seemed to me more than usually morose.

Not long after this interview with Brutus in the Province I set out again for Italy. But before leaving I made arrangements personally for the new settlements where two of my veteran legions were to receive generous allotments of land. I gave the Sixth Legion land from the confiscated territory of Marseilles. The Tenth

is now also in the Province, at Narbo Martius. There are not many
left of those men who marched against the Helvetii and Ariovistus.
Gaius Crastinus and many more lie buried in the plain at Pharsalus. Still more were left at Munda. As they grew older, they were
hard men to get on with. Now they are cultivating their vineyards,
well off as they have never been. I, who have attained everything
which a man may be assumed to desire, have to continue fighting.
I shall find it strange to be fighting without them.

Chapter 14

Conclusion

SINCE MY RETURN FROM MUNDA I HAVE BEEN IN ITALY FOR LESS than a year, and only the last few months of this time have been spent in Rome. My triumph in the autumn was sufficiently splendid, though not quite on the same scale as the four previous ones. There was plenty of entertainment for the people; and, if there was nothing so spectacular as the great sea fight in the artificial lake which I had organized in the previous year, there was a particularly fine display of wild beast hunting, in which four hundred lions were killed, and a giraffe was seen for the first time in Rome. These spectacles and entertainments, at most of which I had to be present myself (though I had far more important things to do), recalled to my mind those seemingly distant days when I had been aedile, with Bibulus as my colleague, and had, with the aid of vast sums of borrowed money, produced a series of shows more splendid than had ever been seen before, and, in the end, ventured to put before the people's eyes again the forbidden statues of Marius. Then for the first time I had heard great crowds shouting out, with enthusiasm and a delighted surprise, the name of "Caesar," and I was elated by the experience. Now these acclamations are everyday occurrences, and if I do anything which falls short of the extremes of grandeur or generosity the people feels itself to have been swindled. They have placed me on a pedestal which is too high for affection, though not beyond the reach of envy. I shall be happier with my soldiers. As for the people of Rome, I doubt whether I shall arouse their genuine enthusiasm again until I am dead.

During my Spanish triumph there were some signs of disapproval and one of the tribunes actually had the effrontery to remain seated while I passed. Some people no doubt felt that I was insulting the memory of the dead Pompey by holding a triumph over armies that had been commanded by his sons. No one, of course, with the faintest knowledge of me could have entertained such a thought. I have never in any official statement even mentioned the victory of Pharsalus. In Rome, after this victory, some of my partisans threw down the statues of Pompey. Recently I have had all these statues restored to their proper places. As for my triumph I held it to mark the end of the civil war and to suggest that those who continually disturbed the peace did not deserve the consideration usually given to Roman citizens. Also I wished to honor the army which had fought the hardest battle in which we have ever been engaged.

I was, I must own, offended by the insulting behavior of a single tribune and slightly annoyed by a few minor manifestations of ill-feeling by the crowd. Yet I am neither vain nor inexperienced. I know that I retain my hold on the people and that it is a hold based, not on fear, but on admiration and fellow feeling. If I were assassinated today, the people, after some time of stupor, would turn upon my murderers and would begin to worship me, much more wholeheartedly than they do now, as a god. But in spite of my knowledge of the reality of power and of the essential triviality of many of the honors with which I am loaded, I am still impatient, as I always have been, with intellectual dishonesty and with that kind of priggish and savage legalism which I have known throughout my life to be used as a cover for blind self-interest and as a justification for oppression and atrocity. So, though in a sense I am amused at the thought of having to ask the permission of some obscure tribune before I proceed with my plans, I am also irritated by the misuse of what should be a genuine respect for convention. In my life time Marius, Sulla, Pompey, and I myself have all, for various reasons (and very often for the good of the Republic), broken the law or distorted it in our own interests. As I have achieved more than the other three, so I suppose I may be regarded as the most revolutionary. And yet I have had a deeper respect for antiquity than any of them. Otherwise I should scarcely have bothered to write nearly twenty volumes on the science of augury, a science in which I do not believe, but one which is an integral part of our state religion, of which I am the head.

I would discard nothing from the past except what must be discarded in the interests of efficiency. For, most important as all convention is, it is only important because it serves the wider purposes of freedom, justice, strength and order. So, when I am asked to "restore the Republic," I should be right in replying that this is precisely what I am doing. True that I have recently been made Dictator for life, and that this is an appointment unprecedented in Roman history. But events have shown how necessary, at least for the moment, this autocracy is. And I have used my powers, both as Dictator and as Prefect of Morals, to strengthen rather than to destroy the existing organs of government. I have greatly increased the numbers of senators. Naturally some of the old Roman aristocracy complain that I have introduced among them people who cannot be described as gentlemen. This is true, and the same people in the nobility used to say the same things of Marius and of Cicero. I doubt whether among the new senators whom I have created a Marius or a Cicero is to be found; yet these new senators are all men of ability who have earned the right to distinction. So too I have increased the numbers of praetors and quaestors not in order to reward my own partisans but because the state requires a larger number of magistrates in order to transact efficiently an increasing amount of business. For the moment most of these officials owe their positions to my patronage rather than, as in the past, to their own efforts, legal or illegal, at the polls. This also is a necessary thing. Rome must have time to recover from this civil war without plunging back again at once into that sorry wasteful strife of personal ambition, accusation and counteraccusation, bribery and corruption which I know so well and which some people still dignify by the name of "liberty." Such people ought to reflect that, in my general control over the election of important magistrates, I have infringed no "liberty" that is of any consequence. No person of ability has been debarred by any action of mine from any position for which he is qualified. Among the praetors for this year, for instance, are Cassius, who, I am quite sure, disapproves of me, and Brutus who, though I love him and trust him, certainly does not share my political views.

But why should I try to justify even to myself my possession of power which I know to be necessary and which I use with moderation? Perhaps when I am in the East I should write some sort of a constitutional treatise in order to define and explain my aims to that very small minority who are really interested. Such a treatise would do me a little good, but not much; since no intellectual argument, however cogent, would prevent most of my enemies, however intelligent they might be, from hating me. Moreover, though I am certainly devoted to the tradition and convention of our race, I should not like to feel myself bound by theoretical prescriptions. I have learned that, both in politics and in war, what matters is speed. At the moment there is much to do, and I simply lack the time to be able to submit my conduct to the processes of prejudiced debate. For the foreseeable future I must retain autocratic power. No one in his right mind could consider me a tyrant; but I am aware that many people are not in their right minds.

Among these, at least so far as politics are concerned, I am inclined to place Cicero. After the end of the African war he made some good and generous speeches. He is genuinely impressed, I think, by the fact that I am averse to shedding the blood of my fellow citizens. Recently, too, he has been the first to propose for me in the senate new, extravagant and unnecessary honors. Yet his language, beautiful as it is, seems to me to belong either to a school of rhetoric or to another age. His brilliant mind has not grasped the simple facts that history is alive and that times have changed. He flatters me in almost exactly the same words he used to employ to flatter Pompey in his youth; and when he speaks with reverent awe of the Republic, he is thinking of something which was ceasing to exist before he was born. He, it seems, has found time to compose a constitutional treatise. Not long ago he showed it to my friends Balbus and Oppius and asked their advice as to whether or not he should submit it to me. They discouraged him and he was, of course, offended. But they were wise to discourage him, as my own comments, I think, would have offended him more. He has good intentions and would wish things to be what they are not. In practice it appears that he has nothing to propose except what he has always imagined as desirable — a state of affairs where one good officer (it used to be Pompey — now it is I) commands our armies in the field, while Rome, Italy and the provinces are governed honorably and patriotically by a senate consisting of public-spirited conservatives with a good knowledge of history, all of whom are assumed to be ready to listen to and be guided by the oratory and wisdom of Cicero himself. His own experience should have taught him that such an assembly does not exist. And he should be modest enough to remember that his own record in politics would scarcely justify an intelligent man in following blindly his advice.

Last December I dined with him at one of his country estates. I was staying nearby with Octavius's stepfather and I was glad to be able to accept Cicero's invitation, though I was rather reluctant to impose myself and my large bodyguard (I had about two thousand cavalry with me) on his hospitality. Also I fear that I may have offended him when he called on me in the morning and I was unable to receive him. I was much too busy discussing various plans and financial matters with Balbus. However in the end everything went well. The soldiers got a reasonably good meal in the garden and I myself thoroughly enjoyed the evening. We talked only about literature and philosophy, and I think Cicero was just as pleased as I was that our conversation was confined to these subjects. He is, I know, only too willing to give me political advice, but his advice invariably takes the form of very harmless generalities which, in the actual context of contemporary events and needs are almost, if not quite, meaningless. He is aware that I have a brain of a rather practical order and am apt to require in a political argument a knowledge of facts which he does not possess and a kind of logical precision to which, where politics are concerned, he is not accustomed. Thus he is frightened at the thought that I might not listen to him with the respect which he considers his due. But on literary subjects he knows that I take every word he says seriously, that I enjoy his wit and admire his learning. Here too he will listen to me without rancor and reply without pomposity. This does him great credit. I am something of a literary man myself and I have observed that in general writers, poets and orators show even less generosity towards each other than do rival practitioners of other professions.

Cicero is an exception. He has given up much of his time to helping young orators and students of philosophy. He recognizes and applauds good work done by others and indeed on these matters where he is really an expert displays none of the vanity and intolerance which he will show when he discusses other topics with which he is imperfectly acquainted. He is now writing a lot of poetry, for which he has an extraordinary facility. He told me that he often composes five hundred verses in a single evening. He is also doing interesting and valuable work in philosophy, creating new words, or devising metaphors, for a number of Greek technical terms for which we have no equivalent in Latin. Altogether I thoroughly enjoyed our conversation together and when I left Cicero I was sincere in wishing my host well. It is a pity that he disapproves of me so much. I should like him to realize that, so long as I am alive, he is safe to pursue his studies and increase his reputation; whereas, supposing I were to be violently removed (and now only assassination could achieve this object), in the kind of disturbances which would inevitably follow, he would be most unlikely to survive. What would probably happen to him is what happened to him in the past. He would be first used and then discarded. I wish that I had ever had in politics any occasion to be grateful to him, since I, unlike the others, would certainly have shown my gratitude.

Just now he and others are no doubt angry and distressed at the thought that I may arrange to have myself given the title of "King." This is a plan which Cleopatra has very often suggested to me. Balbus too is inclined to favor it, and undoubtedly quite a number of my partisans in Rome would like to see me break entirely with republican tradition and make it clearer even than it is already that Rome is ruled by one man. I am not averse to the idea myself. I like distinctions to be, where possible, clear-cut; I am a descendant of the ancient Kings of Rome; and I have a great respect for antiquity. Yet I am also aware that there is in Rome a very deep republican sentiment which, however irrational it may be, is a force to be reckoned with. It is merely the name "King" which people find offensive, and this is because they have been taught to believe that that early Brutus (a rather dubious ancestor of my friend Marcus Brutus) who got rid of the last King of Rome performed a meritorious action in setting up an oligarchical system of government which gradually evolved into what we call "the Republic." We are taught to contrast the idea of monarchy with the fact of this Republic and we are encouraged to believe that our Republic is the best political organization so far devised by man. Such is the effect of prejudice and education that few people allow themselves to reflect that for the last two generations our Republic has proved itself wholly inadequate to deal with the most elementary tasks of government — the maintenance of law and order within the community. During this period more Romans have been killed in battle, robbed or assassinated by their fellow citizens than ever before in any period of foreign conquest or of self-defense.

There was a time when I too used to think in terms of the reform of abuses rather than of a general reconstruction. Now the need for reconstruction is evident and it may be desirable to use new words, or old words with new meanings, to mark the change that has already taken place. It has occurred to me that the word "Caesar" might come to be used to denote the kind of modern monarchy for which I now use the cumbrous title of "Perpetual Dictator." Even now I have the right to wear the purple toga and the high red boots which used to be worn by the old Kings of Rome. It was partly this costume, I suppose, which provoked that demonstration which took place only about a month ago. Many voices in the crowd which surrounded me as I was returning to Rome from the celebration of the Latin Festival saluted me as "King." There was also, of course, something of a counterdemonstration led by some officious tribunes. I replied to the demonstrators on both sides by saying: "My name is Caesar, not King," and it immediately struck me that this name Caesar might not be a bad alternative to the less popular title.

Since then various attempts have been made by my friends to test the strength of public feeling. Royal diadems have been put on my statues and quite an impressive ceremony was arranged exactly a month ago when, at the festival of the Lupercalia, Antony, before a very large crowd, made repeated attempts to present me with a crown. This gesture met with a mixed reception. Probably about half the people present were outraged by the suggestion of an official monarchy. I therefore arranged to have the crown placed in the Temple of Jupiter together with an inscription to the effect that I, Caesar, had been offered the kingship by the people through their consul Antony, but I refused the offer. These proceedings should, I think, convince any fair-minded person that I am averse to offending anyone's susceptibilities. Nevertheless it remains true, as Cleopatra is constantly pointing out, that in the East the title of "King" could be very useful to me. My old uncle Lucius Cotta has managed to produce a statement from the Sybilline books that Parthia can only be conquered by a king, and during today's meeting of the senate (it must be already nearly dawn) he is to propose that, for a combination of reasons, military and superstitious, I should be entitled to call myself "King" outside Italy. The proposal will, of course, be carried; but I am not certain how far I shall make use of this new privilege. I shall have to consider the feeling of the army and the precise advantages to be gained at the particular time. And I have had more important things to think of than the use of honorific titles.

My detractors would be surprised to know how very little time during the past months I have devoted to the consideration of monarchy. I have been more interested in greater projects both at home and abroad. I have also dealt with what I consider to be important matters of detail. I have drafted constitutions for new colonies and settlements. I have gone thoroughly into the plans for the recruitment and transport of settlers to what I hope will be the three greatest of my new foundations — at Troy, Corinth and Carthage. I expect that these cities which in the past were rich, powerful and famous will be reborn and will come to be as great as they ever were. I have discussed the layout of these new towns with the best architects I could find in Greece and Egypt — countries which are still ahead of us both in town planning and in architecture. And I expect to make Corinth an even more important trading center than before by digging a canal through the isthmus which separates northern Greece from the Peloponnese. I have also laid down the lines for a huge program of building and reconstruction in Rome and Italy. Balbus and Oppius will be dealing with these projects while I am in the East. I attach particular importance to the plan for diverting the course of the Tiber and widening its channel, so that good-sized ships will be able to sail from the sea into the heart of the city. The harbor of Ostia, too, is to be enormously enlarged and improved. I expect also to open up near Rome great new areas of land for cultivation by draining the Pontine marshes; and in Rome itself, in addition to the building program which I have accomplished already, there remains much to be done which has been already planned. The most spectacular building, no doubt, will be the great Temple of Mars — the largest in the world — which I propose to have built on the site where, at the time of the Gallic, Egyptian, Asian and African triumphs, we constructed the vast artificial lake for the performance of the naval battle. But I shall be happier still to see the new porticoes, forums, public libraries, theaters and all those other buildings which will at last make Rome, so far as architecture and amenities are concerned, a city not inferior to Athens, Antioch, Alexandria or Pergamum.

I can imagine a Rome that has become the most splendid, as

she is the most powerful, city in the world. I can even imagine citizens living their lives in peace and order, not vexed by open confusion and opposition of interests or by those mad jealousies and desperate rivalries which have filled my own days with blood. But I do not know whether I shall live to see so happy a state of affairs. I may die in Parthia as Crassus did, though I shall not make the strategic mistakes that Crassus made. Nevertheless, and without having made any mistake at all, it is often necessary to expose one's life in battle. Or, as I know well at this age, I may die at any moment from an accident or an inevitability of illness. I may even, I suppose, be assassinated. Certainly I have long been accustomed to consider, as some philosopher recommends us to do, that each day may be my last, though I have never allowed this consideration to influence my actions in the least.

Now I begin to see this day dawn of the Ides of March. Calpurnia, who has slept so uneasily, is waking too. She will be concerned about my health and I shall tell her that this is not the first night that I have spent without sleeping. Her own disturbed rest is more unusual than my wakefulness.

Now the high wind has died down, as it should do, considering that this is the first day of spring. It is no time to be thinking of death, as I was thinking just now, since all the world is coming alive. Last night, at dinner with Lepidus, they were talking of death and of which kind of death would be the one to choose. I interrupted the conversation and said: "A death that comes suddenly." I think that I was right, for, supposing one to have infinite leisure before death in order to reflect upon one's past, as I, in this sleepless night, have been, for a few hours, reflecting, even then how could one be wholly reconciled to the event, or how could one discover or define what it was that, in any case, seemed to make life worth living? As for me, I can see clearly many scenes of danger, of triumph, of love and of achievement. Most clearly of all I seem to see the face of Gaius Crastinus. I see him clearly but I see him as though he were in a dream. If I were to describe to Calpurnia this strange impression, she would no doubt claim that I was being given some supernatural warning to be careful on this day. But it is not like Crastinus and it is not like Caesar to show fear. Today I have a meeting with the senate in one of the halls that adjoin Pompey's theater.